Dead Insid
Dying To Heal

By

Simone Petardo

Dedication

The words in these pages are dedicated to everyone. To my kids - you have been my seven little planets; I have been your universe. I love you all more than words can say, and I will always be here for you, no judgement, just here. To those that saw me – You are my family. I appreciate you. Your kindness was never forgotten and has always been appreciated. To those I have wronged – I'm sorry; I did what I needed to do to survive. To the exceptional people – use your voice! To the normal people – keep blending in. To the garbage humans – You aren't alone. I see you; I hear you; my soul feels yours. To the one I love – You are the only man I have ever been *in* love with. That hasn't changed. I loved you then; I love you; still, I always have, and I always will. To the few people I consider friends – you've cracked through the walls of my heart, and you will live there forever. You will always be in my heart. To those who murdered me – You didn't win. I'm still here. *I am the weapon.* To the world - No. No is a full and complete sentence in every situation. I don't care if a person walks down the street naked; no one has a right to put their hands on anyone without permission. It doesn't matter if they've said yes once or five million times. If they ever say no, stop, try to get away, you fucking stop. It's called self-control and being a decent human being, no matter what class of human you fall into.

Allow me to introduce myself. Once upon a time...wait - that's not right. Those stories end in happily ever after. My name is Simone (not really), and I was born on a cold July morning in 1979, on Long Island, New York. That's where most people's stories start, right? When they were born. Not me, though. My story started when I was...

Eleven

I scribbled feverishly across the page of my black and white marble composition notebook. I remembered to draw a line between each entry. I can still hear the sound of the pencil scratching against the paper. I can still feel the tingly vibration in my hand and hear the scratchy noise. I still hate writing in pencil. I had to get this finished before I got to school. I was behind in my journal entries for my fifth-grade class, and my teacher was collecting them that day. Ms. Olsen didn't collect them frequently, and it had been a while since she had. She would be disappointed if my work wasn't done. It wasn't a lot. A sentence or more on each school day. It didn't matter what it was about, just something on paper. I finished just as the bus was pulling up to the building.

During recess and specials, Ms. Olsen checked our journals and returned them toward the end of the day. I got mine back and checked for any notes she had written. She wrote notes on some pages. If we wrote about an exciting trip or a new pet, she would communicate on these pages how exciting the news was or leave a little smiley face. On the corner of one of my pages, it just said, "See me after class." I wondered why. My stomach filled with lead. Did she know I had done it all at the last minute? Did I write something I shouldn't have? I skimmed the sloppy pages quickly, looking for answers. A couple of days, I had simply written about the weather. We didn't go on trips, have any new pets, or anything new at all, for that matter. I wrote about a boy on the bus who kept picking on me. That was probably it. She probably wanted to know who he was, so he would get in trouble and leave me alone. I felt relieved. That had to be it.

I approached her slowly and cautiously. Ms. Olsen was in a rush trying to help our whole class get ready to leave for the day. She asked me to wait for a minute, and I told her I couldn't because I would miss my bus and have no way home. I went back to my desk and started packing up my homework and books. More work that I would wait until the last minute to do. At eleven years old, I already knew I worked best under pressure. When she had a free second, she came back to me. I left my stuff at my desk while she walked me to a table by the windows. I was unprepared for the conversation we were about to have. Although it was sparked by my own words, my own writing, I was blindsided.

She looked at me for a few minutes in silence. Her dark blonde shoulder-length hair hung limply. Her bangs framed her tan, freckled face. Her blue eyes glowed with caring and curiosity. She wore a knee-length teal pencil skirt, a dark blue flower-patterned blouse, and navy high heels. She was neither attractive nor ugly; like most of the world, she was only plain. This time echoes in my mind. I guess the moments that change your life always seem to last for hours.

"You wrote in your journal," she began, and the curiosity in her eyes depended, "that you have a secret that you cannot tell anyone," She finished without phrasing it as a question. I exhaled and tried to search my brain for having written those words. "I don't remember writing that," I told her. She went to my desk and retrieved my journal. Her heels clacked against the floor with every step. I heard it everywhere, though. Those heels hitting the floor, the desks, the walls, shattering the windows and somehow piercing my heart. She opened my journal and found the dated entry, and there it was. Just a one-sentence entry in my awful handwriting. "I have a secret I can't tell anyone." I tried to find words that wouldn't come. I couldn't actually tell her my secret. If I had been careful and done my work when I was supposed to, I wouldn't have even written that down.

Ms. Olsen continued to look at me. Her soft, caring eyes became more concerned and worried. She asked me so many questions. Was it about the boy on the bus who had been picking on me? No. Was someone in class bothering me? I was a bullied kid, there were plenty of kids in the class bothering me, but no, that wasn't it. Her eyes brightened, and she smiled, "Is it about a boy you like? Is he in this class? I won't tell anyone." I hesitated, "No." There were more questions that were all answered with no. I couldn't do this forever. I didn't know what would happen if I just wouldn't tell her at all. She bent closer to me. I heard the overhead speaker boom announcing buses that had arrived and were ready for kids to begin boarding. The buses always came in the same order, and mine would be there soon. I would have no way home if I missed the bus. My mom worked an hour and a half away and would not be able to come to get me. I had to hurry up. "Look, Simone, no matter what your secret is, you can tell me. I won't tell anyone." Ms. Olsen said softly. The words that I had held in came out as one breathe, "I think I am uncomfortable with the way my stepfather is touching me." The words that I held in, in a secret place in my head and in my heart, were now out.

Ms. Olsen patted my hand and told me to wait. She would be right back. Her heels made no sound as she walked away this time. There was no noise at all. I went back to packing up my stuff. The other kids were laughing, talking, and goofing around while waiting for their bus numbers to be called. I heard nothing as I stuffed everything into my backpack. The world was quiet except for my own words in my head on repeat. I was ready when they called my bus number and started to walk out of the classroom. Ms. Olsen stopped me and ushered me back down the hall, and told me I had to stay. I explained about my bus again, and she said it would be taken care of. She spoke quietly with a male teacher. I sat at a desk as the other kids left, worried about what kind of trouble I would be in for missing the bus. I would most certainly be beaten.

After the other kids were gone, Ms. Olsen let me know that there were people coming to talk to me, and I was going to hang out in her classroom while we waited for them. She wrote our spelling and vocabulary words on the board. She put them all in sentences. I have a brave and beautiful girl in my class; she wrote and carefully underlined the words brave and beautiful. I knew she was referring to me, but I didn't understand why. What had I done that was brave? I certainly wasn't beautiful. She didn't explain what was going on, but we did get to know each other. I already knew it was her first-year teaching. She had told us that on our first day. I learned that she wasn't married, had no kids, and lived with her mother. I asked if I could just go live with her. She smiled softly and said the state would not allow that, and she didn't think her mother would either. If the circumstances were different, though, she would say yes. That was the moment that my plain teacher, who wore knee-length skirts and blouses that hid any feminine features she may have had, became beautiful.

The hours dragged on. It got dark. I wondered if my mom knew I wasn't home yet. She was rarely home from work before nine at night. Would she be worried? Maybe. Would she be angry? Definitely. Did I have any idea what was going on? Nope, not a clue. Would my brother, Brady, have let the dog out? Probably not. Which means the dog would have shit on the floor, and I would be in trouble. He was fourteen, but I was always the one in trouble. I met the school psychologist Mr. P., and Ms. Olsen left. I spent time in his office, and he ordered pizza for dinner. Then there were more people. The principal, the vice principal, and other office people all wanted to talk to me. I had no idea why.

Eventually, two cops came. I never met the guy officer. He left the female officer and I alone. "Hi Simone, I am Detective Lorenzo," she introduced herself. I felt awkward around this woman. I didn't like her. She dug papers and files out of her bag and said, "So you told your teacher something today. A secret you have. I am here to ask you about that." I slumped in my chair. The same chair I had been sitting in hours earlier when I said those words to Ms. Olsen. If I could have disappeared into that chair, I would have. Detective Lorenzo was speaking, but I couldn't hear her. All I knew was that Ms. Olsen lied. She had told my secret. I had trusted her, but she lied. I tried explaining to the detective, whom I liked less and less the more she opened her mouth, that I didn't want to talk about it. She wore too much make-up, and her short red-brown haircut looked like it would be better suited for a hedgehog or a peacock. I told her that I did tell Ms. Olsen a secret, but it was only for her and me to know, not other people.

"Relax. You have not done anything wrong. I just need you to tell me what happened in your own words." It was implied that I wasn't leaving until I complied. I just wanted to go home. So, I told her. I told her that my mom (Bianca) and my stepfather (Griffith) currently slept in the living room because their bed had broken. My mom got the couch, and he got the love seat, even though she was four foot ten and eighty pounds, and he was six feet and over two hundred and fifty pounds. I told her that late at night, after she was asleep, he would stand at the top of the stairs and call me up to him. He would ask me to tell him about my day. So, I would, and we would watch late-night HBO. We would watch things my mother would never have allowed. Then I told her how he would pull me close to him and gently rub down my back while pushing me to lay next to him. Our bodies would be facing each other, and he would pin my leg between his. His hand would go higher and lower on my body. Sometimes coming up to cup the curve of my already large chest and going lower to dip into the back of my clothes and rub my rear end. The detective stopped me several times as she was writing. She double and triple-checked that I would use the words chest and rear end. I confirmed that I would, even though what I would have said was tits and ass. I knew it wasn't seen as appropriate for kids to

6

use those words. When she was done writing, she asked me to read it and sign it if it was accurate. I pretended to read it and signed it in pen. Detective Lorenzo disappeared with her partner, who had been waiting in the doorway.

I hadn't told her everything. I hadn't told her how I could feel something harden against my leg. I hadn't told her how he would press that hard spot against my leg and stomach, rubbing it against me until his body would jolt and there would be a hot explosion against me. I hadn't told her how he would put my hand in his underwear, and I could feel the tufts of his coarse pubic hair. He hadn't actually made me touch it, just close to it.

The psychologist reappeared, and we went to the gym. We played basketball and didn't do any more talking. I felt different. Something was happening. Changing. Things would be different now. Griffith would be gone. My mom, Brady, and I could just have our lives. Mr. P. let me score a few baskets. Or even better, Griffith would just be told to stop, and I could still have a family. As the ball was up in the air and I was laughing, waiting to see if it went in the hoop, I heard her voice, "Simone? Simone?" It was my mom! She was calling me from the corridor off the gym. I ran toward her voice, "Ma!" I yelled back excitedly, searching for where she was. I vaguely remember hearing the now-forgotten basketball hit the gym floor. I saw her and knew immediately she had been crying. I ran to her, and we hugged. I was taller than her; her head rested on my shoulder. I began to cry with her, "I'm sorry, I'm sorry." I repeated over and over as we hugged.

As we left the school, escorted out by Mr. P and the detectives, I felt good. He would not be there. He would stop or be gone, and we could be happy. I saw the truck parked in front of the school, an old beat-up pickup with a cap on the back. A seat had been placed in the back that my brother and I rode on. He wasn't in the driver's seat. No one was. It was over. We got closer and closer, and I suddenly felt uneasy. There he was. Standing outside the driver's door. His large flannel-covered stomach came into view, his bearded face coming into focus. Our eyes met. I saw anger and hatred there. I look back on that moment and see the expression on my own face change. I see my soul leave my body and run back to the school. Run back to the safety of pizza and basketball. Run back and tell them all the things I hadn't before. I remember thinking; They are sending me home with him?! How can they?! It isn't safe! I said nothing, though. I just walked. I turned and looked back once. Making eye contact with Detective Lorenzo. She smiled and held up her hand in a wave. I climbed into the back of the truck and went home without a word.

I still didn't understand the ramifications of my words that day. I didn't understand how allowing that part of my brain to be unlocked and those words to come out could change my life forever. I didn't understand anything.

The days that followed were awful. I do not remember anyone leaving the house. I do not remember seeing Brady at all. That was okay, though. He was a dick that just beat me up all the time anyway. For days Griffith had just sat around on the love seat in his underwear and white undershirt. On the third day, he was sitting in the recliner, and I was sitting across the room while my mom ran back and forth from the kitchen to the dining room. I don't think anyone even said a word in those first few days. Finally, my mom snapped, "Would you two just fucking say something?!" she screamed, as her eyes darted back and forth between us. "Griffith?! Say something?" She yelled a little louder. "I don't know what to say." He replied in a tone that sounded like he was crying, but there were no tears. "Simone?!" Now the angry tone was directed at me and even louder. "I don't know what to say either," I told her honestly. "Well, you are the one who made the fucking accusation!!"

She screamed so loud it was almost inaudible. I said nothing, and the silence continued.

The next time I went to school, there were six or seven girls waiting when I got off the bus. I stepped off, and they quietly sang me a song. "Incest, incest, it's the best. Put your family to the test. I knew it had something to do with my situation, but I didn't really know what it meant. I never told anyone. My well intentioned mom got a set of anatomically correct dolls. Over the next few days, or maybe it was even weeks, she would bring them to my room. "Show me," she said the first time she brought them to me. I looked at her, confused. "Show me what he did to you on the dolls." I didn't want to, but I tried.

I grazed the girl doll's flat chest with the boy doll's hand. I laid the dolls facing each other and showed how he would rub my back and dip his fingers into the back of my underwear. Bianca, like so many others, just asked questions. "Are you sure?" "Are you sure you didn't dream it?" "You have always had an overactive imagination. You used to tell me about ghosts in the other bedroom and dreams about hands that were coming to get you from under the bed. Are you sure you didn't just imagine it?

After being asked these questions many times, it planted a seed of doubt in my mind. He was the only dad I had ever known, and my daddy wouldn't really hurt me, right? I kept trying to show her on the stupid dolls, but it didn't seem to be enough, and she just kept asking the same questions. One day, I had enough, and I exploded. I threw the dolls across the room and screamed, "Fine! If that's what you want to hear, FINE! If you want to hear it was just a dream, FINE! I fucking imagined it! It was a fucking dream!" She said nothing. She just picked up the dolls when she left the room. She never brought the dolls back and never asked again. He wasn't doing it anymore anyway. That was all I wanted. He was my dad, and I loved him. I had just wanted him to stop touching me, and he had.

Bianca and Griffith divorced not long after. I protested it. A part of me was happy about it. I suppose that was the part of me that hated him. The same part of me that knew it hadn't been a dream or my imagination. I was a child, though. A child that desperately wanted a family, and like it or not, this was mine. So, I protested. I felt at fault for destroying our family. Brady blamed me as well. Quietly when the adults were around and not so quiet when they were not. No matter what was said, they were divorcing; Brady and I would spend weekends with Griffith. Griffith and Bianca worked together, so we would all see each other all the time anyway.

Griffith moved into a camper about half an hour away. It was on a property owned by his friend Harry. Harry was old and disgusting. He had property, though, and supposedly a lot of money. He owned a large house, too. People rented rooms out of it. He slept in what had once been the living room, but he converted it into his bedroom. The rooms were all currently full, so Griffith got the camper until a room became available. The camper had one bedroom with two built-in frames for beds. There were no mattresses, though, and the floor was full of holes. The living/dining/kitchen area and a tiny bathroom with no water. That was all the space. The couch folded down into a bed. A kerosene heater was placed on the floor in the kitchen/dining area. I was to sleep on the floor next to the heater. Griffith and Brady were to sleep on the folded-out bed. We would have most meals out, pee outside, and, if necessary, shower at Harry's. We would spend the days at the gift shop that my mom ran, Griffith worked for, and his father (Grandpa W) owned.

Every Friday, Griffith would pick up Brady and me. On our way to his house, we would drink beer. Yes, even me. I sat in the truck between them and would often have to do some of the steering since

Griffith would have had several beers before coming to get us. The drinking would continue until we would pass out. Blockbuster runs were typical since we had a TV and no cable. Griffith pushed one weekend to get The Rocky Horror Picture Show, which I was adamantly against. I didn't want to watch anything scary. I lost that battle. I laid in my sleeping bag and watched. I was enthralled with it. The men dressed as women. The dancing. The make-up. The singing. The sex. It quickly became one of my favorite movies, and I have seen it hundreds of times. On Sundays, Griffith would drive us home sober. Bianca couldn't know how much he drank or that Brady and I did drink. We spent most school vacations with Griffith. Drinking, smoking, and doing whatever we wanted as long as it was out of Bianca's eyesight.

On a wintry night, Griffith suggested Brady and I switch spots for the night. His justification? I was a restless sleeper, and I was going to kick my blankets into the heater. Of course, leading to all our deaths. In my opinion, that wouldn't have been a terrible thing. Brady asked no questions, and they both ignored my complaints. I was just drifting off to sleep when I felt his arm creep around me. Griffith gently turned me toward him as I faked sleep. He kissed the side of my face and breathed heavily against my neck. In my mind, I screamed. In reality, I continued to feign sleep. My legs were pulled open, and he sandwiched his leg in mine. I felt his hardness at once and tried to roll away as if I were moving in my sleep. His hand found the small of my back, and he pulled me closer. Tighter. I felt his fingers dip lower into the back of my underwear as he rubbed me and thrust against my leg. A thought grabbed me. It was my mother's voice. Bianca very clearly asked me, "Are you sure you didn't dream it?" Then another thought, maybe this is just your imagination. My own voice repeated the words in my head silently. "That's it! This must be a dream! I am sleeping! I am just dreaming!" Those were my last thoughts as I felt his hot hand clasp my breast, and my mind floated away. To where? I still don't know. It was just

11

anywhere but there. And just like that, I was ….........

Twelve

I became friends with a woman that lived at Harry's. Her name was Mary, and she was in her early thirties. We would spend time together frequently. She was my escape from Griffith. Mary had a boyfriend named Kurt, who also lived there. He didn't pay much attention to me, which was fine. I didn't really like him. We made plans to do some baking one day, and when I went and knocked on her door, she said she was sick, and we would have to do it another day. I was disappointed, but I knew she couldn't help being sick. Griffith told me Mary had cancer, and if she said she was sick, she was sick. I wound up with Harry, Griffith, and Brady for the day instead. To make it up to me, Mary invited me to stay at the house with her for winter break. I asked Griffith, and he agreed. Of course, Bianca couldn't know.

There was an empty room with a bed, and Harry would never know I was there. The first night Mary went downstairs to get snacks, and when she came up, I took a bottle of Vodka from the bag she had left in my room and began to drink. Mary came up and caught me, "If your dad found out, he would be so mad at me. He would never let me see you again", she half scolded with a smile. "Besides, if I knew you drank, I would have bought you whatever you wanted," she finished her thought with a laugh. "Jack Daniels and he knows; he lets me get drunk every weekend." We both laughed and continued drinking until the sun came up.

The days were long and exhausting. The nights were full and exhilarating. Mary supplied as much alcohol as I wanted and could tolerate, which was a considerable amount for a twelve-year-old girl. Griffith would come and visit, often bringing more drinks. He noticed a Band-Aid on my finger and became concerned about it. I told him I had gotten my period and needed pads; I also needed cigarettes and alcohol in any variety. He seemed hyper-focused and

13

worried about the fact that I had a cut on my finger and my period. These seemed to be odd things for a parent to worry about, especially given the rest of my shopping list. He brought me everything I had asked for and begged me, pleaded with me, to keep anything that was bleeding covered. Sure, I would do whatever he asked if I didn't have to go back to his camper. Back to his bed.

Mary and Kurt got into a late-night fight. I hated yelling. When people yelled, even when it wasn't directed at me, I cried. I was already crying when she left her room and came back to the one I was staying in. I was also drinking and a little buzzed. Mary stormed in in her nightgown, the most girly thing she ever wore, and ran her fingers through her boy short dark red hair mumbling something. It was something about Kurt being an asshole, which I had already known.

Kurt was suddenly in the doorway, and they were screaming in each other's faces. I pressed myself into a wall and cried more. Mary noticed how distraught I was and tried taking the fight to a different room. Kurt smacked her into a wall, and I screamed at him not to hit her. He noticed my presence then and turned his attention to me. "What the fuck are you even crying for? I didn't yell at you! Shut up, you sniveling little bitch!" He screamed while approaching me.

Mary got in between us and started yelling at him so he would walk backward. They each got louder and louder as he stepped backward, and she stepped forward. They got out into the hallway by the stairs, and Kurt pushed her. She lost her balance a little, not enough to fall down the stairs, but she stumbled down a few. She came back up and around him, headed toward their room, still yelling at him. His back was toward my doorway, and I heard her head hit a wall when he hit her.

So, I did the only thing I could think of. I picked up the almost empty bottle of Vodka and came up behind him, and through my tear-filled and half-drunk eyes, I hit him with it. Unfortunately, not hard enough that it broke or knocked him out. I was twelve, and this isn't the movies.

Kurt turned slowly, his eyes clear for the first time that night. I could see he was filled with anger, rage, and vengeance. "You little bitch. You want to protect her? You don't even know her," he said calmly but firmly as he slowly walked in my direction. I had known her for close to a year, and she was my friend; he didn't know what he was talking about.

As he approached me, slowly and calmly, was I scared? Yes. Did protecting my friend matter more? Absolutely. He reached out and slapped me hard across the face. I immediately stopped crying and looked him square in the eyes. "Fuck you," I said coldly. "She is the reason I am this way, and you are defending her. Bitch you don't know her. She will fuck you up too." He told me calmly and then turned back toward her. She had been goading him in her direction ever since I had hit him. They went to their room for a long time. I heard more yelling and hitting.

I finished an open bottle of Jack Daniels and moved on to a bottle of Vodka. There was silence. Long, excruciating silence. I finished that bottle too. What if she was dead? What if they were both dead? The only phone here was downstairs, and Harry couldn't know I was there. He was a pervy dirty old bastard who would watch figure skating and try and finger the women on TV. He already ogled me whenever I was around. I already knew what would happen if he knew I was there. Besides, who would I even call? Griffith had no phone. Bianca? Out of the question. My best friend from school? It was the middle of the night, and she was just a kid. I think that was the moment I realized I wasn't a kid at all. I do not know if I ever was.

I was startled out of these thoughts as Mary appeared in the doorway. She apologized profusely for the night's turn of events. We moved on to a bottle of Tequila. She asked if it was okay if she stayed with me for the rest of the night. Of course, it was. The bed was big enough for two. I was exhausted from the long night of drinking, fighting, and crying. Mary and I had barely slept or eaten in those days; we just drank. The not eating was good for me, though, since I was chubby, and Bianca was forever reminding me I was fat. Most kids' parents offer to pay them for good grades. Not Bianca. She offered to pay me to lose weight. With the night finally over, I knew I would fall asleep quickly. I rolled over, and sleep started to take me immediately. Then I felt her arm creep around me.

Mary rubbed my stomach and started to grind against my ass. She rolled me over and pressed her lips against mine. I felt her leg between mine. Faking sleep wasn't working, and I couldn't force my brain to leave as I had gotten so good at doing with Griffith. I clenched my jaw shut as I felt her tongue force its way between my lips and across my crooked teeth. My escape happened suddenly and without warning. I burst into tears and sat up, running for the bathroom to be sick. Mary jumped up and followed me, pleading, "Simone, I am so sorry. I had so much to drink that I thought you were Kurt", she explained repeatedly. I was twelve, and the explanation made sense to me then. Do I still believe that? No, I don't. When I was done throwing up, I just looked at her and laughed. We laughed. I brushed my teeth, and we got back in bed. Mary told me that Griffith was coming in the morning to give her money so we could go grocery shopping. This time, sleep took me fast, and no one touched me. I woke up to the smell of bacon.

Downstairs, Mary was cooking. Harry was in the dining room pissing into a portable urinal. He had them all over his room and the dining room, the only areas of the house he could get to. After the urinals were full, he would empty them into large coffee cans, and no one was allowed to empty them until they were spilling. The cans and urinals were placed on the radiators, so the house smelled like piss. Everyone justified it as he was old and didn't know what he was doing. I believe he knew, and he got off on it.

"Good morning, sunshine. Your dad brought money. I told him not to wake you. Get dressed, and we are going out." I ran back upstairs, grateful that we would be going out and where didn't matter. I hadn't eaten in days, and the bacon smelled fabulous. If I hurried, I might have time to grab a slice or two. Mary came up and said what I was wearing was too little kiddish and that I needed a more grown-up look. Mary, who had the body (and the haircut) of a twelve-year-old boy, suggested I wear some of her clothes.

So, she stuffed my size twelve ass into a pair of her size five jeans; it would not have worked if they were regular jeans, they were the kind with five buttons, so it squeezed my fat in better. Then she squished my DD boobs into one of her sweatshirts that swallowed her A ones and made her look flatter than she really was. I was always reading, so she suggested I bring a book in case we were stuck in the truck for a while. Downstairs we heard a noise as Beatrice, the old hag that lived around the corner, came in for her weekly visit with Harry.

The old couple droned on about how awful the world was and how the "blacks and spics were becoming too popular." Mary fixed a plate of bacon, eggs, and toast and brought it to Beatrice. "I do not want anything you have touched," Beatrice snapped as the plate was placed in front of her. Mary removed the plate as fast as she had put it down as Beatrice went on, "I know what you have, and I do not want it. You little girl, you better watch out..." Mary grabbed my hand and dragged me out the door. Griffith had left the truck for us to take for the day and was driving Bianca's Ford Escort wagon. Mary explained when we got to the truck that Beatrice thought

Mary's cancer was contagious. "She thinks she can catch my cancer if I touch her food," she explained further. "That is stupid; you can't catch cancer," I said matter-of-factly. "Tell that to the old bitch," Mary yelled laughingly at the house.

We got in the truck and rode away just in time for Beatrice to come out, yelling something at the truck. I was excited to be out doing something. Being with Mary was not hell like being with Griffith. It wasn't boring like being at Bianca's job. It was different. Every day was an adventure. How much of an adventure could we have going grocery shopping?? Well, I would tell you. Except we never made it there.

Mary drove several towns away. She parked in the back corner of a parking lot. I noticed immediately it wasn't a grocery store. Before I could open the door, Mary spoke, "I have some stuff to take care of at that house over there," she gestured at a house behind the building we were parked at. "When I'm done, we are going to have some really good burgers. Have you ever been here before?" I shook my head and left out the fact that I really didn't eat burgers. "Lock both doors and don't open them for anyone but me. Do you understand?" She instructed in an almost motherly tone. It was the first time she had ever sounded like an adult when talking to me. It was also the last.

I locked both doors as instructed and started my book. I took a nap. I read, and I napped. The day didn't seem to end. I hadn't seen which door Mary had gone into, and there were a lot of houses in the area she had pointed out. The burger place was now open and in full swing. My stomach growled with the smells that invaded the little pick-up truck. I read and napped. I finished the book. It was almost dark. Dinner rush picked up at the burger place, and my stomach growled some more. Darkness came. I laid across the three-seater bench and wondered if I was ever leaving this parking lot. As

I drifted back off to sleep, I wondered if dying here would be the worst thing to happen. No, that would be dying in Griffith's bed.

I jolted awake to a knock on the driver's side window. "Hurry up, let me in; it's cold out here," Mary said while laughing. I unlocked the door, and she got in; I was sliding over when she said, "Let my friend in too." I looked to my right and saw a tall, dark-skinned guy waiting. I unlocked the door and slid into the middle. They slammed their doors at the same time, a cold draft coming in with them. "This is my friend, Simone," she told him. "Hey baby, hey baby, how you." he stammered. I was never told his name. I observed her now, more hyper and energetic than I had ever seen her. They spoke to each other rapidly above my head; there was an awful smell coming from them both.

Mary took from her pocket some small white rocks and what looked like a brown, dirty, and stained-glass straw. She placed one end to her mouth, put the rocks in the other end, and lit it. Her friend was doing the same thing on the other side of me. The sickening smell filled the truck quickly. My stomach began to ache. They continued their hyped-up conversation above my head, but for me there was no sound coming from their mouths. "Mary," I interrupted, "Mary, I don't feel so good," I whined while clutching my stomach. "Aw, you don't feel good; what is it? Your stomach?" I nodded.

Above me, she said to the man, "See, this is my friend Simone; I don't remember if I said that already, but she is my best friend." She carefully sat me up and placed the warm glass straw between my lips. "Here, baby, this will make you feel better," Mary said softly as she lit the other end. Above my head: "See, she is my best friend; she is only like twelve years old, and she is my best friend. I feel bad for her, though. Because she thinks I am dying of cancer when really, it's A.I.D.S." I inhaled. She lit it again, and I inhaled deeper. I had no idea that I was smoking crack. Everything went black. Everything was gone.

I don't remember anything else from that night. I woke up in "my" bed at Harry's house before daylight. I was also in one of Mary's nightgowns. Daylight started creeping in the window, and I had a hell of a headache. Mary appeared and sat next to me in bed. "Do you remember what I said last night?" She asked. "That you have A.I.D.S.? Yes, but why didn't you tell me?" I knew now that the cancer was a lie. I felt betrayed. Again.

"I didn't want you to be scared of me. I don't know how much you know about it or how you can catch it." It was the early nineties, and my grade was the first to get a comprehensive lesson on H.I.V and A.I.D.S., so I knew quite a bit. I told her what I knew and asked if that was what Beatrice's problem was. It was, so I told her to just explain it to her. She said she had tried, but Beatrice hadn't believed her. "Do you have anything you want to ask?" She questioned. "How did you get it?" That was my only question. She smiled and pulled up her sleeves showing off her healed track marks. "Oh! I figured it was sex!" I said, surprised. She told me more about her life, her arrests, and her time in jail. She also told me about having sex in jail. "How do two girls have sex?" I asked, genuinely curious. She placed two fingers in a V shape across her lips and stuck her tongue out back and forth. We laughed, and everything was okay.

I had to return home. Bianca was expecting Brady and me. I snuck a couple of bottles of liquor home with me in a backpack. This would become routine. The bottles would go to school with me and accompany me to the bathroom regularly.

I had begun to feel uneasy at home, too. It always felt like someone was watching me. Brady and I were supposed to come home from school, let the dog out and then stay in the house. Bianca would call periodically throughout the day. We were supposed to answer the phone only if we heard her voice on the machine. If we didn't hear the phone or we were in the bathroom, we were to call her back. If we didn't call back, she would call us until we answered the phone. Explaining that it took me so long to answer the phone because I felt like someone was watching me change, and I was scared to open my door wasn't going to happen.

Brady and I were often bored. When I was seven, Bianca packed up most of our stuff and put it in the basement. She was trying to sell the house so we could move closer to her job. The house hadn't sold and hadn't been on the market in years. Our stuff remained packed, though. A lot of the toys that were there we had never even gotten to play with. Including a bike, I had gotten for my ninth birthday. I rode the bike around in the basement at twelve after finding it there. Brady and I also took back a lot of our toys. I never did find my favorite stuffed animal. It had been a little gray seal named Finnegan.

While we were down in the basement, being nosy, we found an old camcorder. We played with it a lot. There were no tapes, so we couldn't actually use it, but it was fun to play with. We pretended to make movies of everything. Our dogs, the house, the toys we took back, even the damn TV. Brady was sitting on the floor in his room, playing with it, while I was checking out his action figures. He asked if I had ever seen a dick. I lied and said I had, so he asked if I thought it would look different on camera. I said I didn't know. He talked me into a game of "I'll show you mine if you show me yours." He went first. I aimed the camcorder at him as he sat on the floor buck naked. I saw his face, his feminine boobs, and his fat rolls and jerked away, turning my back. "Look lower," Brady ordered in a scary, intimidating voice I had never heard from him before. I put the camcorder back to my eye and did what I was told. As the camera focused, I jumped back and shouted, "Ew! It is ugly!" I almost

21

dropped the camcorder, and I ran to my room, placing it carefully on his floor.

Brady was in my room within a few minutes, thankfully, with all his clothes on. I had closed and locked my door, but they were like French doors with a lock in the middle. They sucked, and if you pushed on the center of the doors, they just popped open. If you looked through the split in the two doors, where the lock was, you could see the whole room. Doors and locks were pointless.

"Your turn! Brady shouted at me as he stormed in. "I don't want to," I said as I crossed my arms across my chest. He raised his fist and punched me hard in the side of the head and then kicked my leg. "We made a deal, and it is your turn," he ordered. So, I stripped.

He was fifteen and a guy. I had been learning over those years that you just do what guys say. He watched as I removed my clothes. I sat on the floor with my legs open the way he had. He looked through the camcorder at my whole body. When his vision found my crotch, he said, "Oh, I thought it would be like in the magazines and be like open," disappointedly. Brady seemed to think for a moment, which was unusual; I always thought of him as just an idiot. I started to get up. "Sit back down," his voice boomed. I did as I was told. "Hold it open," he instructed forcefully. I refused. Profusely. Brady bent down to my face and spoke clearly through clenched teeth, "You said you would do it. I want to see it. Hold it open. Or I will." I did as I was told.

After looking for a while, he stormed out. I was almost done dressing when he stomped back in. He handed me one of Bianca's disposable razors. "You need to shave it. Or I will," he said. I went to the bathroom, showered, and shaved. By the time I was done, he was asleep. I went to my bed and hugged myself. I cried until sleep took over. The feeling of being watched increased after that. Once, I snatched the door open and found him there. He was jerking off

22

while watching me. These were my weekdays. Weekends were better. Most weekends, Griffith would let me stay with Mary. Weekends were filled with alcohol and drugs and the ability to be free. I spent the nights high. I smoked cigarettes, weed, and crack; I snorted coke. I drank every bottle. This was me. This was life. This was twelve.

Once it started getting warmer out, I wasn't allowed to stay with Mary as often. Having heat was no longer leverage; Brady and I were rarely at the camper alone, but it did happen occasionally. Griffith had to help Harry's sons with something a few hours away, so we were left at the camper on a Sunday. Brady touched me every time I was anywhere near him. He had begun to grab my tits and ass whenever we were alone, which was frequent. I leaned across the cramped kitchen to grab something off the kitchen counter, and he shoved his dick against me. I pushed him backward, and he stumbled and hit his head. The obvious answer was for him to beat the shit out of me, of course. This was also regular.

Nights in Griffith's bed didn't matter anymore. Those nights were just dreams. Just my overactive imagination. Days with Brady, I couldn't escape. At home one sunny afternoon. He asked me for sex while pressing himself against my ass for the hundredth time. "No!" I shouted, amazed that he would even think such a thing, let alone ask. For one thing, I was twelve, and for another, I was his sister.

He had the audacity to ask, "Why not?" I had become better at thinking quickly to avoid things, and obviously, the fact that I was twelve and his sister didn't matter because if they had, he would not have thought it or asked. "Well, what if I got pregnant? It could happen, you know." He looked at me dumbfounded. As I said, he wasn't the brightest. I had been doing his classwork and homework for him all school year because he didn't understand how to do any

23

of it. Brady dropped the subject until he found a bag of balloons. He was overly excited about these balloons. "Big deal Brady, they're balloons; what are you, five?" I teased him. "I can cut this end off," he said, pointing to the mouthpiece, "And use it as a condom," he said flatly. He didn't do it at first.

The first time was at the camper. Griffith had left us there to go help Harry's sons again. I went to the tiny bathroom and changed. I was at the kitchen counter making a sandwich when he grabbed my tit from behind. I elbowed him, but he caught it and pushed me down on the tiny counter. "I just want to know what it's like," he said desperately. "I don't!" I yelled at him.

"Come on, just let me do it one time," he begged, holding a pre-cut balloon. He was already pulling my pants down. Brady must have had his pants down when he grabbed me because I could already feel his skin against mine. "I will tell mom!" I yelled defiantly. He had me pinned against the counter and was putting the balloon on. "She won't believe you. She will say it's just your imagination," he said as he tried to force his balloon-wrapped dick inside of me. It wouldn't go in, and he kept pushing. I yelped in pain as he pushed harder. There was a gallon jug of water on the counter; he poured some on his hand and wiped it all over me and his balloon. Then he pushed harder. It went in. He thrust over and over again. I laid face down on the counter as he held my head down. I cried silent tears that no one would ever see. That no one cared to see. Nowhere was safe. Not for someone like me. I was dying inside a little more every day. Why couldn't I die for real? My mind drifted away to wherever it went that it was safe. I knew what was supposed to happen to girls after sex. There was supposed to be cramping and bleeding. It didn't happen, and I didn't know why.

When my mind would disappear, I never knew where it went. When it came back, I would always be in a different place than when it left. This time I was on the convertible couch in Griffith's camper. My clothes were on, and Brady was making a sandwich and throwing bread at me. "Eat, you asshole," he said, so I did. Balloons became common just like everything else did. Until he ran out; by then, he didn't care anymore. I would thank God that I didn't get pregnant, but I had stopped believing in God when I was eleven. Once while laying on top of me in my bed, "Have you kissed a boy before?" Brady asked, with his face just inches away from mine. "Yeah," I lied. "Well, do you want to? Just to know what it's like?" He asked with curiosity as he was forcing the life out of me with each thrust. I could smell his foul breath lingering in the air as his body pressed against mine. "I have already kissed guys; I already know what it is like." I lied again, and thankfully he just let it go.

I got Griffith to let me spend some weekends with Mary. This was one of those weekends. The liquor flowed, and the drugs took me away. It was a warm sunny day. We had spent the morning at the methadone clinic, so Mary could get her medication that she would trade for crack. "We are going to my parent's house today. You have to be good. They can't know we're high. They don't like it." I agreed to be good and gave no indication that we were high as we smoked crack on our way to their house. When we got there, I claimed I was really tired from all the studying I had been doing and asked if I could take a nap on their couch. I didn't know how to appear to be not high other than to just be asleep. I faked sleep as I listened to Mary tell her parents about me. She told them how I was good for her, that I kept her straight, I kept her good. As they finished dinner, Mary "woke me up," and I cried because there was mustard on my hot dog. I hate mustard. It was a child-like moment. It was good for Mary. It showed her parents she was an adult that was washing mustard off a hot dog for a helpless child.

That night we sat in "my" bed at Harry's, talking. She told me how she had known Griffith since before she lived there. Mary told

25

me he had worked at a strip club she used to dance at. She told me about what a great guy he was, and I struggled to keep my secret in the vault. Alcohol made that hard. Mary told me that she and Griffith had decided to tell me she had cancer together but that he had known the truth. "Your dad loves you so much, Simone. You are so lucky to have him," she had continued her thought, and my words just fell out, "But he doesn't love me the right way," I blurted it out with a chug of Vodka. She looked at me, confused, but her face told me to go on.

"I don't like the way he touches me, and he isn't my real dad." I chugged some more. I didn't notice then, but when I go back to that night in my memories, I can see the pain on her face. "I know he isn't your dad, but he is the only dad you have ever known; he is your dad. You have to be mistaken; he would never. He is such a good man; he just wouldn't do that; Do you mean it was someone else? He takes care of you. He takes care of me. I am in love with him, and if I didn't have A.I.D.S., we could be together. You have to, you just, you're wrong..." All of her thoughts came at one time, and she walked away in the middle of them. She didn't stay with me that night; she stayed in her room with Kurt.

The following weekend, Mary and Kurt moved out. She was rambling to Griffith about being late on rent and that she had to go, she would send the money as soon as she could. She wouldn't even look at me. I was standing right next to Griffith, but I seemed to be invisible. This woman who had been my best friend for over a year, this woman who had given me salvation and destruction without knowing or even trying, could no longer see me. Mary got in Kurt's car, and they drove away. She didn't even say goodbye to me.

For the first, but not the last time, I went upstairs to say goodbye to the space of a person I loved. I went to her room; the only sound was the echo of my shoes on the wooden stairs. Her room was littered with needles, bent spoons, crack stems, baggies, weed seeds, and stems. The smell of crack, which I had grown to love, lingered in the air. The room that I had often stayed in was open, and I saw two bottles on the bed with a note. Jack and Vodka, my favorite and hers. The note simply said, "I'm sorry; I love you." On a hunch, I lifted the mattress and found the stash she had left me. Not a lot of anything, but some weed, crack, and coke. It wouldn't last me long. I put the stash in my pocket, threw away the note, and walked away with the bottles. No one would think anything of me carrying around liquor; that was just another day.

I had begun sneaking out of the house while Bianca was at work. I was restless. I met people. Older people. People with drugs. Older guys with drugs. They didn't care about my age. I didn't have to pay them, which was cool since I had no money. Once they were high, they rarely knew what they were doing, and I learned that quickly. They didn't notice which way or to whom they were passing the joint, stem, or straw. If they did, I would flirt a little, something I learned how to do way too young, or I would claim I was just holding it for them. They were careless and dropped things often, things that I picked up. As long as I was back in my window before Bianca got home or Brady noticed my absence, it was all fine.

Only once did I get home to find my window closed and locked. Bianca's car wasn't there, so I knew Brady had gone looking for me. I was trying to find a way to get the side door open when he heard me and opened the door. Brady grilled me about where I had been. I didn't lie; I told him I was out with friends. He hit me a few good times and yelled at me, "If mom found out, I would be the one in trouble for not watching you, you little bitch." While I was on the floor recovering from the punches, he kicked me in the ribs hard. I heard and felt a crack.

When Bianca got home from work, and I heard her coming to my room, I forced myself to lay down and act like I was asleep. The pain was excruciating, and I struggled to breathe. I peeked through the sliver of the one eye I dared to leave open. Once I knew she was gone, I sat back up and painfully gasped for air. I crept silently to my closet and my stash. There was no way I was going to be able to handle the pain, and I already knew telling her was pointless.

I had a collection of alcohol-filled beverages and a small number of drugs. I knew I couldn't smoke weed or crack; someone would smell those. I selected Mary's bottle of Vodka and drank deeply. I drank until the pain was bearable and then a little extra, just in case. I didn't sleep much after I got back in bed; what sleep I did get, I was sitting up.

The next morning before school, I sipped from the bottle slowly before putting it in my backpack. I left the house and then decided not to take the bus. I walked the mile and a half to school instead. Every step and every breath was agonizing. When I got there, I went right to the bathroom to drink. I went to the school bathroom a lot that year.

I had two groups of school friends. The goodie, goodie smart, and unpopular kids were Sophie, Heather, Jessica, and Joanna. Then there were the also unpopular loser kids, Tiffany, Nate, Nora, Tyler, and Kristen. I had a couple of other random friends also, the ones that didn't really fit in anywhere, like me. Raynelle, whom no one liked; everyone said she looked like a boy. I always thought she looked like Freddy Mercury from Queen, which I thought was cool. Then there was Kyle. Nora and I had met Kyle when I was twelve, and Kyle was fourteen. Nora and I both had a crush on him, but he said we were too young. "You guys have probably never even kissed a boy before, and I have had sex with five different girls," he told us with a cocky attitude once. We didn't see Kyle often.

Nora taught me how to shoplift, and I became addicted to it. It was just another self-destructive thrill. Bianca was one of the only thin people in our family. I still swear that the worst thing that could have happened to her was to have a fat daughter, and that is what she got. Brady was big also, but I was a girl, so I got more of the backlash, which led to her being controlling and overly restrictive with food.

We were allowed no junk, ever. Our cereal was set out on the counter each morning, pre-measured, and covered in Saran wrap. The milk for the cereal was also pre-measured in the fridge in two separate cups. The gallon jug was marked so she would know if we took any. We were only allowed healthy cereals. After school, we were not allowed to use the stove to make dinner; we were allowed to eat peanut butter and jelly and use the microwave only. There was never more than half a loaf of bread in the house, and it was often moldy.

I learned how to make boxed macaroni and cheese in the microwave before the cooperate world did. I had to make Brady's food as well as my own because he swore I did it better; I complied because I would be hit if I didn't. MicroMagic sandwiches and fries were often dinners. They were a great concept, but they tasted like their cardboard packaging. These things were allowed because they were measured and consistent; it didn't matter that they were actually crap food and not helping our weight. The fact that we were not allowed outside and were just supposed to sit on our asses didn't help either. So, when Nora showed me how to shoplift, I stole candy. Loads of it. Brady never found my drug or alcohol stash, but once he did find my candy stash. He demanded to know where it came from, and I didn't lie. He made me steal double so he could have some too.

On the weekends, when we were at work with Bianca, meals were often forgotten. Breakfast would be at the local deli or nothing. Lunch was nothing unless Bianca wanted something. Dinner was usually pizza. If we were with Griffith, he would let me get whatever I wanted and as much of it as I could handle. He had always picked on Bianca for being too thin or exercising. I think he liked fat girls. I also think he thought getting me whatever I wanted would buy my silence. Little did he know I had no conscious thought or memory of whatever he was doing. My mind left the second I was alone with him. So, I guess I should count my addictions. Drugs, alcohol, shoplifting, and food. I would be lying if I said it ended there, but I would develop more as the years went on. I still struggle with them all to this day.

Bianca found my stash of candy once and demanded to know where it came from. I couldn't tell her the truth. I couldn't tell her a friend bought it for me; she would call the parents of whatever friend I named. I lied and told her Griffith had been buying it for me. She called him and told him off. He didn't deny it and never said anything to me about it. He took the heat for that.

I completely stopped taking the bus to school. I had to walk past most of my loser friends' houses to get there, so I would walk to each of their houses, and we would walk together. I feel bad for it, but I was embarrassed to be friends with Tiffany. I was already a loser. An outcast. She was more so, and it made me a bigger loser by association.

Nora and I started skipping school often. I would leave the house, walk to her house, and then we would double back around to my house. Bianca was usually gone by the time we got there, and if she wasn't, there were plenty of places we could hide until she was gone. The school would call and leave a message with every missed day, but I was there to delete them from the machine. We didn't really do anything when we skipped. We sat in my room and listened to music, smoked cigarettes in my yard, talked about boys, or gossiped. In some ways, these days of peace were better than the high I got from drugs.

All of my loser friends smoked. All of their parents smoked except mine. Bianca had quit when I was seven, and Griffith had never picked up the habit. They would all sneak a few cigarettes from their parents. I would sneak some from my Grandma when Griffith would bring us there to visit. It was Bianca's parents, but she didn't get along with them and rarely brought us to see them. Grandma smoked three different kinds at once. She always had three packs open at each of her frequently stopped locations, by her bed, the table, and her bathroom. On a good visit, when most of her packs were close to full, I could walk away with over a pack. We all shared our stolen stashes and smoked on our way to and from school. Griffith would also buy them for me, but usually only on weekends, and he would only let me smoke them at his house.

I often faked sick or injured during gym class. Seriously, what fat girl wants to change in the locker room and then participate in activities meant for skinny people? Not this one. Gym class has always been a breeding ground for bullying, and the locker room was worse than the class. My boobs were huge, and it was just more ammunition. Bianca told me, "Those girls make fun of you for having big boobs because they are jealous that they don't have any," it may have been the only thing she was ever right about. I went to the nurse's office for almost every gym class. "Simone, I am glad you are here. I have a list of absences here for days that I know you were here," Nurse Nancy greeted me during one of these days. I was lost for words and looked at the paper she was holding out to me. I didn't realize I had missed that many days. In a way, it had become just another addiction.

"How do you know I was here?" I asked her nervously. "You walk to school, and you pass my house on the way." Shit. "Oh, really, I didn't know that; where do you live?" I asked her to try to both stall and calm the rising panic. "I live on Dragon Tree Road. The big brown two-story with the flowers out front." Fuck, that's just a few houses before Nora's. I pointed at the first date on the list and told her I had gotten sick while I was walking and turned around to go home. I struggled to find explanations for the other days. I picked a couple of others and told her I had gotten sick those days, too. I was honest about one day. I told her I had fallen on ice and laid there for hours before I could get up again. I had fallen and hit my head pretty hard. Once I could get up, I chose to just lay there and hope for death. I didn't tell her that. In the end, lost for any other excuses; I told her some of them must be teacher errors, and the rest I just didn't remember. She sent me to talk to the attendance office secretary, Mrs. G.

I explained the situation to Mrs. G, who said I needed to talk to the teachers about the days that I felt were errors, and we would discuss the rest afterward. I went to the teachers of my four core classes and had them almost convinced that I had been there, and they were wrong. I had done and turned in every missed assignment on time. They agreed that if I could produce my notes from class for the seven days in question, they would change them. I spent lunch quickly copying Sophie's notes for all four classes. Those seven, plus three, I claimed I had gotten sick and one I had fallen on ice. Ten days were crossed off the list. There were still over twenty on it, though. I told Mrs. G. and Nurse Nancy with teary eyes that I just couldn't remember what had happened those days. They agreed not to call Bianca but made it clear that on any days I missed going forward, they would call her at work instead of at home. I didn't know then why they let me slide; now I think they knew that something was wrong in my life, just not what. I started writing notes for missed days and forging Griffith's signature. I couldn't forge Bianca's. She wrote too fancy, but Griffith's handwriting was worse than mine. Forged notes and a splint shoplifted from Super X got me out of the next six weeks of gym class. No sixth-grade square dancing for this fat girl.

I continued using drugs. I pocketed what the hardcore addicts would drop or forget about; that way, I would have something for when I really needed it. I met a dealer named Todd. He wanted me to shoot heroin, and I wasn't interested. I wasn't scared of needles, but I was scared to end up like Mary. I was scared of A.I.D.S. Todd was twenty-four and stood about six foot three inches tall. He was also over two hundred pounds of solid muscle. I probably should have been scared of him, but I wasn't.

Nothing much scared me anymore. I knew my place in all situations that I was familiar with. I knew when to cry quietly and when to cry loudly. I knew when to open my mouth, and I knew when to shut the fuck up. Todd was different, though; he was hard to read. A "friend" had arranged our meeting when I said I needed more than what I was able to get by sharing with those I met. I had been given no information about Todd other than he could help with what I needed. That he would often trade free drugs for selling for him, that was a deal I was interested in.

Todd looked at me hard. "How old are you? Fourteen?" He asked with a smirk. He was looking at my face, and not my tits, which was uncommon with men, and I didn't really know what to make of it. "Twelve," I matched his cold eyes with my own and sat down in the chair he had offered. He rolled his eyes. "You are just a kid, and you think I should trust you with my shit?" He looked right through me; I may as well have been invisible. "I only look like a kid when you look at my face," I could match his attitude all day. Todd glanced down, smiled, and said, "Point taken." Todd was silent as he looked through me and thought. "Okay, I will let you have free

33

of charge all the weed you want if you make me five hundred dollars a week. The crack and coke you have been after are different. I will give you some if you do this," he placed a syringe in front of me. "I just need a little rock; I am not doing that for some rock," I told him, but little did I know I was about to make a deal with the devil.

"You don't even need to do it yourself, kid. I will do it for you." He had a baggie of crack in his hand that he shook in front of me. I could almost taste it. I could almost smell it. I could almost feel the sweet nothingness it brought. I knew the needle was clean; I had seen him open it. "Fine," I snapped, "but only one time." His eyes changed; they softened, and he knew he had won. "Good girl, now let me see those big ass titties you flaunt in my customer's faces, so you get your high for free." I stood and took off my shirt and bra, and sat back down. Todd stepped closer and lifted one of my "big ass titties" while telling me, "We don't want any visible marks now, do we," with a twisted smile. I tried to back out of the deal, but he kicked the chair, and I fell backward, smacking my head into the floor. Todd straddled me, and I thought, "Okay, rape. I can handle that. I am used to it." He tied my hands and feet, put me back in the chair, and tied me to the chair. He carefully and surprisingly gently lifted my breast again and successfully injected the heroin. I hadn't had time to think; I was already gone. Sweet, peaceful nothingness. I know now that it was going to happen no matter what. It didn't matter. It was all just another way of dying inside.

I worked with Todd for a while. He shot me up many more times, more times than I care to admit. I only had to be tied down once in a while. I had many different lives in those days. I was able to keep them all separate, even though I still don't know how. Not only did I keep up with my schoolwork, but I also had to do Brady's. I played all of my roles well. The friend, the daughter, the loser, the student, the sister, the thief, the dealer, the addict, the punching bag, the molested, the raped, the drunk. The dead.

I got sloppy shoplifting. I had gotten greedy, and I had a need for sugar all the time. I didn't know then it was from the drugs. I had cut a big hole in the inside of my coat, and I would fill it, along with my pockets, inside and outside, and sleeves with candy every few days. I was loaded down with as much as I could fit in my coat and headed out the door when the store manager popped up in front of me. "Are you going to pay for the candy in your pockets?" He asked me. I had no money.

Nora covered a couple of dollars for me, but it was her uncle's money, and she couldn't use much of it. I started filling a basket with what I couldn't buy, and that was only from my regular coat pockets. "I have one question before I call the cops. Why?" The manager asked. I saw my fate. I knew the beating this was going to lead to. I cried at the thought and told him, "My mom works far away. There is no food at my house. This is for my brother and me to eat," It was a half lie. He escorted me to the back room and simply said, "Wait." When he came back, he gestured for me to follow him. I did. When we got to the front of the store, he handed me two full brown paper bags from the neighboring grocery store. The bags were full of food, actual food. He held the door open for me, and on my way out, he very sternly told me, "Do not come back to this store. Ever." I never went back to that Super X, and I became scared to shoplift from any other stores, too, at least for a little while. Time was passing, and I was...

Becoming a Teenager

The teen years are supposed to be filled with wonder and new experiences. What new experiences could I have at thirteen? The truth is, I don't remember much of that year. For my thirteenth birthday, Bianca had promised to take me to the mall. We were going to go shopping, and she was going to get me new clothes, hair stuff and have lunch. It was going to be just the two of us. I was so excited to finally be doing something with my mom. It didn't even really matter what it was.

Bianca woke up that morning with a migraine, though. I spent the day taking care of her. I put wet wash cloths on her head and neck. I held her hair while she got sick. I helped her undress, got her into a warm tub, washed her, dried her, and dressed her. I held water for her while she sipped it. I tried not to be disappointed, or at least not to show it. She was my mom, and she was sick; she needed someone to take care of her. Bianca always was sick when she was supposed to do something with me, though. I had really been looking forward to that day, and it was ruined because she was sick. I felt a heaviness in my heart that I now know was resentment.

Eventually, she was feeling better, and we went to the mall. We would not have much time, though, and we would not be able to go to many stores. That didn't matter to me; what mattered was that we were going at all. She was insistent that we get clothes from stores like 5-7-9, but stores like that didn't have anything that fit me. I was a size twelve. That was simply unacceptable to her. We wound up in Claire's because if she couldn't find me girly clothes that she found acceptable, she could at least find me girlie accessories. I found a hair straightener that I really wanted. I had had long, beautiful thick hair, but when I was eleven, she swore I didn't care for it properly and had most of it cut off. The little hair I had piled on top of my head in curls wouldn't do anything. It was the source of a lot of my bullying. If I could straighten it, then that would be one less target for the bullies. Bianca didn't want me to have it but agreed, letting me know it would be all I got. I got it, and she complained about it the whole way home.

I went to Griffith's house that night. I was sitting on the edge of his bed. He had moved into Harry's house not long after Mary and Kurt had moved out. Griffith had their room. When Brady and I were there, Brady slept on the floor, and I slept in Griffith's bed. No matter where in that room I fell asleep, that was where I woke up. Griffith brought me my birthday gift. It wasn't in a box; there was no wrapping paper or bow. He handed me a simple but pretty ring. It was gold, and the four prongs on top all twisted to the side like they were reaching out for something. "This ring is special. Do you know what it is?" Griffith asked. I shook my head as I spun it around in my fingers. "This was my grandmother's engagement ring. I want you to have it. There is no stone in it. I will take you to have a stone put in it when you are older. When you are eighteen." That made sense. I was an irresponsible kid, and no one gave expensive jewelry to irresponsible kids, right?

Christmas wasn't a big deal in my house. No holidays were. For Christmas that year, I got nothing but clothes. I know, most thirteen-year-old girls dream, but I really wasn't a girlie girl. I also didn't have the same taste as Bianca. She got me an assortment of shirts in bright colors with matching pants. The pants were all spandex. If you were a nineties kid, you understand the stigma of spandex. It would be one more thing for me to be bullied for. The fact that they were bright, and in some cases, even neon colors, didn't help. Bianca told me years later, "I thought it would help you to lose weight if the other kids were picking on you." Yes, my own mother set me up to be bullied intentionally. That isn't particularly surprising. She tried everything to bribe me into losing weight. She offered money, a flat rate for every five pounds lost, and a bonus for every twenty pounds. She offered me a new wardrobe if I lost enough to be a size five. She even promised they would be name-brand clothes. It wasn't that I didn't want to lose weight; it was that I didn't know how. Her comments were hurtful, more so than the kids at school. Griffith was also constantly stuffing me with food. I was pulled in two different directions, and neither seemed right.

The middle school social worker, Mr. K., had arranged for me to go to a camp that summer. Bianca would not have to pay a dime. It would be my first time away from family overnight, and it would be the first time I would have no drugs or alcohol in two years. Griffith and Bianca drove me there and dropped me off. Again, I was a loser. I didn't have anything to kill the pain of my existence. I also didn't have anyone sticking me with things, dicks, or syringes, so I took the trade-off.

I was miserable. I always felt sick. I was nauseated, vomiting, had migraines, and was super emotional. I cried over everything, which was very unlike me. The camp counselors and nurse were convinced I was just homesick. I didn't believe that, but I also didn't know it was withdrawal until years later. On the second to last night of camp, they had a big dance. Attendance was mandatory, but you had to answer a question to get in. They thought it was a witty question, and a lot of the kids struggled to produce an answer deemed suitable. I thought it was stupid. If we had to be there, we shouldn't have had to do anything to get in. The question I also thought it was stupid. It was my turn, and two preppy counselors blocked my entrance to the dance that I didn't want to attend to begin with. "What is the meaning of life?" They asked me with ridiculous matching smiles. "It means you aren't dead," I told them with a flat tone and a flatter expression. I was granted admittance at once, and my answer was voted best of the night.

The camp nurse had given me extra Advil for the headache that had plagued me since my arrival. It wasn't doing anything. They gave us punch in plastic cups, played all the popular songs, and had crepe paper strung from the ceiling. I wished for Vodka to spike the punch and some crack to deal with the noise of the kids surrounding me. They were all laughing, talking, dancing, and plain loud. My stomach ached, and my head pounded. The whole thing was fucking stupid.

A teen male counselor approached me. He smelled like weed, so I didn't mind. I thought about asking him to share, but I didn't. "Hey, Simone. You know you may have enjoyed it more here if you had given it a shot. We all know the signs of a troubled kid, and you have a troubled kid written all over you. Let yourself have some fun." He was right. I did talk to a couple of other kids. I danced with a boy whose name I never knew because he wasn't important enough to know. The next night we had a huge campfire. I had extra Advil again. It still did nothing. I tried, though. I participated in roasting marshmallows, and I responded with words instead of my middle finger when someone spoke to me. My headache was still awful, but my stomach was calming. I decided that night I would not use drugs anymore. I would stick to alcohol and weed.

Griffith and Brady picked me up the next day. Five minutes after we left the camp, Griffith passed me a beer. I crushed it in two gulps, and Brady handed me another. Several miles and several beers later, Brady was asleep against the passenger side door. He fell asleep telling me some new guy named Brad had moved into the large bedroom at Harry's. I really didn't care. I just wanted more to drink. Something stronger than beer would have been great. I leaned a little and started to doze off. When I felt Griffith's hand sliding up the leg of my shorts to my ass and then his fingers forcing inside of me, it didn't even matter. My mind was already gone.

Griffith woke Brady and me when we stopped for dinner at a diner. I got out and noticed I was sticky and not from sweat. I looked down at myself and saw that I was dripping blood. It was already down to my calves. Brady got in the back of the truck and got me a change of clothes and a sweatshirt that was tied around my waist. Most of the blood was on the back of me. Griffith walked into the dinner with his right hand stuffed deep into his pocket and asked for a table for three and the location of the bathroom. I departed them at once for the bathroom. I cleaned myself up and changed my clothes. With my blood-soaked clothes stashed in a plastic shopping bag, I peeked out of the bathroom to see where Griffith and Brady were. I found them quickly and joined them at the table; when I got there, Griffith went to the men's room with his right hand still stuffed in his pocket.

The rest of the ride was quiet. We had to stop frequently so I didn't keep bleeding through everything. Brady complained about the stops. Griffith stayed quiet. His cold hard eyes never even glanced in my direction.

I wasn't back long before I was leaving again. I hadn't even had time to go to Griffith's house between trips. My friend Jessica's family was going away on vacation. As a reward for good grades, her parents Dean and Dawn, allowed her to bring a friend. Her sister Jean would have been allowed to bring a friend also, but her grades were not good enough. The five of us would be going to Assateague Island, Maryland. Jessica's aunt and uncle were going too, but they had their own vehicle and would be in their own tent. We drove to Rhode Island and took a Ferry the rest of the way. When we needed supplies, we would take a Ferry from the Island to Ocean City.

The island was beautiful. There were wild deer that roamed free, and we were right on the beach. Jessica's parents had a two-room tent. The small front room went to her dad, and the bigger back room went to us four girls. On our first night there, I woke up with sudden lower abdominal pain. It raced across me from side to side. I was in tears as the pain intensified. In a sudden rush of relief, I peed and then collapsed back into sleep. The next day we took the ferry to Ocean City, where all the sheets were washed, the air mattresses were dealt with, and we got some groceries. No one in Jessica's family ever said a word about it. They never knew how much I appreciated that or that I still do. Luckily, it didn't happen again.

The island was a peaceful time for me. Jessica, Jean, and I ran around the beach freely. We laughed, we talked about school and boys, we ran in the water, and occasionally got to pet one of the wild deer. Mostly, we were just kids. I was a kid. Except for the water balloon fight. Jessica's uncle asked Dean, "How old is she?" With a lustful look in his eye that I knew well. "Almost fourteen. But look at those tits! Watch this." Dean replied as he launched a water balloon at me. It hit me in my tit so hard it bounced off and broke in the air. I was soaked, instantly turning my shirt see-through. I later approached with a water balloon that I was going to throw at Dean. "If you hit me with that, you are walking home," he said when he saw me coming. I turned and smashed it on the ground. A wave of anger flared inside of me. Why was it anyone could do anything they fucking wanted to me, but I could do nothing back to them?

On a day trip to Ocean City, a deer chewed through our food tent. I will never forget the big bite mark on the side of a watermelon and a box of cereal. I overheard Dawn say, "At least the cake is in the cooler." Jessica replied with a quick "Mom!!! Shhh!" That night Jessica kept trying to keep me in the camp bathroom. Finally, she told me they were setting up a surprise birthday cake for me, and I had to wait. I had already known when I heard her mom's comment earlier. When she let me out of the bathroom, I acted surprised. It was the nicest thing anyone had ever done for my birthday. It was a beautiful, thoughtful gesture. I slept peacefully that night. In the morning, we loaded up and got back on the ferry to go home. I wished I could get lost on the beach. I wished I could live the rest of

41

my life in the wild with the deer. I wished to be a kid on the beach forever. It was time to go back to the real world, though. The world where I wasn't a kid. My birthday was the next day, which meant it was.

The Summer (and more) Of '93

It would be my first time at Harry's house with Griffith in a few weeks. The morning of my fourteenth birthday, I was in the kitchen when the new guy came downstairs. I saw him, and it was like breathing for the first time. He was so cute. My heart thumped like a wild horse and beat in slow motion at the same time. He didn't notice me. This seemed utterly impossible to me. Men noticed me. Even though I was fat, ugly, and had fucked up teeth, they just noticed me. His shaggy jet-black shoulder-length hair was striking against his milky white skin with unusually unmasculine rosy cheeks. "I am going to fuck him," I declared in my mind as he grabbed something to eat and went back upstairs. I spent as much time as possible over the next several days in the shared areas of the house.

Just hoping to be around him. To just breathe the air he gave me from his own existence. He struck up a brief conversation with me once over something he had read in the newspaper. As the days stretched, our conversations increased. I always replied as sarcastically and nonchalantly as I could. He worked at McDonald's and didn't have a car. He was complaining one hot afternoon about having to walk to work; he said he hated to walk to work alone. "I will walk with you," I offered. "Really? You don't have to," he said with a hint of happiness. "Yeah, sure. I'm bored anyway."

We left and talked the whole way there. I was in heaven listening to him. It didn't matter what he was saying. Just as he was talking, I learned that he had moved there from Poughkeepsie, where he had been cheated on and dumped by a girl named Crystal. When we got there, he thanked me for walking him and asked me to meet him when he got off work, too. I didn't show my enthusiasm in front of him. After he was inside, though, I squealed like a cheerleader. I spent the day counting the hours until it was time to go meet him.

This also became regular; I would walk him to and from work every chance I got. When he wasn't at work, he was hanging out with me.

We smoked cigarettes, listened to rock and classic rock music, and talked. I started hanging out with Raynelle a lot, also. Her mom would drop her off at Griffith's, and the two of us would sleep on the floor in Griffith's room. Brady had taken over the smaller room that no one ever wanted to rent. Sometimes, I would wake up in Griffith's bed. Neither Raynelle nor I knew how I got there. The days were spent hanging out with Brad. The three of us were inseparable on days he didn't have to work. His smile lit up my heart. By early August, I began to see a spark in his eyes when he would look at me. It reflected the spark I felt in my own eyes every time I saw him. When Bianca would demand I come home for a few days, I would spend as much time as possible on the phone with him. Or I would be at the community pool with Autumn from down the street. She was a friend I had known since I was six and never really liked; Bianca approved of her, though.

Brad would sometimes go away and stay at his friend Will's house for a weekend. Brad had told Griffith that when he wasn't there, Raynelle and I could stay in his room. We could when he was there, too, if we didn't mind sleeping on the floor. So, we did, whether he was there or not. I would still sometimes wake up in Griffith's bed, and no one would know how I got there.

Around mid-August, Brad, Raynelle, and I were hanging out laying on the front lawn at Harry's. I went inside to get us drinks, and when I came out, they were hysterically laughing. After they had calmed themselves down, Raynelle said they had seen a cloud that looked like a dick, but they gave each other a look. Raynelle went home that night, and Brad had to work. I stayed on the phone with her all night; we did that a lot when she couldn't be there; it was another way to stay safe. I wasn't allowed to stay in Brad's room when Raynelle wasn't there. It was the first rule Griffith had ever given me. When she wasn't there, I had to stay in Griffith's room, in Griffith's bed. After Raynelle and I had stopped giggling for a moment, she was able to squeeze in a confession. "I have to tell you something," she began. I was instantly nervous, and my breath caught in my throat. "When you went inside today...Brad asked me if you like him," she said the words in slow motion. "Oh my God! Ray, you didn't tell him? Please tell me you didn't?! I asked her frantically. "I didn't know what to say, so I said yes, no, maybe, well yes, but don't tell her I told you. He then asked me not to tell you that he asked." I didn't blame her for spilling my secret. All the big ones were locked in my vault. No one had access to them. Not even me.

The next morning when Brad got up, he came right to Griffith's room. I was sitting on the bed leaning against the wall, smoking, and listening to Brad's Motley Crue tape for the millionth time. "Hey," he said as he flopped into the chair, I returned his hey, and then we just sat. We sat in a silence that stretched an eternity. "She told you, didn't she?" The question snapped accusingly from his mouth. "What?" I asked, trying to play dumb. "Ray told you I asked if you like me. I am not stupid; you won't even look at me. I didn't want you to know because now things are going to be all weird," Brad whined.

"Okay, yeah, she told me," I looked into his eyes. He sounded mad, but that wasn't what his eyes showed. "Well, it isn't like I won't want to hang out with you because you like me. I want things to stay how they are. I don't want it to be weird. You're my best friend." His voice softened as he finished his thought. "Well, don't make it weird then," I snapped at him. He went back to relaxing in the chair. Brad muttered something that I couldn't hear; I asked him what he said. "I can't talk to you about it. Not right now. I think I am going to go to Will's house for a few days," he said as he walked away without looking at me. He didn't want things to be weird, but he couldn't talk to me, and he was leaving. Right, that made a lot of sense. I waited until I heard him leave to cry. Loudly.

A few days later, he was back, and he acted like nothing had ever happened. I was again sitting on Griffith's bed smoking with the music loud when Brad popped in and asked me to turn the music off. "I wrote you a letter. I want to give it to you and sit here while you read it. But you have to understand that you can't keep it. After you read it, we have to tear it up and burn it." Of course, I agreed.

Brad brought me a two-and-a-half-page letter. I wish I could still remember the letter word for word. I can't, though. I remember his neat, clear, cursive handwriting. I remember seeing the way he looked at me out of the corner of his eye as I read it. The gist of the letter was that we had become best friends, that I had helped him ease the pain of losing his last girlfriend, and that he was falling in love with me. That loving me was wrong because of my age, which was why he sometimes left; sometimes, he had to be away from me to ease his feelings.

I read it once, twice, and three times. I lifted my head, and our eyes met. I saw the spark there that had been building over the weeks, it was intensified now, and I saw fear. I wondered what he feared. That I would treat him differently? Not a chance. That I would reject him? Never. That I would tell someone? Not even if hell froze over. "So, you wrote me a letter to tell me that you are falling in love with me, but we can't be together because I am fourteen?" He gave no response, but his eyes got colder.

"Do you think I don't already know we can't be together? I am fourteen; I am not fucking stupid. Big fucking deal, I have a crush on you. Woohoo. It isn't like I expect anything to happen." There was more silence, but neither of us looked away. I handed him back the pages, and he tore them up. We went to the bathroom and burned them together, dropping the remnants into the toilet and flushing as they fell. When Griffith and Brady got back from work, Brad and I were sitting on Griffith's floor watching The Simpsons and laughing as usual. Things were back to normal. His letter and his words filled my heart in a way I can't describe. It felt like my heart was pumping fire instead of blood.

Summer ended, as did my endless days with Brad. I returned home to Bianca's with Brady. That first three-day week of school lasted forever. I went out the window nightly to kill time. I hadn't done any drugs all summer, but this was a different place. I could manage most of the days, but the nights were harder. The nights I got restless. I couldn't wait until Friday. As always, when Griffith got there, I chugged a beer. I drank another two on our way to his house and another when we got there. It was the weekend after Labor Day in 1993. Brad's door was closed when I got there, and I didn't see him that night. I could smell his Preferred Stock, a smell that I had grown to love that summer. The first scent to make my heart flutter into my stomach and awaken a sexual urge inside of me. A smell that my heart still remembers.

Saturday, Brad was off work. We were playing around wrestling in Griffith's room that early afternoon. The sun was shining, and my laugh was easy and real. Brad tackled me on the floor, putting both arms around me and throwing his leg over me, "There, now I have caught you, and you can't go anywhere," he declared. We were facing each other, my face by his chest, breathing in his smell, breathing in the life, I didn't know he was giving me. I was utterly relaxed and calm. I was wrapped in the arms of a man, yet I was safe.

Brad's next actions were unexpected but not unwelcome. His middle finger touched my chin, his index finger my cheek, as he gently lifted my face upward toward his. Our lips met with a burning passion, a longing that we had both been feeling for weeks. Our lips began to part, and our tongues met in an even greater passion. My first real kiss. With a man I knew I loved. We rolled around on the floor, kissing for what seemed like forever. Brad gently kissed my neck and then back to my lips. His hand moved gently up and down my body while his other hand held my head and neck. Brad opened his pants and put my hand on his dick. I began to rub him through his boxers while he opened my pants. Brad's warm hand slipped down my pants, and his finger found its way effortlessly inside of me.

The kissing was amazing and seemed last an eternity. My stomach had been bursting with butterflies since the first touch of our lips. I felt a hot wetness that I had never felt before. Brad stopped as suddenly as he had started and looked down at me, "Do you wanna do it?" I nodded. "Are you sure? Because you can't tell your dad or your friends about this?" I nodded again. "I'll be right back. I have to go get a condom," he said as he held his pants up on the way out. Brad put the condom on in his room as I laid there waiting. When he came back in, he laid on me, and we kissed again as he took my pants halfway off. He entered me, and two seconds later (two if I am being generous), he was done. "Now I feel guilty," he said as I thought, "What, that's it?" We went to the bathroom, flushed the condom, burned, and flushed the wrapper. He would not look at me. "I am going to take a nap," he said as he went to his room and closed his door.

What had I done wrong? Did he not want to? He had certainly seemed to, and he started it. He initiated the kiss, the touching, the fondling, and the sex. I had completely let him lead the way. Did I do it wrong? Was I a lousy lay? I cried myself to sleep. When I woke up, his door was still closed, but Griffith and Brady were back. Which meant so was the beer. I went to the yard to drink with them

48

and all the guys that hung out there. When Brad got up, he came down and sat in a chair on the porch, smoking and staring out into the distance. His eyes were dark, brooding, and unreadable. "I am going to Will's for a few days," he said to no one in particular. After he was gone, I went to his room and clung to one of his shirts, breathing in his smell while I cried on his floor. Griffith came in and told me I wasn't allowed to stay in there if Raynelle wasn't there. I walked to the door slowly, "Go fuck yourself," I said firmly and slammed the door.

Brad had gotten his own phone line in his room; he didn't call me that night. I spent Sunday alone. Alone with your own thoughts in my life isn't a good place to be. I thought of killing myself. I thought about just walking away. I thought about drugs. A lot. I thought about calling Todd; he would have delivered. That was part of my other life, though, and my lives couldn't ever mingle. I also didn't want to know what Todd would want for a delivery fee.

Griffith and Brady had left that morning before I got up, but they had left me breakfast and money. I did what came naturally. I drank. I finished off all the beer Harry had in his fridge. I drank the open bottles of Jack, Vodka, and Rum that I had stashed throughout Griffith's room. I went out to the barn, and I drank the warm beer that was stored there. By the time Griffith and Brady got back, I was sloppy drunk and still looking for more. I went right to the cooler and chugged a can. "Shit. Why the fuck would you get drunk like this on a Sunday? You know we have to go home, Simone!" Scolded Brady, "I will get her sobered up," Griffith said with a kind, understanding tone while trying to offer me his coffee. "Ew fuck no, coffee is gross. It is fine. Bianca will never notice."

When we got home, I told Bianca I needed to shower and do homework. I did shower, but then I went out the window. I walked, smoked some weed, and went back home. I packed extra alcohol in my backpack for the next day. Did I really need the books? School sucked, as it always did. The home was simply a place to be that was near the phone. I hoped, with everything in me that was still alive, that Brad would call. He didn't. I was convinced after that weekend I had done something wrong. I punished myself in every way I could, under eating, overeating, drinking, smoking, drugs, and getting attention from boys. Then the non-stop questions ran through my head. Was I a bad kisser? A lousy lay? Too fat? Too ugly? Did I not do something I should have? Did I do something I shouldn't have? Drugs were the only way to make my mind shut the fuck up!

I didn't hear from him until Wednesday. He still wasn't home; he called from Will's house. Neither of us brought up that we had sex or anything about us. There were a lot of silences that I wished didn't exist. I was about to ask if he was still there when he said, "I miss you," and hung up. The next night was a little more normal, but he was still at Will's when I got there Friday night.

Another Saturday, I spent alone in his room, smoking cigarettes and listening to his tapes. Brad appeared in his doorway in a hurry. "Hey, I am just here for clothes. I have to go to work," he said without looking at me or getting too close. "I am going back to Will's tonight. Stay by the phone. I will call you." He was gone. He did call that night, and things were, again, a little more normal. I stayed in his room on the phone with him for a couple of hours and slept with his shirt again. His distancing from me was at least shrinking, but things were not the same.

Griffith also called every night. We were on the phone when I heard Brad's voice in the background. "Is that Brad?" I asked, trying not to sound eager. "Yeah, he just got home from work," Griffith replied emotionlessly. Then there was Brad's voice, "Hey, is that Simone? If it is, tell her I am going to take a shower and call her." Griffith didn't relay the message; he knew I had heard. Griffith had started looking at me differently that summer. He knew I liked Brad. Everyone knew, even Bianca, who generally knew nothing. Everyone said the same things about it, "It is just a phase. It is just a crush; she will have plenty of them. She thinks she is in love with him; just wait until she is older, and she will realize it wasn't love. She is just a kid; she doesn't know what love is." I never contradicted these statements. I also never told anyone I was in love with him. Not then. I didn't want to grow up and see it wasn't love and have anyone be able to say, "I told you so."

Brad called, and we talked about our lives. He asked about school and my friends. I asked about work and Will. Will had met a new girl, and Brad thought it was going too fast. Will didn't like me. He stared me down hard every time he was around. At the time, I thought he was jealous. Brad introduced me to everyone as his best friend, including Will. That had been Will's position before Brad met me. I would soon learn that wasn't the case at all. Will knew how I felt about Brad and knew that Brad felt the same way.

Boys at school had started to notice me. Older boys that Brady went to school with noticed me, too. There was a snotty girl I went to school with who, like me, was exceptionally large-chested. She wore tight shirts all the time to try and show it off; I had tried to hide mine. I primarily walked to school. I only had to deal with Cathy on the rare occasion I took the bus. "Simone, look at this new top my mom got me last night," Cathy called to me while slowly unzipping her windbreaker. The boys, of course, looked. I was feeling a little petty and vindictive that day, so I said, "That's nice, Cathy. Look at this new bra I got!" I lifted my shirt. This also became routine, and in time, I just stopped wearing a bra. My hometown nickname became "Flasher."

I was juggling too much. Bianca's house, my schoolwork, Brady's schoolwork, both of our homework, doing drugs, selling drugs, friends, Brad, it was becoming overwhelming. I needed to let something slide. I thought about not doing Brady's schoolwork, but he would beat me up if I didn't. He didn't understand his work, homework, or projects. I would do it all for him. I didn't have time to read the books for his high school book reports. I would read the first and last pages and whatever was on the inside cover and write him a five-page book report. I had to keep selling for Todd; that was how I got what I needed, which at that time was primarily weed. There was no way I was letting go of Brad. So, I stopped doing my schoolwork.

Brad was back that weekend. That house was insufferable without him. He greeted me with a hug when I got there Friday night, and we hung out a little. He closed his door when he went to bed, though. I curled up in the chair in Griffith's room after I was sure he was asleep. I woke up with my shirt open. Saturday morning, Brad came to Griffith's room and did his signature flop into the chair. "What are you doing today?" He asked. "That depends. Are you working?" I asked, hoping he wasn't. He shook his head. "Well, then, obviously, I am hanging out with you." I smiled and threw a pillow at him. Just like that, we were back.

We goofed around for the rest of the morning. We walked to the store. We made fun of Harry trying to finger girls through the TV. Back in Griffith's room, we stopped laughing, and he asked, "Did you tell anyone?" I looked him in the eye and lied, "No." I had, of course, told Raynelle since she was the only one of my friends who had met him. Then she told most if not all, my other friends. Sophie's reaction of "I knew they were going to screw" was the funniest. It was before the days of cell phones, texting, and camera phones, so there was no proof I said it at all, and I would have denied it if anyone of importance had asked. None of my friends would have reported it or told their parents, though. Brad kissed me. "Do you want to do it again?" I nodded, and we kissed some more. I gave him a blow job; he got a condom, and this time I got on top of him. It still lasted two seconds, and I am still being generous.

Griffith was rarely home before dark. I did have the thought as I climbed on top of Brad that afternoon of what would happen if Griffith got home earlier than normal and walked up those stairs. We were on Griffith's floor with the door wide open. Griffith was at least twice the size of Brad; he would pulverize him. But would it be a dad protecting his daughter or fighting over me in a different way? I chased these thoughts away.

I had begun asking Griffith since I was eleven when he was going to get a girlfriend. Bianca had been dating before the divorce was even finalized. She dated Jay for a while and was dating Liam. Bianca and Liam were talking about selling my house and getting a place together, an idea I didn't approve of. Whenever I would ask Griffith about getting a girlfriend, he gave the same answer, "Probably after you turn eighteen." Back then, I thought he was trying to be a good parent. I thought he meant he was putting Brady and me first and that relationships could happen after we were grown. I know better now.

Griffith allowed and paid for Raynelle and me to go to a movie. Brad wanted to go and, of course, had his own money. He called Will to cancel plans he had with him that day. Will wanted to go too, and he wanted to bring his sixteen-year-old brother Matt. Raynelle, and I picked our seats; there were several seats available on each side of us. Will insisted that he and Brad sit in the row behind us and not with us. During the endless previews, Brad was goofing around, throwing popcorn at me; I, of course, was picking it up and throwing it back. Just before the movie started, I heard Brad say, "Nah, fuck this, I am moving." Brad left Will and sat next to me. Will glared at me intensely, which got him an eye roll.

Matt had tried talking to me and even flirting with me when we first got to the theatre. I wasn't interested. Raynelle was so she flirted with Matt. Halfway through the movie, Matt also left Will and went to sit with Raynelle. It was dark, and no one saw when Brad started holding my hand. I knew Will had hoped Matt and I would hit it off, but he kissed Raynelle all the way back to Will's car. Brad had stopped at the bathroom, and Will warned me, "I know you have a thing for him. You are a kid. He could get in a lot of tro-." I cut him off by laughing in his face.

"Will? I get you are jealous because I am his best friend now and not you, but you said it yourself. I am a kid. Do you think Brad would be stupid enough to do anything with me?" Will didn't have a chance to respond; Brad was there with his arms around me, "How is my best friend? "He joked. I tossed my hair in his face, "I would be better if my hair didn't smell like popcorn, you dork." Will and Matt went home, and Griffith came and picked the three of us up. When I went into Brad's room, Raynelle was already laying on the floor, and so was Brad. He opened his arms for me to come to lay with him. So, I did. I looked over at Raynelle, and she mouthed, "Oh my God!" I just smiled and went to sleep with my popcorn-smelling hair in Brad's face.

Brad and I continued having sex. He would bring up sex at the most random times. Once, we were having a regular ordinary conversation when he found a screw on the floor, and he said, "Wanna screw?" Of course, I did. It didn't matter that he finished quickly; just the kissing was enough for me. His kiss took me away to another place. It was a high that no drug could touch. Nothing else in the world existed as long as I was lost in his kiss. I was addicted to his scent, his laugh, his smile, his gentleness, his kiss, and mostly, his safety.

He was laying on Griffith's bed, and I was sitting up with my legs draped over him; we were both bitching about one thing or another. For him, it was work, and for me, it was school. He knew I was bullied, and he didn't understand why, either. He felt everyone would be lucky to have me as a friend. Brad sat up and kissed me, "They don't see you for who you really are. I promise it will happen when you are older," he told me. We kissed a little bit more, and he once again asked if I wanted to. I did, I always did, and I always would. "We can't, though. I am out of condoms," he said disappointedly. "So? I don't care," I told him honestly. He glared at me with a little bit of anger in his eyes. "Well, I do. I'm going to take a nap." He went to his room and closed his door.

What the fuck had I done this time? I also laid down and took a nap. Two hours later, I woke up to Brad rubbing my back and asking me to come to his room; he wanted to show me something. I stood and stretched; Brad took my hand and led me to his room. He had cleaned no one in that house ever cleaned. He had converted his closet into a bedroom; it was almost big enough to be one. His bed was really just a cot, so that and a nightstand fit just fine. In the bedroom, he had laid some blankets and pillows on the floor to lay on and watch TV.

His arm was wrapped around my waist, and his hand was casually on my ass. We were talking about his new arrangements when he turned my head and kissed me. We used his floor of blankets this time instead of Griffith's; not having a condom suddenly didn't matter. I honestly didn't even think about pregnancy. I did, very carefully, shoplift some condoms later that week, though.

On Sundays, Griffith would come back a little earlier. We would go to the laundromat and eat dinner at the pizza place next door. Brad and I were sitting on Griffith's floor playing cards, and the bedroom door mostly closed because the laundry bags had fallen on it. We had been laughing so hard we didn't hear Griffith's truck pull in or Brady climb the stairs. The door started being shoved open, and I shrieked, "Oh shit," as the door almost hit me. "Get ready to go. We are leaving in ten minutes. And do not be in here with him with the fucking door closed," Brady yelled because he suddenly felt he was in charge of me.

Brad and I started cleaning up the cards, but he kept looking at the door. "You know if he ever touches you, I will fucking kill him, right?" Brad asked rhetorically with an angry tone I had never heard before. His eyes darkened, and I saw an evil there that I was unfamiliar with. I stayed quiet and looked down. Brad reached out and touched my face; he lifted my chin gently, the same way he did before he kissed me, "Has he?" He asked gently but firmly. "I don't know what you are talking about," I replied, but I couldn't make eye contact with him. I didn't want to have this conversation with anyone at all, especially not Brad. "I can tell by the way he looks at you, and he is really jealous of us hanging out. If he ever touches you, tell me, and I will fucking kill him," The sternness in his voice was somehow calming.

I was quiet, too quiet. "He already has. Fucking son of a bitch," Brad was on his feet and headed for the door. "No, Brad, please, don't. If you do, I will never see you again. Please? I need you." I begged him and said some of the words that neither of us had ever dared to say. Brad's arms surrounded me, and I felt his body shake as he cried. I didn't know if he knew I was crying, too. I know now what I hadn't known then. He knew because they both looked at me the same way.

On weekends, we stayed inseparable that September. He got a new job at a restaurant that was a closer walk. It wasn't a small town, but it was small enough that people did talk. It got around that I was fourteen, and he was, well, not. I started seeing pointing and hearing whispers when we would go anywhere together. By the end of the month, I had earned a nickname in Griffith's town as well. "Jailbait."

I was no longer concerned about school at all. I was smart; I knew it, and everyone else knew it, too. I just didn't care. Or, as the school would often say, "I didn't apply myself." With Bianca working so far away, my house became the place for all of the outcasts to hang out. I wasn't popular, far from it, but I was a popular outcast. I knew some of them didn't actually like me; they just liked having my house to hang out at. I didn't care. The outcasts came over, and they brought outcast friends. They all knew about Bianca's random check-in phone calls, and they knew if the phone rang to shut up. Tyler, who I wasn't close with, asked if there was somewhere he could be alone with Kristen; she talked about me behind my back. Neither of them really mattered to me. I told them they could use my room, and there were condoms in the toy box. My stash of alcohol and drugs had been moved when people started coming over. Tyler and Kristen didn't have sex. He put the condom on, she touched his dick, and he was done. I guessed it was a guy thing. It certainly wasn't like the movies.

Fall was here, and I felt some tension between Brad and me. Sometimes when we would go for a walk, our fingers would touch, as we would almost hold hands, only for a second before I would pull away. It wasn't that I didn't want to, I did, but I did understand the ramifications of those actions. Just our fingers touching would give me butterflies.

I did understand that I could lose him forever, and I did understand that you never know who is watching. I knew we were not in a relationship, and I wasn't disillusioned enough to think we ever would be. The thought, the fantasy, of us continuing the way we were until I was eighteen never occurred to me. It bothered me the way people talked about us. I overheard a group of women that were around forty talking about me being jailbait and a slut, that I was always with men and never boys my age. I stood in front of them and told them if they were not careful, I would fuck their husbands and their sons too. Their jaws simultaneously dropped, but they shut up until I was out of ear and eyesight.

Bianca invited Brad over for dinner. Griffith was his ride since he still didn't have a car. I snuck Griffith's wallet off the table and stuck it on the couch. I knew he always checked his wallet before he drove. This would ensure that I would be able to walk Brad out to the truck alone. Once Brad and I were alone in the dark and couldn't be seen from any of my windows, we were able to sneak in a quick hug. I had been hoping for a kiss. Brad called when they got home. The dinner had gone surprisingly well. Bianca later told me she invited him because "If he is going to be spending time with you, I should get to know him." Griffith had grown very quiet and sullen whenever Brad was around.

In mid-October, after another episode of floor sex with Brad, I told him, "You need to get a girlfriend." The surprise on his face, I expected the hurt in his eyes I didn't. "What do you mean? Why would I need a girlfriend? I hav-" I cut him off; I couldn't hear the rest of that sentence.

"People are talking." Silence. "I don't care what people say," he finally snapped at me. "I don't care what people say about me either, but they are talking about us," I told him softly. "I haven't heard anything." He was getting argumentative.

"Open your ears and listen then. Everywhere we go, people point, whisper, and stare. Besides that, everyone calls me jailbait," I said as I crossed my arms and rolled my eyes. "You don't need to be serious about it. You don't even have to like the girl. Just ask a girl from work out to dinner or something. Go on a few dates. Shut people up." I said it angrily to try and ease the pain I felt. He was quiet; the silence that hung in the air was painful for both of us. Brad never noticed the hot tears that ran quietly down my face. The silence was broken by the sound of Griffith's truck pulling in and the realization that neither of us had pants on, plus Brad's door was closed. The only two rules that I had at Griffith's house were that I couldn't sleep in his room unless Raynelle was also there, and I couldn't be in any room with Brad with the door closed.

Two weeks passed, and it was Halloween. It was the only childlike thing I still enjoyed. However, I had pretended I didn't want to go Trick or treating because I didn't want Brad to see me as a kid. Griffith said he didn't really want me going by myself, and he had to work. Brad offered to walk with me. I don't remember what I dressed as; it was probably something slutty; Brad went as a football player. He had tried to teach me about football and his two favorite players. I pretended to understand and follow along, but I only knew the players by who had the nicer ass. Brad and I had been bickering a lot that night. Actually, we had been since the girlfriend conversation. We were on our way back to Griffith's when I told him,

"Well, I would get a boyfriend, but it wouldn't do any good to get a boyfriend at home when people need to see it here, besides I am too fat and ugly to get a boyfriend." Brad turned to face me, walking backward, "I don't want a girlfriend. I don't want you to get a boyfriend, either. And as far as you being fat and ugly goes, you aren't fat, and this," He grabbed his dick, "doesn't leave my pants for anyone ugly."

This was the streets of Long Island, New York. There were people everywhere, and he hadn't said any of it quietly. We sat on the edge of his tiny bed. Brad was silently thinking. I was silently crying. His hand found mine, and our fingers tangled together. It gave me butterflies almost as much as kissing him did. We didn't look at each other; he sighed and breathed deeply. "Maybe you're right," he said sadly. I said nothing because I knew I was right, and I also thought he was crying.

I fought every instinct of love that I had to pull him into my arms and tell him I loved him and that everything would be okay and we would find a way to make it work. The instinct for my lips to kiss his and to undress and have sex in a way we never had before. I knew that that wasn't possible. I knew everything would not be okay. I knew that kind of sex wasn't for us. Besides, with all of the times we had been together, he still hadn't seen me with my clothes off. Then he would see how fat and ugly I really was. Instead, I walked him to the blankets on the floor, turned on the TV, and closed the door. I laid on my side, and I pulled him down to me. His arms fell around me just right. We both fell asleep right away. I fell asleep breathing him in, feeling him hold me, wrapped in his safety. I woke up in the morning still wrapped in him, we hadn't moved, but the door was open.

We could hear Griffith in the kitchen slamming shit around as he made Harry's breakfast. "I will handle it. Stay here." I told Brad and made my way down the stairs and into the kitchen. "Not sleep well?" I asked him, leaning on the doorway with a knowing smile on my face. Griffith looked up at me and glared hard, his blue eyes cold, stoney, and red-rimmed. "I told you not to be in there with the door closed," he said with an accusatory pointing finger. "Harry had his figure skating really loud last night. He was grunting while poking the TV. We could barely hear the movie, so I closed it, and we fell asleep. Nothing happened." He just glared at me. I smirked and walked back upstairs. It was handled, and I knew it. I knew it in his stare. I also knew what I had to do about Brad, and it was going to hurt us both.

In my outcast friend group, Nate liked me, and I knew it. He didn't hide it. I didn't like him; he wasn't my type. He was a nice kid, and I knew I would hurt him. Kristen and Nora bugged me to go out with him, so I told them if he asked, I would say yes. The relationship lasted three whole days. In those three days, I gave him his first kiss and several more, and he got to feel my boobs. On day three of dating Nate, Nora had the idea that I should call Kyle, whom we hadn't seen in over a year. I left a message on his machine, and a couple of hours later, there was a knock on my door. "Hey, I am looking for Simone." Asked a much cuter and taller Kyle. "Kyle? It's me," I said as his eyes ran up and down my body. My hair flowed over my shoulders as I tossed it back to give him a better few.

My shirt was off the shoulders, black, and every other line was sheer. When Bianca bought it for me, she made me promise to wear something under it. She didn't say a black Bra didn't count. Kyle stared at me so long and intently that I should have felt violated. I didn't. I was used to it. That was just how guys looked at me. I used it when I needed to. I was the only one in all my friend groups who could buy cigarettes and alcohol or get tickets to R-rated movies. I just knew I had to go to the register with a guy working.

Most of the group had rules and curfews. I did too, but mine didn't really matter. I wasn't supposed to leave the house, ever, except to go to school. I left almost nightly. Kyle, Nate, Nora, and I wound up outside at the library that was next to my house. We stayed outside so we could smoke, and so we could see if Bianca pulled up. Kyle's eyes again ran up and down me. I had told Nate an hour earlier that we had to break up because my family said he was too young for me.

I leaned casually, knowingly, against a wooden framed trashcan. I watched as both boys took in every inch of me; Nora bummed a couple of cigarettes and left. I leaned my head back and pulled my shoulders together, making my tits more visible. "Mmhmmm. Why didn't I get with you when I had the chance?" Kyle asked, more to himself than me. I rested my head on my shoulder and batted my eyes up at him. "Who says you don't?" I could still see Nate out of the corner of my eye. He turned his head and looked at his feet, but not before I saw the heartbreak across his face. I cared because he was my friend, and I didn't want him to be hurt. I didn't care because I was playing the role I had been trained to play, and I was a bitch. "You mean I still have a chance?" Kyle asked incredulously. "My mom says I can't date until I am sixteen. So, I guess you will have to ask her." I walked over to Nate and hugged him, knowing all eyes were on me, then I gave him a nice long kiss.

Bianca no longer owned or ran a shop. Hence she got home earlier than she used to. I needed to make sure I was in before she got there; I walked away from both boys, not looking back at either, but knowing what they were both thinking. I waited for the phone to ring; Brad called every night at nine. I didn't tell him about Nate or Kyle; it wasn't time yet.

After school the next day, Kyle was waiting for me. The high school and middle school were next to each other. He walked me home, and I told him when to come back to talk to Bianca. He was late, and I thought he had chickened out; he made it through and followed through with asking her. She confirmed that I wanted to date "this boy." I lied and said that I did. Kyle was cute, but I didn't really like him. I acted happy about him wanting to go out with me, and she said yes, then she gave us permission to go to the library for one hour. That was perfect; it would be nine-thirty. Kyle told me how beautiful and sexy I was. I wondered if he was blind or just needed someone to fuck.

I returned home on time, and Bianca let me know Brad had called. I was told not to stay on the phone too long. I took my time to call him back. "Hey," he answered before the first ring finished. He was obviously happy to hear from me, which made my heart thump hard with my own happiness and then shatter at what I knew I had to do.

"Sorry, I missed your call," I lied; I had missed his call on purpose. "I was out." A long pause. "What were you out with your girlfriends?" He asked in a teasing voice. I laughed. "No. I was out with my boyfriend." This wasn't a good pause. I could hear his pain in the silence. I could hear his breathing. The breath that had given me life. I could smell him through the phone. I could feel him holding me. His arms surrounding me with the forbidden love we shared. "You have a boyfriend now?" His voice quivered.

"Yeah, for like a whole hour," I said with a laugh, trying to soften the blow for both of us. "That's cool. Did you have sex with him?" There was a twinge of anger in his voice. "Umm, no, it has been an hour," I said with my own anger. "Okay, well, tell me about him," he was calmer. "He is sixteen. He goes to school with Brady, but I don't think they have any classes together. I met him a couple of years ago, and I liked him, but he said I was too young. I guess I'm not anymore." I tried to sound excited. "Okay, I gotta go; I will talk to you tomorrow." Click. I had hurt him enough to make him hang up on me. I hurt myself even more.

The next day was Friday. I told Kyle how incredibly sad I was that we wouldn't be able to see each other over the weekend. I was happy that with school open, Raynelle wasn't coming to Griffith's much anymore. How would I have been able to spend time with Brad with her there? Like clockwork on Saturday morning, Brad came to Griffith's room and flopped into the chair. He moved quickly to the bed and laid down. I flopped my legs across him, and he was hard at once. He pressed against me, "I would ask if you want to fool around, but you have a boyfriend," he said, trying to sound emotionless; I could still hear the pain, though. "So?" I asked him with a smile. Brad sat halfway up and grabbed my chin more forcefully than usual to look into my eyes. "You have a boyfriend," he repeated. I smiled at him, "I don't care." He must not have either because his lips were on mine at once. We kissed on our way down the hall to his room, closed the door, and found the floor. He still didn't have condoms, and neither of us cared.

I had been more defiant with Griffith in those months. When Brad wasn't there, I would often wander the streets drinking. I would always manage to wind up back at Griffith's, though. I never knew how I got there. Sometimes I would wake up in his truck. Sometimes in the bathtub. Sometimes on his floor. Sometimes in his bed. Sometimes I was missing clothes. Sometimes I had bruises, cuts, or scrapes. I never knew how any of these things happened. I didn't care. Not remembering was the key to my life. When Brad was there, I slept in his room. With his arms around me. And the fucking door closed. I would look at Griffith in the morning with an "I dare you to say something about it" look and walk away.

Brady still fucked with me every chance he got. That was why I had my outcasts, though. I kept people around as much as possible. I had told both Bianca and Griffith about him watching me change, not the rest, though I couldn't bring myself to say the rest out loud. Griffith offered to talk to him about it, with his angry glaring eyes not directed at me for once. I asked him, not knowing Brady would beat the shit out of me, and he didn't. Bianca, on the other hand, did say something to him. He denied it, beat the shit out of me, and she claimed to believe him. She made comments like, "Boys are curious. They like to look." Which I countered with, "Shouldn't he be looking at girls he goes to school with?" That was met with, "Look at him; he can't get a girlfriend. What girl would want him?" So, I guess it was okay with her since he was a pathetic blob who couldn't get a girlfriend.

Kyle and I had been dating for three or four days. We were sitting in a chair together at the library, kissing; we had already been warned twice to take a breather. "Do you want to go outside? " Kyle asked eagerly. I nodded, and we went. We leaned against the cold brick wall and kissed some more. There was snow falling lightly around us from the trees above. Kyle pushed on my boob; like it was a button, which made me smile a little. He clumsily reached down and grabbed my crotch, I felt him in return, and he pulled back. "Do you want to go somewhere?" I nodded slightly, and we walked away.

Across the street from my house was a dead end, some woods, and some power lines. If you cut all the way through, there were houses on the other side; Kyle lived in one of them, so he knew the woods well. We stepped through the snow in the dark woods until he found a fallen tree covered in ice. "This will do," he said and began kicking the snow and ice off the tree. Once it was clear enough, he gave me a quick kiss and opened his pants. He was still mostly hard and huge. When he pulled it out, I won't lie; I was scared. I was also surprised; as grown as I was, I didn't know that a guy asking if you wanted to go somewhere was an automatic "We're fucking," situation.

I had thought, go somewhere to fool around more, or even talk, hell, play a fucking board game. I did what was expected, though. I pulled down my pants and laid on the cold hard log. Kyle didn't know how to put the condom on, and it took him forever to do so. Once that was taken care of, he started trying to shove it in. There wasn't a drop of moisture coming from me. Well, maybe some from the snow melting under my ass. He pushed harder and harder. There was no kissing or touching. There was no emotion. He got his dick in the general vicinity of where it was supposed to go and pushed, "There is it in? Nope, not yet," he spoke to himself. Then he pushed HARD. Now it was in. It was awful. It felt like it went on forever. It was probably only twenty minutes, though. His gush of cum filled the condom, and I was filled with a gush of relief for it to be over. We pulled our pants up, he gave me a quick kiss, and we walked in opposite directions to get to our respective houses.

By the time I got home, I could barely walk. There was a horrible burn that made me not want to be a girl. I wobbled to the bathroom, hearing the phone ring and knowing it was nine without looking at the clock. I peed and noted the blood, some fresh and some already dried, that had dripped down my legs. I could hear Brad's voice on the machine, "Simone, it's me; call me back," for the first time ever, his voice was just background noise. I cleaned myself up and grabbed the phone to call Brad back. I kept my cool and didn't cry; there was no time for that. "Hey!" he shouted when he answered, "I was worried about you. Where were you?" He asked. "I was peeing," he laughed. "Oh, I thought maybe you were out with your boyfriend again," he teased. "I was. I had just got home when you were calling, but I really had to pee." There was that painful silence. "Did you have fun?" I could hear the pain dripping from his words. "I guess," I lied. "Did you have sex with him?" He asked with a clear expectation of no. "Yeah, actually, I did. Before Brad hung up, he said, "I've created a monster." Click. I had been holding in tears since I was laying on that log. They started to leak slowly as I brought the phone back to the kitchen.

I was in physical and emotional pain when the phone rang again. "Hey, you hung up on me," I answered. "Simone, what are you talking about? I didn't hang up on you. I need help. My dad kicked me out because I was late getting home. I don't have anywhere to go." Kyle said.

I didn't want to look at him or talk to him. "You can't come here. Bianca would never let you stay here. Call a friend."

66

I hung up on him. What the fuck did he want me to do about it? I didn't have a place to put him. Hell, after that experience, even if I was grown and had a house, I would tell him he couldn't stay, especially if it meant I would have to fuck him again. Why did I have to make the adult decisions anyway? Had it escaped the entire world's attention that I was fourteen? I wanted to call Brad back and tell him I was sorry. I wanted to cry and tell him I only did it to push him to date someone. I wanted to tell him what I knew I never could.

I called Todd. He came right away. Bianca had gotten home, though. Todd knew to wait until her light went on. He came into my window quietly. I had used some of his crack and coke when that wasn't part of the deal. I knew I owed him. Freebies were over. I took him into my closet and gave him a blow job. It made up for what I owed him but not what I needed. I begged. He took pity on me but made it clear, never again. I did some coke and stayed up all night. I smoked crack behind my house in the morning before school. When I felt like I was going to crash in school, I went to the bathroom and did a line of coke. The biggest relief was that Kyle wasn't waiting for me after school.

A couple of days later, he was, and he wanted to "go somewhere" immediately. I gave him the benefit of the doubt; maybe he had just been nervous or something. It was daylight this time, so at least I would be able to see. Before we got started, I felt him a little through his pants; the damn thing was curled up like a snake, but hard. We went to different woods this time, not as secluded, but there was flat ground, and there was no more snow. I dropped my pants and sat, waiting for him to get the condom on. Kyle opened it, unrolled it, and tried to get it on. I guess he didn't pay attention in sex ed class.

After several minutes of watching and waiting for him to try and put the condom on wrong, I reached out to just do it myself, and he broke it. I took his last one, opened it, and rolled it on; he looked shocked. There was no kissing, touching, or feeling. Just being ripped apart. I turned my head and let the hot tears fall into the cold leaves. Once he was done, he rushed back to catch the train, explaining that his guidance counselor had gotten him into a shelter, but he had to make curfew. Kyle called that night. I didn't answer. Brad called at nine. He asked a girl out on a date, even though he didn't like her. I told him how great that was. It didn't hurt. I knew why he did it. I knew he didn't like her. I knew it would not last.

Raynelle started hanging out at my house a lot on weekdays. It was unusual because both of our mothers were strict, and we didn't live within walking distance of each other. Her mom was dropping her off several times a week, though. At least she didn't drink, and I didn't have to worry about hiding my alcohol. She also never said anything about my drinking. She was the only person my age who knew about it, and I don't know if she knew how much I actually drank. Raynelle still came to Griffith's house sometimes, but it was only for the day.

Brad and I continued having sex. He went on a few dates with girls he worked with. Kyle waited for me after school two or three times a week. He ran out of condoms and had no money. Mine were long gone; the outcasts and I used them as balloons. I wasn't shoplifting more to have sex with Kyle. We walked into the woods side by side, and he put his arm around me in a short squeeze, "It's okay. It's not like we are having sex with other people," he said with a smile. If only he knew the truth. Kyle stopped at a clearing and dropped his pants, "We could always do something else," I suggested quietly. "Are you saying you don't want to? Cause we don't have to," he said with a bit of anger.

"We can go back to my house and hang out? I can call some people to come over?" I said hopefully. Kyle pulled up his pants and said, "Go ahead; I will catch up." I started to walk away feeling relieved. He said I didn't have to; I just figured I did; if I knew I didn't, I would have said so sooner. I didn't get far when something hit me in the back of the leg and knocked me down. I yelped in pain, like a wounded dog, as I rolled over to see what had happened. Kyle was approaching, pants down, erection throbbing, and a large rock in his hand. The rock came crashing down on my thigh, "Okay, okay, it was just an idea," I stammered as I pulled down my pants.

He shoved it in hard, and I felt another piece of me being ripped away in death. Kyle took longer than usual. I thought of Brad. His gentle touch, his safe arms. If he knew what I had to go through to keep him safe, I wondered what he would think, what he would say. I didn't allow myself to wonder if he would save me, protect me. After it was over, Kyle saw I was bleeding, "Oops, I guess I was a little too rough," he said with a chuckle. I bled every time I had sex with him. He walked me home and then went to the train station; he called when he got back to the shelter. I didn't answer. I never answered his calls.

I knew the next morning that I needed to break up with Kyle. I needed to wait until after his birthday; it would suck getting dumped for your birthday. His was in early December. Not long before that, I was at Griffith's for a weekend. Friday night, Brad popped his head in, "Hey, I have a date tonight, and I can't decide what to wear. Help me?" He said excitedly. I acted as if it was a chore. But I knew it was an excuse for him to get me to be able to go to his room. However, I was happy to pretend to help. Brad's eyes were glowing that night. I went to his room, and he exclaimed, "I think I might really like this one, Simone!"

"Her name is Marissa, and she started working there around the same time I did, but we've only worked together a few nights," he told me as we looked at his clothes. His words sliced my heart, and I felt the blood stop flowing in my veins. I acted like I didn't care; everything was fine. After he was dressed, I wished him luck. Brad got to the top of the stairs and then came back; our eyes locked, and he glanced back at the door. "I almost forgot something," he whispered. His hand grasped the nape of my neck, his fingers tangled in my hair, and our lips found each other for the thousandth time. It was just a quick kiss, but it was all I needed. The butterflies flew through me to mend my slowly breaking heart.

After a big hug, he left for his date with Marissa. When he got back, I was on the small back porch, drinking alone in the dark. "How did it go?" I asked, and in response, he grabbed my hand and walked me upstairs. We went right to his room and laid on his floor, cuddling. "How is Kyle?" I couldn't lie to him. "I guess he is okay, but the sex sucks." Brad laughed and asked what was so bad about it. I told him that there was no foreplay; Kyle would just shove it in dry. I didn't tell him that I didn't want to have sex with Kyle and only did because I had no choice. "That's why I make sure I get a lot of foreplay in. I know I can't last," Brad said with a laugh.

I didn't respond; it wasn't a lie. He rolled me onto my back and laid half over me. Brad looked me in the eyes, and I held his gaze; I hoped he couldn't see the pain I held inside or how much I loved him. I could get lost there in his eyes. If I had died in that moment, physically died, I would have died happy. "I didn't have sex with her, you know." I could tell it was important for him to make sure I knew, and I had known the second I saw him. I nodded, and we kissed. We kissed and kissed and kissed. We had sex with Griffith and Brady down the short hall. With the fucking door open.

It was mid-December, and I hadn't seen Kyle in over a week. I also hadn't answered any of his phone calls. The last time I saw him, he slapped me across the face. I knew that the next time I saw him, I was dumping him, and I was doing it publicly, so there was less chance of him hurting me. So, when I saw him that sunny and oddly warm winter day, I gathered my outcasts. Tiffany, Nora, and Nate walked right behind me as I approached him. "I don't want to go out with you anymore," I said straight to the point as I walked past him. I crossed the street in front of oncoming traffic. "If I had known that, I wouldn't have waited. Now I'm stuck here until the next train, bitch," Kyle yelled. "If you came around more often, you would have known. You only come around when you want to get laid," I yelled a little louder. "What the fuck am I supposed to do? I got kicked out of my house because of you!" Kyle screamed across traffic. "That's not my fault. You were late because you wanted to get fucked! I didn't even know you had a curfew!" I was even louder as drivers started opening their windows to listen. "Stupid, fucking, worthless, bitch. I come around when I want to get laid because that is all you're good for! A good FUCK!" Kyle screamed his last words, and they almost echoed.

I stopped walking and faced him from across the street; I was sure my eyes were shooting flames at him. "At least I'm good at something! Your stupid ass can't even figure out how to put a condom on, AND you're a bad fuck! At least YOU aren't the one who might be pregnant!" My words echoed through the street as I started to walk away, I glanced back once, and he was standing there staring at his feet with his mouth open. I walked away with my head held high.

***

The nagging thought of pregnancy had been weighing me down for weeks, I asked my friends not to come over, and I went home alone. Now that I had said the words aloud, it felt more real. I was sitting at the table crying when Brady came up to get dinner and grilled me about what was wrong. When I finally told him, he said, "You dumb bitch. How could you be so fucking stupid? You are telling mommy when she gets home," he smashed my head into the table before storming back to his room.

When Bianca did get home, I had moved my pity party to my room, and Brady had gone to the table to wait for her. I heard him as soon as she walked in the door, "Your daughter did something stupid, and she needs to talk to you." She came to my room immediately and started asking what was wrong. I cried and laid my head in her lap; I just needed to be comforted. I needed to be comforted and told that one way or another, everything would be okay. And one of those sticks to pee on. The words "Mommy, I think I might be pregnant" came out before I was ready for them too. She stood up, flinging me off of her, "How? Who? That boy Kyle? Why would you do something so stupid? How late are you?" She squawked angrily. "Five days and yes, Kyle," I lied through my sobs. I had not had a period since October before I even started dating Kyle. "We will wait and see," she said, looking next to me. It would be weeks before she looked at me again.

Bianca wouldn't get me a pregnancy test. It weighed on my heart, not knowing. I shoplifted several tests and stole some money from Griffith's wallet to buy some. In the end, I took thirty-five pregnancy tests. Every single one of them was positive. If you have not been able to do the math, that would mean I got pregnant before I started dating Kyle. Griffith and Brady hadn't had access to me because I kept myself surrounded by people. It was Brad's. I cried hard. I didn't want anyone to know about us, but with a baby, how could I hide it? Of course, everyone would just think it was Kyle's baby, and I would have gone along with that, but it felt so wrong. I was torn into a million pieces.

Around two months into my period being "late," I was struck by pain so severe I fell to the floor. I had felt off for a few days, but this was excruciating. Not long after, I started pouring blood. I always had heavy periods, but this was different. It didn't take me long to realize I was having a miscarriage. I laid on the bathroom floor crying, not for the loss of the baby, but because I was so alone. I just wanted someone to comfort me, hold me, and be there for me. I wanted desperately to tell Brad he was my best friend, but he was also the father. I bled heavily for two weeks; I suffered quietly around everyone else and loudly alone. My bedroom and the bathroom floors absorbed so many of my tears those weeks and several more weeks after the pain and bleeding had stopped. I needed comfort so badly, but there was no one to turn to. I had told Bianca when I started bleeding that I had gotten my period and that it had just been late. She said nothing else about it. The miscarriage was for the best; I knew that then and now. Between the drinking, drugs, Brad, and my age, there would have been too many risks and complications. I still mourned, though, for the baby and for myself. It is still one of my most painful memories. Going through a miscarriage at fourteen, completely and utterly alone, was an indescribable pain even to this day. I didn't admit to anyone that any of this happened until 2022.

Todd came for his money, and I was short. I didn't know that many people used drugs, and I had slowed down. Todd tied me to a chair and whipped my back. Apparently, the fact that I didn't cry was payment enough. Brad went on several more dates with Marissa, but he was still having sex with me. After the first time he did have sex with her, he came home and told me all about it. He told me how bad it was and laughed at her for being a lousy lay. He had showered right after he had sex with her, again the next morning, had sex with me that afternoon, went to work, and then went on a date with her. I hoped he smelled like me.

Days and weeks passed, we were moving, and I was pissed. This was my home. This was where I had lived for ten years. The house we were moving to was smaller; I would never see my friends, and, well, teenage angst. A lot of the outcasts had stopped coming over. Raynelle was still there frequently. We were running around outside of the library, throwing leaves at each other, she fell on the ground laughing, and I buried her in leaves. She stopped laughing and became serious, "I have to tell you something," she began, "it's about my brother Stevie," she looked into the distance. "He tried to do things to me. Like he touches me and tries to have sex with me." My vault cracked. Two years of snapshot memories came flooding back. Two years that, my brain had gone somewhere else and locked it all away.

Griffith carried me from Brad's room while Brad and Raynelle slept. Griffith picked me up from various locations and brought me back to his house. Griffith put me in his bed, removing my clothes, touching me… touching me everywhere. I could feel his hands on me. I could feel his hand sliding down my breasts, his tongue flicking at my nipple, rubbing ice between my legs and across my chest. Rubbing his dick on me and releasing his disgusting mess on my leg, back, stomach, and ass. I saw it all in just a moment, memories mixed with flashes of light like a camera taking pictures. "My mom knows. That's why she has been letting me come over so much while she is at work. So, I won't have to be alone with him." I sat next to her. "Griffith does stuff to me too." Our eyes locked now bound by our dark secrets. "That's why I liked you coming over so much and why sometimes I stay on the phone with you all night." She nodded. We sat in silence, alone, invisible, but exposed.

She spent half of the following weekend at Griffith's with me. Friday night I spent with Brad, we had sex Saturday morning, and she came over Saturday afternoon. The three of us stayed up late Saturday, watching movies, laughing, and throwing things at each other. When Brad was tired, he again laid on the floor and stretched his arm out for me to join him. I obliged happily, and his arm fell around me. Big spoon and little spoon, we always fit together perfectly. Raynelle laid a couple of feet away, facing me. I looked over at her, and she smiled at me; I smiled back. I knew what she was thinking. I knew how happy she was that I had Brad, and she was most likely the only person who knew how we truly felt about each other. When Brad and I got up in the morning, Raynelle was getting in the shower, and I couldn't help but notice Brad's boner when he stood up. I laid back down and gave him a knowing look. "What this? It's morning wood because I have to pee." Brad and I did not have sex that morning. We kissed, but he was worried Raynelle would come in. I thought, "You're quick, and all I need is your kiss," as we walked down the stairs, and he pressed his dick against me playfully.

Raynelle's mom was working overnights the following week, so she dropped her at my house a few times. I told her I had cleared it with Bianca, and she could spend the night. It was a good thing she never wanted to talk to Bianca because she didn't allow sleepovers. I would have Raynelle hide under my bed when Bianca would come in from work until after I knew she was upstairs in her room. In the mornings, she would climb out my window and sneak around to the front of the house; then, we would walk to school. She came to Griffith's that weekend, and the three of us fell asleep the same way we had the previous Saturday. Only I woke up in Griffith's bed.

The door was closed, and I had no clothes on. I found my shorts under the blanket and grabbed my shirt off the floor just as the door cracked open. "When did you come in here?" Raynelle whispered. "I don't know," I whispered back. Her eyes widened, "How did you get in here?" She whispered a little louder. I looked at her and wondered what showed in my eyes, the fear? The anger? The embarrassment? "I don't know," I whispered, yelling back through clenched teeth. There was a noise behind her, "Is she in there?" It was Brad! Brad couldn't know; I would die if Brad knew, and not in the way I was used to dying. "Yeah, she is getting changed. She will be out in a minute," she told him. The clothes I had quickly put on were the clothes I had gone to sleep in, so I grabbed a change of clothes, and when the three of us got near the bathroom, I yelled,

"First dibs on the shower!" Brad asked, "If you just got changed, why are you taking a shower?" When you have no answer to give, answer with another question. "Since when do girls make sense?" I asked, and that was that.

Brad started staying at Marissa's sometimes. It hurt, and I am sure he knew it. I am also sure, in a way, it hurt him too. I got his room to myself when he wasn't there. It was always where I fell asleep and sometimes where I woke up. It was where I could be alive. I could listen to our music. Our songs. The sounds of UB40's Promises and Lies, Meatloaf's Bat Out of Hell 2, Bon Jovi's Slippery When Wet and various others could be heard blasting all day and played quietly at night. The scent of him, the feeling of his arms around me, and the thought of his kiss on my lips got me through each night there. Brad called me every night, still at nine on the dot, no matter where I was. If I didn't answer his phone, he would call Griffith. I knew he was having sex with both Marissa and me. But was that any different than what I had done? He kept coming back to me, but he was laughing at her less; he was spending less time with me. Before he went on a date with her, he always hugged me goodbye Until one day he didn't, which was also the day he asked me to leave the room so he could get changed.

I couldn't hide Raynelle at my house anymore. We were mostly packed, and my mattress was on the floor. Bianca would not have allowed me to be on the phone with her all night. I had no way to keep her safe. On weekends, we would stay on the phone and plot ways to get even with her brother. He demanded she get him a glass of lemonade, and I told her to piss in it. We giggled endlessly.

In some ways, those weekends were hell. I knew things were happening that I didn't like, but there was also freedom. I stayed drunk; my mind still often wandered to where it was safe, which had been getting harder since Raynelle, and I had exchanged our deepest secrets. I didn't question the odd places I would wake up. I couldn't and would not admit that somewhere in my mind, I knew how it happened. I didn't know how he would always find me. I didn't want to know any more than what I already knew. Griffith started letting me control his checkbook and finances. I controlled the grocery shopping, made sure he had money to do laundry, and I made sure there was a hefty budget for drinks.

Shortly before we moved, Brady came to get me alone one Friday night. He tossed me two beers and said, "You are going to need them," I drank both and got in the truck. Brady handed me two more; this wasn't going to be good. We were almost there before Brady spoke again, "I have to tell you something," he began. I could feel him looking at me. "Brad moved out." My heart exploded with pain. It was a burst inside of me, unlike the pieces I had felt slowly die or be sliced away before. I felt it as the blood from my exploded heart dripped through my entire body. "He would have told me. You are lying because you and Griffith are jealous and don't want me hanging out with him." I knew they were jealous, and I also knew he wasn't lying. "He left you a letter. We didn't read it. It is in his room by the window."

When we got to the house, I went in first, through the kitchen and down the hallway to the stairs; I heard Brady tell Griffith, "Yeah, I told her, but-" I turned his voice off as I climbed the stairs. His door at the top of the stairs and to the left stood open. I had been able to smell him halfway up the stairs. I walked in and saw almost all of his stuff was gone. Some of his tapes were still there; his phone still hung on the wall. His Elvis poster and TV were gone. The floor was littered with trash, ashes, and cigarette butts. One of his shirts laid amongst the mess. I stood in the center of the room in disbelief. I spun slowly, taking it all in; this wasn't real; it couldn't be real. The warm feeling of my blood spurting from my burst-open heart continued to spill into every part of me that was otherwise icy and dead. I saw the envelope by the window. *"Simone,"* it read across the front. Inside was just one piece of paper, written in his neat handwriting, that I can almost still see in my mind. It just said

"I will call you.
Always
Brad"

The warm blood from my heart filled my stomach, and I ran to the bathroom to be sick. His phone rang at nine o'clock. Of course, it was him. I hid my pain the best I could; he apologized for not telling me. He had made the decision to move in with Marissa the week before and couldn't tell me face to face. Why? Because he knew he would see the hurt in my eyes and not be able to go.

"You know I needed to, though, right? You know it was time. You know why I had to, right?" His voice was pleading for my understanding, and I did understand, and I made sure he knew that. As we got off the phone, I knew he would go to bed with her, thinking of me.

I spent the weekend in his room. Either Griffith or Brady brought me food that I didn't eat or alcohol that I did drink. I clutched the shirt he left behind and cried. The tears would never stop. My shattered heart would never heal. Brad said he would call me but not as often now that he was living with her, and he gave me her number in case I needed him. Marissa didn't like me and didn't like him being friends with me. I had overheard her once asking how I could be his best friend when I was just a kid. Yeah, I was a kid, but I was also the one he was fucking behind her back for weeks. He was mine first. The phone in his room would only be on for another few days, and we were moving. We didn't have a new number yet, and it was the nineties; this was before bringing your number with you existed. I didn't think I would ever hear from him again.

We moved, and as expected, it sucked. My new school was enormous. It was so big there was a bridge connecting two buildings so kids could get to their classes in the allotted three minutes. I was a target of bullies from day one. I sat alone in the cafeteria as I wasn't accepted at a table; I would find a seat along the walls of the stadium-style seating. My first class was Mr. Holbert's science class. Every day for the first fifteen-twenty minutes of class, he just sat there reading the newspaper. The rest of the class talked, laughed, and gossiped. I sat there and waited for the teacher to do his job. I was there for about a week when Mr. Holbert decided he had a problem with that. "Ahhh, Simone, who has to stare at me every day. What can I do for you today, Simone?" I gave no response, so he continued. "What is it you find so fascinating about me reading the paper? Is it my sophisticated good looks?" The class laughed as my face filled with heat. "Oh, I don't know, Mr. Holbert, I just thought a teacher was supposed to, ya' know, teach." Then the class laughed at him; he clasped his hands together and began the day's lesson.

I sat at a lab table with a fat kid; his last name was similar to Loser, so of course, that is what everyone called him. I didn't call him that; after all, I was a loser too. To me, he wasn't Loser; he was Mike.

We worked well together, and he was nice; it was clear pretty quickly that he liked me. Mike asked me out, and I told him I wasn't interested in a boyfriend right now, just friends, and we would see how it went later on. It wasn't a complete lie. But then the new kid walked in. My heart thumped. His name was David, and he was hot. He exuded the bad-boy attitude that I knew so well and was drawn to. David was immediately accepted by the other kids, unlike me.

I got his attention easily enough; it is called tits and body language that says, "I know what I am doing." A carefully dropped pencil picked up in a way he could see down my shirt, and it was game on. David was leaning on my locker right after class. "Hey sexy," he greeted me. I opened my locker between us to hide the smile I couldn't help. By the time I closed my locker, the smile was gone, and he was waiting patiently. "You, uh, you wanna go out with me?" David asked while looking me in the eyes; I nodded while playfully nibbling at my lower lip. "Cool," he said and kissed me passionately against the lockers, his hand sliding across my hip and landing on my lower back. No butterflies, but not bad, either.

As the kiss ended and my eyes opened, I made eye contact with Mike, who was walking past; he hung, his head and his face flushed as he kept walking. I had seen that look before. I felt bad, but I got lost in another kiss with David. We dated for three weeks. We cut class together often, hiding under the bleachers or on the football field; we made out a lot. I jerked him off; he fingered me; he always finished, but I never did.

Brad did call. I would go to the basement to talk to him privately. Sometimes our feelings for each other hung in our silence; the air between our phone lines would sit heavy with lead as neither of us said the words in our hearts. I think we both knew if the words were said, he would come back, and we both knew that couldn't happen. I also did call him every so often. Marissa's sister answered once, and as I waited for Brad to pick up, I heard them arguing. "I know twelve-year old's that are more grown-up than you, Brad. Grow up!" She screeched at him. I heard the phone moving and thought I heard him quietly say, "Yeah, well, I know a fourteen-year-old that is a better fuck than you." To this day, I don't know if he really said it or if it was just wishful thinking. Or, as Bianca would say, my imagination. My heart smiled as I heard him say, "Hello," we talked, and asked if I had heard any of what was said before he picked up. I lied.

Brad had gotten a second job at a grocery store, so naturally, I changed where Griffith did his shopping. Just hoping to see Brad once in a while. I did run into him, and the joy, happiness, excitement, and love that sparkled in his eyes every time he saw me was undeniable. Did he see those same things in my eyes? I would walk there some Saturdays and see him when he was on his breaks. It was before the days of cameras everywhere. We were out behind the store, and he was getting ready to go back to work; I flicked my cigarette and was about to walk back to Griffith's.

Brad turned around and came back to me. His arm wrapped around my back tightly, and his hand held the nape of my neck. I imagined him kissing me as he hugged me. The energy between us was fierce, passionate, and loving. Brad hugged me tight as I breathed him in deeply. My soul was trying to cling to the life he had brought back in me; it was trying to heal. He breathed and sighed softly in my ear, his arms released my body, and he walked in the back door without looking back. Not long after, he was fired for doing a Beavis and Butthead impersonation over the loudspeaker. He had done that while I was there one day to make me laugh. Most of the time, we talked two or three times a week. But I never saw him again.

I was identified at school as a kid who may be having trouble fitting in. I was invited to join a group of loser kids for a loser kids club. They didn't call it that, of course, but that is what it was. We met during lunch and met for group sessions with a counselor. Mike was in the group also; things had been tense after he asked me out, and the counselor picked up on it. Mike had an attitude with me during the loser club groups. That was okay; I deserved it. He invited us to meet with him together, but it wasn't really optional.

It was oddly like marriage counseling. Neither of us would say anything; Mike just looked at the floor; I looked at him, taking in the pain I had caused him. The counselor left us alone to take a call, which is when Mike spoke, "You could have just told me you didn't like me," I saw he was crying. "Mike, it isn't that I don't like you. I have problems; I am trouble. I don't want to hurt you and trust me if you date me, you will get hurt." again, this wasn't a complete lie. It was all of that, and I didn't like him. It's cliché, but it wasn't him. It was me.

Mike smiled, "I would be nice to you, though. I would talk to you during class and not just make out with you in the hallway." I moved to the chair closest to him. "Mike?" He still would not look up at me. I touched his chin and lifted his head up the same way Brad had done with me less than a year earlier. "I am sorry," I said as our eyes connected. He smiled and said okay, and we hugged. Friends again, and when the counselor came back in, we were laughing and playing some card games. Mike reminded me a lot of Nate. I could have liked them both in time, but right now, they were both just kids. I didn't need a kid.

David and I didn't actually break up; we just fizzled out, which didn't matter any more than he did. He hadn't been what I was looking for. I didn't know what I was looking for or that I was looking for something. We stayed on good terms, which was nice, he did a science project with Mike and me, and the three of us got along just fine working on it.

Not long after we turned it in, Mr. Holbert asked me to stay after class. David was the last to leave the room and told me, "This is weird. Let me know what he wants and if you need me," on his way out of the room. What was wrong with a teacher wanting to see a kid after class? It seemed like the most normal thing in my life.

Mr. Holbert shut the door behind David and paced around the front of the class. I was sitting on one of the front-row tables, as usual, waiting for him to speak. When he stopped pacing, he sat on his desk, which was really just another larger lab table. "I have seen your test scores, and there is no denying you are smart, but you aren't doing enough in my class. I know you are a new kid and all that, but you have got to start doing more." I had heard this speech before; he should move on to the next one. Mr. Holbert got off his desk and made his way back to the door while he spoke, "You also seem to be a different kind of kid. One who maybe will not need school to get by." Okay, David was right; this was weird; I slid off the lab table and threw my backpack over my shoulder. He pulled down the shade of the small door window, and I heard the soft click of the door lock. FUCK!

He turned back toward me and started walking, slowly, intently, in my direction. I stood my ground. I knew this game, and I played it well. I also knew I wasn't failing his class; I had a solid C. Sure, I could do better, but that didn't matter. All that mattered right then, at that moment, was getting the fuck out of that classroom without getting fucked. Just inches away from me, he unbuckled his belt, his hand came up, and he grazed the side of my breast with the back of his hand and then cupped it with an open palm. "I am not failing your class, Mr. Holbert," there was more I wanted to say, but I didn't think I had time for that. He walked away, and I backed up to stand by a chair that was pulled out. As he paced, "You aren't failing, but you aren't doing well. Besides, you are the kind of girl who has other assets and other things to offer. If you don't do this, you will fail. If you tell anyone, they won't believe you. Everyone has seen the way you behave with boys. Stringing one along while doing God knows what with the other. If you do this, I will give you this as a token of my affection," he placed a new, unused book of hall passes on his desk. This man, this teacher, thought I was going to fuck him for some hall passes. That wasn't going to happen, but I said nothing.

"You have been at this school for what three weeks? Four? You already have a reputation." I slid the chair out further; I wasn't fucking this teacher. "I have seen the way you look at me during class. You should stop wasting your time with that little boy and see what a sophisticated man has to offer you. Has that little boy ever even made you have an orgasm?" He was halfway between the window and the door. Now was my chance.

I grabbed the chair, lifted it into the air, and threw it at him. I saw that it grazed his back before hitting the chalkboard behind him and crashing onto the floor. I didn't see it land; I didn't see if anything broke. I was already gone. I had snagged the book of hall passes on my way out. I was speed walking down the hall when I noticed a voice coming from behind me, "Simone! Simone! Wait up!" it was David. He had waited for me in the hallway. Once he caught up, he walked with me, asking questions about what Mr. Holbert wanted. Why did people have so many fucking questions? "I am fine, David. He wanted to talk to me about my grades, and he offered me extra credit." Our eyes met briefly, and I knew he saw the lie. I walked out the front doors of the school with so many of my own questions screaming inside. Was I born with a sign on my head that only men could see that said, "I like dicks?" One that said, "Fuck me?" How about "Beat me, I like it?" I also questioned one thing Mr. Holbert said. Girls had orgasms?

Griffith had gotten me a purple and black mountain bike that year. I loved that bike, and I rode it everywhere. He always bought me things. Things Bianca wouldn't let me have, things I wanted and things I didn't, things I didn't know I wanted until after I had them. I think that was around the time I realized, vaguely, that his gifts came with a price tag. I never asked for any of the things he gave me. But in the days afterward, he would always be more aggressive toward me, physically and touchier. I would always be more drunk.

84

I found a new way to freedom at the end of that winter. Everyone knew the move had been hard on me. Bianca was adamant that I don't see my old friends and just make new ones. Griffith didn't agree. Most Fridays, he started picking me up and dropping me off in my hometown. I always told him I had a place to stay, usually Tiffany's or Sophie's. I didn't necessarily have a place to stay when he dropped me off, but it usually worked out that I was able to crash at one of their houses. Their parents liked me; all their parents liked me. Tiffany's parents probably liked me more than they liked her; I didn't actually like her either. On the nights I didn't have anywhere to go, I just walked. This was New York, and there was always some place open if I got cold or needed to use a bathroom. I always had my backpack with a change of clothes, at least one bottle of liquor, and cigarettes. I tried to always have weed too, but that wasn't always possible. Potheads were cool, though, and always willing to share, plus easy to find. During the day, I could nap in the library's rarely used downstairs.

A weekend came when I had nowhere to go, and I wandered those streets. I walked along next to the fence of my old house. Whoever lived there didn't belong there. I hated them for existing. I hated everyone for everything and nothing. For almost a year, I had found salvation with Brad. I still had his phone calls, but it wasn't the same. I thought of him as I walked; I could picture him there, walking with me; I could conjure his smell and the feel of his arms around me in my mind. I missed him; I needed him. I was so lost in a mental image of his face as I drank and walked that I didn't hear anything behind me. A huge arm seized me from behind, and an equally large hand covered my mouth, "Do not scream cunt," Todd growled in my ear. I bit his hand, and he flung me forward; I spun around and saw that I had drawn blood. Good. "You probably just have me rabies, whore." I didn't try to run, I saw his car pulled over on the side of the road, and I knew it would have been pointless. I crossed my arms and gave him a look that said, "You deserved it."

He got close and towered over me; I showed no fear. What did I have to be scared of? What was he going to do? Kill me? Who cared? I was better off dead.

"You moved and didn't tell me. I found your new place. Not so easy to get into that one, and your mom's room is too close to yours. Where is my money?" I held his stare, "I don't have it. I ran out of toilet paper and used it to wipe my ass." His fist connected with my stomach in less than an instant. I coughed and panted but didn't give him the satisfaction of tears. "Is that all you've got as big as you are?" I smiled in his face as I regained my stance and footing. He had a gun, and I intended that night to push him to use it. I was empty inside, and, at that moment, I was fearless. I felt how dead I was inside; Todd couldn't do any more damage. He lunged for me, threw me over his shoulder, and brought me to his car.

I heckled him from the backseat as he started to drive, "If you wanted to give me a ride, all you had to do was ask. "Todd's cold blue-gray eyes stared at me in the rearview mirror; I didn't look away. I caught the reflection of my own face as he turned his eyes to the road. I wore a coy smile and eyes that showed absolutely nothing except a sparkle that was looking for danger. Looking for death.

Todd drove for a long time. I had no idea where we were or where we were going. Every time he looked in the rearview mirror, his eyes met mine. I knew after he killed me, those eyes, my eyes, would haunt him until the day he died. We pulled into a hotel, and he gave me the command of "Wait" while he went into the office. When he came back to get me from the back seat, his directions were clear. "Get out. Walk. Do not try anything stupid. If you do, I will shoot you. Don't say you don't care. You may not care about your life, but remember, I will also shoot anyone that sees or hears anything." I obeyed.

Once we were in the room he had rented, he pushed me toward the bed. "Strip. Let's see those tits and ass." I sat down and crossed my arms, daring him to make me. "You like it, don't you? The way everyone talks about you? Flasher? Or are you jailbait this week?" I laughed loudly, "Todd, are you just upset that you aren't getting any?" Our eyes had locked the minute we were in the room, "I am tonight. It is time to pay up. We can do it your way or mine," Todd said as he pulled handcuffs and rope from his pocket. I stood and stripped, never letting my eyes leave him and never showing the fear he desperately wanted to see. For the first time, I saw Todd really smile; it was pure evil. As he climbed on top of me, I smelled his sweat, his desire, and his hatred. Todd had a gun in his hand, which he used to open my legs. He held it in front of me, finger on the trigger; I didn't look away. "Let's lube you up, don't want to go in dry and hurt you," he said as he dragged the gun up my thigh; I could see he wasn't hard yet, as he pressed the barrel to my most sensitive parts. It was a pain like nothing I had felt before as he pressed it inside of me. I felt the stinging tingle of a tear forming and fought it away. That is what he wanted. No pain. No fear. Only the weak cry. Where had I heard the phrase before? I couldn't allow myself to think about it; I couldn't allow my mind to wander.

I needed to stay where I was completely present, no matter what because I had no idea what I physically did when my mind left. The gun pressed in and out, in and out, as I saw him become aroused. "Good bitch," he said as he pulled the gun out for the last time and put on a condom, "Got to be safe, I don't know where you've been, and I don't want to catch anything." While Todd was inside of me, I didn't move one time in any way; in the end, it was him that broke eye contact. His weakness showed and not mine. Good. We left the room as the sun was coming up, it hurt to walk, but I didn't let him see that either.

Todd dropped me off a few miles from the hotel near a diner. "We're even," he said as he slipped some cash, a bag of crack, and some coke into my hand. I didn't ask him where we were or which direction to go, I didn't need him, and he couldn't think I did. I got a soda from the diner and used their bathroom to get high. It was Sunday, and I needed to find my way back to my friend's house before Griffith came to pick me up. Bianca had no idea that I really wasn't at his house on most weekends. I found a highway and stuck out my thumb; getting a ride was easy, no matter where I was.

I don't remember most of the people who gave me rides, but I managed to get pretty close to where I needed to be. I walked the last several miles and barely made it back in time to do some coke in the White Castle bathroom before Griffith showed up and I got in his truck. I never saw or heard from Todd again; I heard he got shot in the parking lot behind my old house. Some people said it was a drug deal gone bad; some said it was his own nephew Mickey who shot him. Mickey was a friend of mine, I asked him, but he would never give me a straight answer. Mickey himself later disappeared, I always suspected something gang-related, but I will never know. Associating with people whose real names you don't know has its downsides.

Griffith started taking Brady and me to our grandparent's house frequently. My aunt Tina also lived there. Tina was permanently sitting on the couch, or her stuff was there. So, there were two chairs to sit in, with matching ottomans, and the floor. Brady always had his feet up, which left me on the floor or the ottoman in front of Griffith. I was told by both Griffith and Tina to sit on the ottoman. I adored my Grandma, disliked my grandpa, and was pretty indifferent to Tina. She had been cool when I was a kid, but now, she was a giant blob who never left the house and only wore oversized tee-shirts, no pants, and often no underwear either. Grandpa spent most of his days outside in his garden and most of his evenings in the dining room, reading. His seat gave a clear view of the living room, so the ottoman seemed safe for me to sit on. The chair ottoman matches were rockers, so with your feet up, you could rock your whole body. Griffith would pull me back, so I was laying in his lap, using the excuse he couldn't see the TV through me. Tina and Grandpa would go to bed at around the same time, and Brady would fall asleep in the chair or be talking to Grandma downstairs. Griffith would rock, which would also rock me; his hand was positioned in a way that it would rub against my chest every time he moved back. If I tried to sit up, his other hand clamped down on my shoulder and pinned me to him. When we were alone, he told me that when we were there, I should just sit in his lap; this, in time, became an order. As the order was obeyed, he touched me more. Griffith rubbed my crotch through my pants and rubbed himself against me as he rocked. Why didn't Grandpa see these things? I swear there were times I saw him glance over the top of his book.

Tension built everywhere. I seemed to have completely lost the ability to make my mind go away. I didn't have regular and consistent access to drugs, not the kind I needed anyway. Weed was great for getting high and laughing, but I needed darkness. I needed the kind of drugs that made my reality black. Alcohol didn't even do that anymore. Every Friday night, he rubbed against me until he released his filth on me, and most Saturdays, too, as I pretended to be asleep. Raynelle's visits became rare, as did our all-night phone calls. We had protected each other the best way we could the previous three seasons, but time changed everything.

I hated Bianca's boyfriend, Liam. Did I have a reason? No, not really. He was a retired cop, and I wasn't fond of cops. He was uninterested in everything except football. He would ask Brady and me about school every now and then, but it seemed obligatory, and I was always sarcastic in my replies. Brady was coming to my room frequently; I awoke several times with him pinning me down with his pants down and holding his hand over my mouth. When he would move his hand, I would threaten to scream or tell Bianca.

He made sure I knew she would not believe me, or he would tell her I started it, which she would believe. Bianca and I fought often. Sometimes I hit her. I am not proud of it, but I am not ashamed of it either. I hated her then. I felt justified in my hatred. She was my mother. She was supposed to protect me from these things, and she didn't. She was blind to everything. Everything everyone did to me and everything I did to myself. She didn't see. She wasn't really around a lot; she was always at work. But there were still things she should have seen or words she should have listened to, or my troubling behaviors that only got worse.

When Bianca and I would fight, I would threaten to leave, and she would tell me no one wanted me; I would tell her that Grandma would take me, and she would tell me she didn't want me either. Once when Griffith brought me over there, I asked her if she would let me live with her, and she said yes. I asked because I really needed to know if anyone wanted me. The last fight with Bianca happened in the kitchen of our new house, which I hated. "You are just upset you didn't get your perfect little daughter, Skinny, girlie, loves hair and make-up, and you could dress up like a fucking doll! Instead, you got me, a fat kid who likes jeans. If you hate me so much, I will just fucking leave!" I screamed in her face. "Oh yeah, where are you going to go? No job, no money. Who would take you in?" Bianca yelled back. "Grandma will take me! She wants me!" I yelled just to piss her off and to hurt her. "Yeah, right, she wouldn't want you either," she said coldly and calmly. "Wrong, you fucking CUNT, I already asked her, and she said yes!" I was going to hit her. My fists curled, and in those moments of blind rage, she deserved it.

Brady had come up quietly behind me and wrapped his arms around me. I tried to smash my head into him, but he was stronger and a lot bigger than I was. Brady lifted me off the ground as Bianca and I continued screaming at each other. My attitude and mouth were worse than she could even dream of being, and I knew how to hurt her with words. I actually knew her when she didn't know me at all. I also had the power of being fluent in several languages; English, Sarcasm, Mean, Bitch, Cunt, with a heavy helping of Cruel.

I enjoyed watching the look on her face go from "I won" to "severely hurt" I also liked that she was scared of me. Brady didn't think when he lowered me enough to let my feet touch the floor; Bianca got closer, screaming at me with words she intended to hurt me with. I couldn't even hear her anymore; I was quiet but combative. Brady's grip around my arms and torso was tight. I waited for her to get close enough, and I kicked her hard in the knee. In those days, I wore four-inch heeled combat boots, and she felt every bit of it. Bianca cried out in pain as she fell to the floor, clutching her leg. Brady threw me backward onto the floor and ran to his precious mommy. I smiled as he helped her up, but I was angry. No one ever helped me up, no one ever protected me, and I was the fucking kid. After that, Bianca got a person in need of supervision (PINS) petition against me; it basically meant that if I hit her again and she called the cops, I would be arrested. I always thought she did it to scare me. It didn't work.

I still took comfort in Brad. His voice on the phone would sew dissolvable stitches in my heart. I listened to the tapes that he had left behind repeatedly. He had also left behind some newspaper clippings of community service projects he had been involved with in high school. The articles had pictures of him, and I taped them to the side of my dresser so I could look at them as I fell asleep. It made it easier to pretend his arms were around me. I took over his room at Harry's when I was being defiant, I thought about cleaning it, but I didn't do it because I was afraid it would erase his smell. Brad's cot-sized bed, rough pillow, and shirt held me anytime I was there. I played his tapes until they broke. I looked at the small blue The Wall sticker on their corners. The Wall was a music store that guaranteed your tapes and CDs (which were not big yet) for life, you could break your shit on purpose, and they would replace it. I thought about bringing them in, but they would not be the same. The words would, of course, remain the same, but they would just be different.

Bianca came to talk to me one night. It was unusual I existed in her world; it was more unusual that she was nice when I did exist. I don't remember why she came to talk to me or what about, but she did talk about Brad. "I know you are in love with him," she said warmly. I said nothing because I didn't know what to say. She droned on and on about how it was okay and she was there for me; she said she understood the pain I was feeling. For the first time that I could remember, I felt I could talk to her and confide in her. I showed her the newspaper-printed pictures next to my bed and told her how they made me feel closer to him and helped me sleep. She left as abruptly as she had appeared.

I had wanted to watch something on TV, and my TV stopped working; Brady said I could watch it in his room while he did his homework. It was strange of him to be nice, but at least he was now doing his own work. I was sitting on the edge of his bed when the show came on, and suddenly he was behind me, trying to touch me. I told him to leave me alone and let me watch the show. He did, and every time I glanced in his direction, he appeared to be doing his homework.

He left his room and came back with a drink; he closed the door when he came back in. Brady pushed me down on the bed and held me down; his hot breath was burning my eyes. I had learned long ago to just let it happen or be beaten. I don't know what happened, but I snapped. I broke. My knee came up and connected with his balls, he rolled off of me, and I got up. Brady grabbed my leg before I got to the door; he got to his feet and started hitting me.

Strength came from somewhere deep inside of me, and I fought back. I punched, kicked, and clawed until I could get that door open and walk away. I was almost to my room when he hit me from behind; I turned and attacked him in a hate-filled rage. I won the fight as his nose bled, and he called for a truce. He was getting up off the floor when Bianca came in and asked us what was going on and who had started it. "Go ahead, Brady, tell her," I said with hatred, violence, and vengeance. His surety that she would believe him over me waivered that night, and he said, "It's nothing, we're fine," he said as he walked back to his room. I was and am still one million percent sure that she would have believed him over me. He never touched me again.

We hadn't lived there long; I had been enrolled in that school for an entire six weeks. I moved in with my grandparents shortly after the last fight with Brady. They didn't actually have a room for me there. Grandpa had the master bedroom, Tina had the other two bedrooms, and Grandma had the whole lower level to herself. A "room" was made for me on the lower level; out of old bookshelves and filing cabinets, an old yellow curtain was hung as a door. Grandma and I were a lot alike. We both stayed up all or most of the night; we were both sarcastic, and we were both known for being honest to a fault.

I started my third school of the year with only six weeks left in the school year. All of the schools were vastly different, and the requirements varied. I failed my science regent's exam placement by one point, and the teacher changed it to pass by one point. He didn't even expect anything for it. I started French in my first school in eighth grade, and I continued in my second school, but they started language classes in that school in sixth grade, so I was already behind. The third school didn't have French for eighth graders, and if I failed a foreign language, I would fail the grade. I didn't know any Spanish, which was all they had for my grade.

Arrangements were made with the high school French teacher that she would provide worksheets and a textbook, and I would do it while sitting in a Spanish classroom. Then she would schedule me privately to take the three-part regents exam. I got two As and a B on the tests, which isn't bad, all things considered. I qualified for regents in every subject, well, except science, and they had taken pity on me with that test. Brady moved in with Griffith at the end of the school year, leaving Bianca and Liam alone. They moved to an apartment a few miles away from me.

Riding in Cars with Men

I turned fifteen that summer. It wasn't very eventful; Bianca did stuff for my birthday. It was the first time in a while. I think it was because she felt guilty. Yes, I had threatened to leave, but in the end, she had told me to go. I had wanted her to want me; I wanted her to be a mom and care for me, love me. It seemed no one loved me. I began to see myself as unlovable, worthless, useless, helpless, and hopeless. These words all became synonymous with my existence. I still spent a lot of time at Griffith's, but my grandparents did make me come home for a few days here and there. Of course, every night that I wasn't at his house, he came to see me. Bianca thought he was having an affair with Tina. Most of the days I was at Griffith's, I was alone, which was good but boring.

Tina had given me some of her old clothes from when she was smaller. Amongst the pile was a couple of body suits. One was green with a low scoop neck, and the other was blue, low cut, and crossed at the breasts. Both looked great on me; they made me look thinner, especially with a pair of baggy jeans. I was out of cigarettes, and there was a guy working at the gas station; I threw on a light flannel jacket (to hide more fat) and started walking.

It wasn't a far walk, a couple of corners away and on a hill. I hadn't gotten far when a white van went past me in the opposite direction. A young guy was driving with his head hanging out the window, looking at me. "Nice tits!" yelled the guy with reddish brown hair and dark sunglasses. I yelled back, "Thanks," and kept walking. I didn't notice he turned around until I heard tires pull up close to me. "Hey, you want a ride?" He asked with a smile. "I'm just going to the top of the hill," I nodded in the direction I was headed. I leaned on the passenger side door, looking into his sunglasses. "Well, do you want a ride? To the top of the hill?" His smile widened, and his cheeks flushed. I stepped back a little so he could see more than just my face, "I'm fifteen," I told him honestly. I felt his eyes all over me, "You aren't fifteen. Come on; I will give you a ride." I got in and told him again, "I am fifteen." He drove straight, but he was looking at me more than at the road. He passed the gas station and went a few more blocks before making a left; as he turned off onto a side street I didn't know, he said, "I'm just turning around, I'm not, you know-" He didn't finish the sentence, as he drove back up the hill and passed Harry's house.

You want to take that jacket off so I can see you?" I sat up and slowly slid it down my shoulders, giving him the view he was asking for. "You are beautiful," he said as I leaned back again and watched him look at me from my peripheral vision. "Can I see your tits?" I pulled them out. "Can I feel?" I nodded slightly. I wasn't used to being asked, and I liked it. "You want to go somewhere? Somewhere and park?" I now knew, thanks to Kyle, what going somewhere meant, and I again nodded. I started to pull my clothes back up and was half covered when he asked me to leave the other tit out. He touched me again. "What's your name?" He asked with a smile that didn't go away. "Simone, what's yours?" He reached to touch me again; Joey, how old are you really?" I laughed, "Fifteen." I took one of his cigarettes from his shirt pocket and lit it. "Why? How old do you think I am? How old are you?" He eyed me up and down while still fondling me, "I am twenty-four, and you are, I don't know? Twenty-six?" I laughed again. We had pulled into the back of the movie theatre parking lot. I finished my high-jacked cigarette. We talked for a couple of minutes. He didn't live there; he lived about thirty minutes away; he just worked there and just got the job. He didn't know anyone or really where anything was. I eyed his tented pants, "Do you want to uh, uh?" He didn't seem to know how to finish the question as he opened his pants and exposed himself.

I didn't know if he expected a hand job, a blow job, or to get fucked. But I kneeled down between the two seats and gave him a blow job as he squeezed that tit he seemed awfully fond of. Joey didn't take long, less than five minutes; when he was about done, he started pushing me back a little bit. I didn't stop. "I'm going to cum!" He said, still pushing me a little. I didn't stop, he finished, and I swallowed.

First time for everything, right? I sat up while pulling my clothes back up; I could almost see his eyes through his sunglasses, "Holy shit!" he shouted. "Not bad for fifteen, huh?" I asked with a smile. I sat back and stole another cigarette. I expected him to tell me to get out and walk; it wasn't that far back to Harry's, I guess a few miles, but I had and have no concept of distance. Joey stared out the windshield in shock for several minutes before starting the engine and driving. Joey asked where to drop me off and if he could see me again, "I don't live around here. I'm here for most of the summer and then only on weekends," I told him. "Can I get your number?" He had been nice, and I had been nicer, but that seemed fine. "Yeah, I will give you my grandparents' number; I won't be there much until the summer is over, and don't call after nine. My grandmother will get pissy. Got a pen?" His expression changed a little.

As he felt around the dash, his pocket, and wherever else he could reach, something seemed to dawn on him. "You can drop me right there," I pointed toward Harry's driveway. "Oh shit!" he yelled in shock. I turned and looked at him; Joey had gone white as a ghost; his mouth was open, and he wasn't looking at the road at all as he made the right-hand turn into Harry's driveway. "You're not-? You're not that girl I was warned about? The girl they call jailbait?" I smiled, "Yup. That would be me. Still want my number?" He was now looking a little green. "Uh, no, I uh, don't want to bother you," he said as I got out of the van and waved goodbye with a smile. My reputation was stronger than I knew. I went into the house and realized I never got cigarettes. I went back out and made it to the store and back this time. I went to Griffith's room and wrote I 'Heart'

Joey on his wall. I liked to piss him off, and that would. Not because I wasn't supposed to write on walls, Griffith wrote most numbers he needed on the wall. It just pissed him off when there were any guys around me. Then I went back to Brad's room.

Brad's shirt had lost his smell, as did most of the things in his room. I could still smell him faintly on his pillow. I found an almost empty bottle of Preferred Stock under his bed and sprayed what I could onto the bed and his shirt. I laid there until I slept. Brady woke me up when dinner was ready; I didn't want it. I thought of Joey; he was probably a good guy. I don't think he would have laid a hand on me if he believed I was fifteen. I knew I wouldn't see him again; I did try, though. I walked down the street at around the time he had picked me up a few times a week.

I had plenty of other guys stop, and most of them I got in their cars. Most of them didn't try anything and just stared at me. I didn't let them see anything or touch anything, and I didn't touch them unless they had something to trade. Drugs would get a guy a hand job or a blow job, depending on what it was, how much, and if he seemed like a dick or not. Some of them complained and told me to get out; some jerked off while driving and looking at me. I found it all intoxicating. Getting in cars with strange men was a whole new world of addiction. It was different from the high I got with drugs that could make my reality go black; this was a danger that I was always aware of what I was doing. It was an exhilarating danger that I could control.

I had drifted apart from most of my friends in my hometown; sometimes Griffith would still drop me off there, though. Raynelle's grandmother was going away for a week and wanted Raynelle to house-sit. She didn't want to do it alone, so I got to spend a week with her.

On Saturday nights, Griffith and I would watch America's Funniest Home Videos, which I honestly didn't find very funny. It was usually just a bunch of guys getting hit in the balls with random objects. Then we would watch Saturday Night Live. I would try to be asleep by the end of the show, or at least fake asleep. If he knew I was awake, he would tell me to get in his bed. If I was "asleep," he would sometimes leave me alone.

Grandma liked to order things from catalogs; she ordered me two new bathing suits for that summer. They were both the same thing, in two different colors; the bottoms looked like shorts, and the tops looked like a flowy tank top, one in purple and one in black. I would always bring at least one of them to Griffith's with me, I never knew where I was going to end up, and I knew several people with pools. Harry's house also had no air conditioning, and fans didn't do much, so bathing suits were great to sleep in.

A sixteen-year-old boy named Chris started doing odd jobs for Harry. We became friends, and he asked me out; I said yes, much to Griffith's dismay. Chris never did a thing to me; we held hands, we kissed a few times, and that was it. His name went on Griffith's wall, along with Joey's and a lot of others. I enjoyed seeing his eyes fill with anger when he would see another name added to the wall. Harry was really noticing me; he gave me a birthday card with twenty-five dollars in it that summer, but he gave Brady nothing. I caught him a few times watching me, with his eyes squinted tight so hard they would almost look closed. His hand would raise, and one gnarly finger would poke out toward me, and he would stab the finger at me in the air. People that didn't know would think he was trying to get my attention; those of us that knew him knew what he was really doing. I don't care how people tried to justify his behavior. He knew what he was doing and knew it was wrong. Harry never did it when Griffith was around; the second Griffith would come around the corner, Harry's hand would fall back into his lap. Chris saw him do it once, "I guess I'm not the only one with a crush on you." he joked. I laughed, even though I didn't think it was funny. Harry was a true piece of shit. Not just for his TV habits or for the way he looked at me. Harry, in his younger days, was a proud member of the KKK. At dinner, he would often talk about the "good old days" when you could lynch black people and beat "The gays" in the streets. I hoped the old mother fucker would die at least once a day. I wished someone would lynch him while beating him in the streets. This story isn't about him, though. Just to clarify, I am anti-racist and far from homophobic.

On a particularly hot night, I fell asleep in Griffth's chair in my purple bathing suit. I had felt off since dinner. As I was sleeping, I felt my body shifting; I felt like I was falling and then flying. I lifted my head as high as I could, which wasn't far, and even that was hard. My head was so heavy I opened my eyes as much as I could; a sliver was all I could manage. I saw Griffith holding me, "Daddy, I don't feel good, and it is so hot," I said groggily. I heard him speak and could make out, "I'm going to cool you down," before my body went limp, and I was again unconscious, as I felt him laying me down in bed.

I felt something icy cold wrap around my side, across my waist and abdomen; it was refreshing and welcoming. As the iciness faded, there was something warm behind it that wasn't pleasant. There was more icy coolness as I felt my body rolling onto my back; it didn't feel like I was moving on my own. The top of my bathing suit was lifted, but the built-in bra remained in place; that was see-through, though, and I felt exposed. The ice was back, placed at the top of my cleavage, and as it melted down me, I felt sweet relief. The coolness was welcome, but I felt fear; I tried to reach to pull my top back down, and I could barely lift my arm. Trying to stay even a little conscious was nearly impossible. The only thing that kept snapping me back was the feeling of cold. When the iciness was gone, whatever was warm behind it made my skin crawl, and my mind would slip back into the darkness.

Ice again, this time dripping on my lips and down my neck. I opened my mouth and felt the coolness drip on my tongue. I was drenched from my mouth to my lower abdomen. I laid relieved and started to fall back asleep when the cold came again. This time it was across my entire chest. I felt my nipples harden from the cold and again tried to pull my top down, but I again failed. I couldn't lift my arm enough. The warmth was touching where the ice had hardened me. It made me want to scream as it burned my flesh. I tried to open my mouth to let the scream out, but all I could produce was a squeak through barely parted lips. I tried to open my eyes, and again, it was just a sliver. Where was I? More ice. It started at my neck and went all the way to the bottoms of my bathing suit. There was something warm on one nipple and ice on the other. What was that? Was that a mouth? Who was touching me? I didn't like it, but my body was responding to it. Why was that happening? It had never happened before. Why couldn't I move?

More ice moved lower. My thighs and between were touched by the cold. Heat on my chest and ice everywhere else. The ice seemed to be awakening me, while the warmth made my mind slip further. I heard a voice, "Yeah, you like that?" Whose voice was that? I wanted to respond, "No! Stop!" But when I tried, all that came out was a gurgle. The gurgle started with the N sound, though, so it was an improvement. The ice was going inside of me as I felt the heat kissing down my cleavage. The ice started to hurt; the heat was making me want to scrape off every bit of my skin it was touching. I wanted to set myself on fire.

The pain of the ice on my thighs and inside of me made my eyes snap halfway open. I could lift my arm more now and grabbed at my top to pull it down. My hand was smacked away. Why were people always touching me? Who was touching me? A tongue licked down my torso, and my back arched in reflex. I was so confused. A new heat began to build behind my eyes and then cover my eyelids. I tried not to let the tears out as I felt one slide down into my ear and then one from the other side. "NO! Don't cry, Simone! DON'T CRY! Remember always, only the weak cry!" My own voice screamed inside my head. There was that phrase again. Where was it coming from? Could I move my head? A little. The heat of whoever was touching me was low now, almost at my hip bone. I tilted my head, put my chin on my chest, and opened my eyes as much as I could. My eyes met his as his tongue stuck out to lick the lowest spot on my stomach. Griffith.

I turned my head back to the ceiling and tried not to cry. I tried to wipe a tear away, and I could move my arm fully. My head turned easily but sluggishly, and all my thoughts were in slow motion. But I could move. I felt the tears flowing, one after another, as he licked from my navel to my bathing suit bottoms. I tried to keep my breathing even so he wouldn't notice I was crying. I tried to keep my shit together and just get through whatever was going to happen. Just get it over with without being beaten. I failed.

I exploded in a burst of hysterical tears and jumped up just as he was about to pull the bottom of my bathing suit down. I walked as quickly as I could to the dresser while sobbing on my legs, that were shaking. All of me was shaking. My legs were having trouble supporting me. I didn't know why and didn't have time to think about it. I grabbed a pair of shorts and slid them over my existing bottoms. I collected the cash I had stashed (stolen from Griffith), my cigarettes and lighter got jammed into my pocket, and I grabbed the unopened bottle of Jack on my way out of the room. I flew down the stairs on legs that were still shaking. I don't know how I didn't fall. I passed Harry's room loudly, the bottle smacking into the wall as I staggered. "Hey, you! Girl, come back here! Help me!" Harry yelled. I turned and looked back to see Harry jerking off in front of his TV. I gave him the finger and kept going to the fridge. I drank three of Harry's beers consecutively. Schmidt's gross beer, I don't think, is made anymore; it would have to do, though.

I slammed through the door, not bothering to close it behind me. The storm door slammed shut behind me on its own, echoing my anger and defiance. Fuck them all. I cracked the bottle open beside the house and began to drink as I walked. I stopped in the gas station, at the top of the hill, for more cigarettes after stashing my Jack outside. The guy working asked if I was okay, which is when I realized I was crying uncontrollably. My eyes must have said it all; he didn't say a word as he gave me my change. I retrieved my bottle; it was already a quarter gone.

I had nowhere to go, and even if I did, I didn't have enough money to get anywhere. I walked, drank, and smoked. I walked until there was nothingness. Pitch black. Darkness. I woke up in the morning next to a dumpster on a cardboard box. My bottle was still in my hand but empty. I tossed it in the dumpster, noticing the homeless man that was sitting not far from me. "You dropped this, miss," the man said as he held out some cash. "I didn't want no one to take it; I held it fo' you." I looked into his kind eyes, "Keep it," I told him as I lit a cigarette. The sun was shining; my body hurt; I had scrapes and bruises on my legs and arms. I had no idea where I was. My head was clear, though, and it was time to walk. I walked back to Griffith's and was relieved to see his truck was gone. Harry was asleep, and I took a long hot shower. I climbed the stairs and gathered most of my stuff from Griffith's room; I brought it all to Brad's room and wished that the door had a lock.

There was no scent of him left at all. I tried and tried to find it. I needed it now more than ever. I stood in the center of his room with my eyes closed. I could see us in my mind. I could almost feel him here with me again, almost feel his safety, but I couldn't find his smell. I tried to bury my face deep in his pillow; I clung helplessly to his shirt. There was nothing. I cried more than I thought I had ever cried in my life. On his trash-littered floor, on my wounded knees, holding his shirt, my tears filled an ocean. When the flood was over, and I had rebuilt the broken damn, I knew it was time. I got up and cleaned his room. Then I took it. By the time Griffith and Brady got back, I had moved my radio, clothes, and almost all my other things into Brad's room, except for that purple bathing suit. I left that on the floor next to Griffith's bed. I never wore it again.

I did call Brad while I was gathering my things. We talked about the basics and caught up even though it had only been a few days since we had talked. Brad asked if anything was up or if anything was wrong. I lied and told him no, just a shitty day, and I needed to hear his voice. He said he needed to hear mine too, which I already knew. I could hear it when he answered the phone. When we talked, I could almost smell him. Almost.

I didn't leave Brad's room that night. Brady brought up a plate of food, a cold six-pack, and a bag filled with Jack and Cigarettes, letting me know, "Daddy said to give you this shit." I didn't speak. As he was pulling the door shut, he looked back at me, "You know you can't stay in here, right? It is for rent." Fire shot from my eyes like bullets as he shut the door. I didn't eat the food. I didn't drink the alcohol; I stashed it in my backpack instead.

The next day, after the guys were gone, I got dressed and went out walking. Only this time, I was looking for something, and I knew what I wanted. I was looking for a guy. I was looking for trouble. I met a boy named Luke. He was seventeen; he had a license and a truck. He would do. We talked for hours about absolutely nothing. He asked if he could pick me up that night and take me to a movie. Of course, I said, "Yes."

Griffith was in the kitchen that night making dinner when I happily bopped in and announced, "I have a boyfriend. His name is Luke, and he is seventeen." I had to make sure he knew, even though I had made sure to add Luke to the growing list of names on Griffith's wall. Griffith's eyes turned cold as they traced my body from head to toe. My hair was done, my make-up was on, my shirt was tight and low cut, my skirt was mid-thigh, and my legs were bare to the tops of my combat boots. Griffith asked me to cut the onions for dinner. He was allergic to onions. Well, raw onions, anyway. He could eat them if they were cooked, but if he ate them or touched them raw, he would break out in a painful rash. As I diced the onions, filling a big plastic bowl with them, I told him all about Luke. I didn't look at him, but I could feel his angry gaze. He didn't speak. "So, Daddy, Luke wants to take me to a movie tonight. He will be here any minute to pick me up. Can I go?' The question was rhetorical, and we both knew it. I looked at him then and saw the anger in his eyes had intensified to a degree I hadn't seen before. His pants were falling down, as they always were; I saw him unbuckle his belt to re-tuck his shirt like I saw him do at least a dozen times a day. He was speaking, but I only heard one word, "Slut." His pants were still low, and his belt was open as he stood there staring at me with eyes that would kill me if they could. I heard Luke's truck pull in, and he honked the horn. I took the bowl of onions and walked the few steps to Griffith. I grabbed the elastic waistband of his tighty whitey briefs, my eyes never left his, as I dumped the entire bowl of raw cut onions into his underwear. "Jealous," I accused while staring him in the eye. I snapped the elastic against his skin as I let go and walked to the door. I turned to him just before walking out the door, "If you think I' m a slut, don't forget, you made me this way, asshole." I half ran to Luke's truck and made sure to put a smile on my face when I got in.

Griffith left me alone for a couple of weeks. When he was home, he laid in his bed with a bag of ice on his crotch. I could see the rash had spread down his thighs, and it made me smile. I saw Luke a few more times. He liked to invite me to movies and out to eat. We would drive to those places and never make it inside. We would just sit in the parking lot, listen to music and talk about nothing. I would lay across the seat of his truck with my head in his lap and laugh at his stories about his brothers or his friends. We kissed a few times, but nothing else. He was sweet. The school year would be starting soon, though, and with me going back to my grandparents' house, we wouldn't really be able to see each other. So, we stopped seeing each other amicably. Which was fine, I never really liked him anyway, and he served the purpose I had needed him for.

Grandma ordered that I spend the last two weeks of summer vacation at home. Griffith came almost every night, sometimes with Brady and sometimes alone. That's when it started. Again. He had made it clear that I was to sit in front of him or on his lap. Bianca knew about me sitting there and would complain to me about it. Grandma started calling me a "Cow" anytime she saw me sitting in his lap. I had been told she also didn't believe me when I was eleven, that no one did. Why would I tell them again now? They had already chosen their side. They had already failed me. Betrayed me. I did try and tell Bianca once that he would tell me I had to sit there, and she didn't believe me.

When he would rock the chair and touch me, I would jump up, claiming to need the bathroom. When he would pick me up and put me in his lap, there was no way to get away. Griffith had begun rubbing my crotch as he would dry hump me in the chair. If I simply said I was going to bed, he would follow me to "Tuck me in." On those nights, his hands would go to any number of places.

School started, and I tried to be excited and interested. I hoped this year things would be different. It wasn't only high school, but I was pretty new since I had just moved there at the end of the previous school year. No one knew me; I wasn't a flasher or jailbait; I could just be me. The bullying started on day one. Frankie, the most popular boy in ninth grade, passed papers back to me in Spanish class and announced, "Oh, look, another loser." That was all the rest of them needed. Some girl accused me of staring at her boyfriend; I didn't know who he was or what she was talking about. She pointed him out; he was cute, and he would have been a guy I would have gone after if he was single. She harassed me that I had been staring at him until I fled the cafeteria to cry alone in a bathroom stall. I had never wanted to take Spanish; I wanted to take French because my entire family told me, "It will be too hard for you. You will never make it. You will fail." I wanted to prove them wrong, but the teacher who had been so kind to me the previous year had retired. They couldn't find a new French teacher, so I was stuck in Spanish.

I did make some friends, which was all I needed. I never wanted to be the most popular kid in school; I just wanted to not be tormented. I was bullied for everything, my clothes, hair, weight, boobs, even my fucking name. Patty was the first friend I made, and she lived close to me. I asked her if she knew where to get weed, and she hooked me up with her cousin Greg. Greg liked me, so I got free weed; from there, I met some of his other friends, and they had other drugs. They never told Greg, so Patty never found out. Usually, I got free weed, sold some, and used the money to buy what I needed. If that wasn't an option, blow jobs worked.

News travels fast in schools, and kids have big mouths. A girl named Dierdre approached me in the lunch line and asked to buy enough weed for a joint; cool five bucks, please, and thank you. She said she lived near me and asked me to meet her at a park near us both. When I got there, I found out it was her first time, and she wanted me to smoke it with her to show her how. My favorite kind of customer. They pay, but I get high. Dierdre became one of my best friends. Raynelle visited my grandparents' house a few times, but there were no more sleepovers. Brad still called, but the calls were getting less frequent, and they were not as long. I only called him when I really needed to hear his voice. When I just couldn't breathe.

I was in Brad's room the weekend after Labor Day. It had been a year since we had sex. A year since his kiss forced a burst of life through my heart and soul. I could hear our music in my head. *Soul Asylum's Runaway Train and Bon Jovi's Never Say Goodbye and Always* played on repeat at a max volume just for me. I had a candle burning in the window; I watched the flame dance as my burning tears ran down my face in an endless stream. I accidentally knocked the candle over, and in an attempt to catch it before starting a fire, the wax spilled across my arm. The pain was refreshing, rejuvenating, almost living. The heat didn't last long enough, but I became fascinated by the sensation it gave. The pain would spark momentary life inside of me.

I was asleep in Brad's room. I had fallen asleep quickly after dinner feeling sick with a headache that had the potential to become a migraine. By the time sleep took me, I was nauseated, dizzy, and thought my head might explode. Then I was moving. Floating in the air. There was light. Maybe I had died; maybe my head really did explode. There was heat on top of me, heavy breathing. My shirt was raised, and I was again exposed.

I choke down vomit as my pants are pulled down to the tops of my combat boots. I was able to clench my fists enough to feel my nails dig into my palms. The pain sparked my brain to work a little. It kept my mind in place. A mouth on my calf that worked its way up to my inner thigh. My body flips over like I weigh nothing. Hands, hot and hungry, grab at my ass. Fingers fall between my legs, and I am flipped again. I squeeze again and feel a flex in my forearms. I twitch my toes. I alternate squeezing and twitching, and each time I can feel it a little further up my limbs. It distracts me from the feeling of his mouth and hands sliding around my body. I squeezed and felt it all the way up to my collarbone. I twitch and feel my knee kick just a little. I get flipped again, and he is kissing my ass. I don't even wonder who it is; this time, I know. He speaks, but I cannot understand what he is saying. Squeeze and twitch. The backs of my shoulders started to flex, and the back of my thigh twitched almost to the ass he was just kissing. I get flipped back onto my back. I know I don't have much time left. I feel his fingers almost inside me; I let one tear fall. My eyes snap wide open; I lift my leg and kick as hard as I can. In a falling run, I am up and yanking my pants back up. I have no doubt that this time he is behind me. I look back and see that my boot has collided with his dick, and he is a fat crumpled ball of shit on the floor. He looks at me with pain and hate in his eyes. I took the cash out of his wallet on the dresser while he watched. "Don't fucking touch me," I spit the words out at him before I could even think.

I closed my pants and, on my way, passed Brad's room; I grabbed my already packed backpack. I had started leaving it by the door at all times. I fled as I had before. I fled this disgusting house filled with its sick secrets. As I approached the front yard, I slipped a hand into my backpack; I knew where everything was. I grabbed the bottle of Jack, cracked it open, and gulped. Again, I drank, walked, and smoked until there was darkness. Again, I woke up in a cardboard box by a dumpster. The same homeless man was there. I had felt him the night before, making me a blanket out of newspapers. I reached into my bag and grabbed two beers. I passed him one, a five-dollar bill, and a few cigarettes. I sat there with him in the early morning silence as we drank our beers together, but alone. On my way back to Griffith's, I cracked open my second bottle of Jack and finished it before I got there. Griffith didn't stop touching me.

Time bomb

In mid-late September, Brady picked me up alone again. There was a stack of cold beers in the center seat. This wasn't going to be good. I got in, slammed the door, opened one, and chugged. I had finished three by the time he started the ignition and began to drive. "I have t-" Brady began, "Just fucking tell me," I snapped while drinking beer number five. "Someone moved in. Someone moved into Brad's room." One can hit the floor, and another opens. Brady started telling me all about Drew, the new guy. Brady said Drew was really cool; he set up the bedroom to have a living area with a love seat and TV, and there was the bedroom area with a big bed and a weight bench. I was silent. We were almost there when Brady let me know Drew had invited us to watch a movie with him that night.

As I started up the steps, the world moving slowly, I saw that the door was closed. Good. Motherfucker didn't belong there. There were TVs on throughout the house, but I couldn't hear them. The only sound was my boots thudding on each wooden step and the sound of my blood crashing furiously through my veins. I needed to get out of here; maybe Todd's number was still good. I dropped my bag on Griffith's bedroom floor and was about to head to the phone when Brad's door opened. "Hey! You must be Simone. I have really been looking forward to meeting you. I heard you were really close with the last guy who lived here and that you would be upset, so I really want you to see how I fixed it up. Did Brady tell you I have it set up as a bedroom and a living room? You guys want to come to watch a movie with me?" I wished the fire I could feel in my eyes could actually set him on fire. I wanted to scream at him to get out. But time with him was better than the alternatives...maybe.

The Three of us sat together on the small love seat. It was a good thing Drew was a twig because Brady and I were both big. If Drew had been any bigger, we would not have fit. When the movie was over, Drew started to put on another one, but Brady said he needed to go to bed and walked out. "Oh, I guess you do, too, then, huh?" I slid over and grabbed another beer, "Nope. Not really." Drew thought about it, "Yeah, you should probably go. I don't want your dad to get mad that I kept you up too late." I grabbed my backpack and took one step toward the door, and I froze. The tears were coming like a tidal wave.

Drew was unremarkable. I don't even really remember what his face looked like. He had long, dirty blonde hair, he was scrawny, and he was thirty-one. I would never have been interested in him. I took another step, and the tears fell. The waves crashed through me, and I ugly cried in front of this man, this stranger. I pushed the door shut and squatted, trying to get myself together. Drew sat, repeatedly asking what was wrong. He tried to pat my back and awkwardly hugged me. He tried to comfort me, "Hold on, Simone, I'll go get your dad." As he grabbed the doorknob, my reflexes kicked in, and I grabbed him and sat him back down on the loveseat without a word. "Your brother? You want Brady instead?" I shook my head. They would have lied. They would have said it was because I missed Brad. I did, and being in this room was physically painful, but that wasn't what was wrong with me.

Brad's room being taken was only the nail in the coffin. I paced back and forth in front of him; I was prepared to knock him down if he got up. I just needed time to get a grip on myself. I couldn't go in that room; I just couldn't do it. Drew sat, obviously uncomfortable, watching me pace and cry. "Simone, if you don't tell me what is wrong or how to help, I'm going to have to go get your dad," he finally dared to speak. "No," I growled at him. He sat with his feet apart, so I stood between them, making sure I was perfectly positioned to put him back down if he dared to move at all.

I wasn't used to being like this; I didn't know how to turn it off. Drew told me several more times that he was going to go get my "Dad," but he didn't move. Every time he said it, it was like my brain cracked open, and the years of being held in tears would stream more. Finally, my mouth started to leak, too, "He isn't my dad, and he does things to me," he looked shocked. "Griffith? He's your dad. He seems like a good guy. Oh, you mean your stepdad does? Oh, okay." He rationalized mostly to himself. I squared my feet between his and stared directly into his eyes, "He isn't my dad. He is my stepdad, and he does things to me," I told him again as he stared in disbelief. "Nah, nah. Where is your room? I will walk you to your door. No one has to know about this. I won't tell anyone." Drew started to get up and had one hand on my shoulder. Why didn't anyone fucking listen to me?! I put him back in his place and again stared into his eyes. "Idiot. Fucking listen to me. How many bedrooms do you see here? If I leave this room, I have to go to his room. His room is my room." I could see the lights popping on in his head. "But there is only one bed in there." He said, and stark understanding clarity appeared on his face; his eyes widened as they locked on mine again. "He isn't my dad. He's my stepdad. And. He. Does. Thing-" I was silenced by Drew's kiss.

My shirt was over my head, and my bra was off as I walked backward toward Drew's bed under his guiding hand. His shirt was off, his pants were down, and his dick was in my hand. His hands moved quickly over my body. My pants came down and tangled in my boots. We fell and laughed. Drew lifted me onto his bed and took my boots and pants off. Then he was on me. I opened my legs willingly to this man, this stranger, as he slid inside me. He was rough, and it was painful. Not as painful as Kyle. We fucked almost all night.

Shortly before sunset, I dressed, and Drew peeked out into the hallway. The coast was clear. I left his room laughing. There had been no orgasm. Good old Mr. Holbert must have lied about that. I dropped my bag just inside Griffith's doorway and went downstairs just in time to hear his alarm going off. I decided as I opened the fridge that beer would make a good breakfast. I brought a six-pack to the back porch and waited for the shit to hit the fan. Griffith came outside after making Harry's breakfast; he hadn't known I was there. "Where did you sleep?" I gave him silence. He asked again with his hand squeezing my thigh, "I didn't," I told him, my eyes glittered with hate. He squeezed harder, and I knew it was going to bruise. No pain. No fear. The damn of tears had been released, it was resealed now, and I felt a ticking inside myself.

I never loved Drew. I never liked Drew as anything more than a friend, and even that was questionable. I fucked him, though. As soon as he was up that Saturday, he invited me back to his bed, and we fucked most of the day. I went out walking that night and got back after Griffith was asleep. Drew and I drank and fucked all night. Over the next several weekends, I learned that Drew liked to give and receive oral, which was a new experience for me. However, he also liked to bite; I asked him and told him several times not to bite me before warning him that if he bit me again, I would bite him back. He didn't listen, so he got bit. We were so drunk that he laughed about it more than he complained about it. Drew talked me into trying anal. Once I finally agreed, he bent me over his weight bench. As he entered the "wrong hole," it hurt so bad I shot forward into the wall, hitting my head. My ass hurt more than my head did. We laughed about that, too. We tried it again with me on top of him, it was better when I had more control of the situation, but it was still the wrong hole. I never tried everything he tried to talk me into. Drinking his urine was out of the question.

Over those weeks, I started telling people. I told Griffith's neighbor, who was also a friend, Richie. He was a big dirty man, but I had always liked him. He had never looked at me in a way that made me want to burn off my flesh. At first, he tried to tell me the same thing everyone else did. No, no, no, you must be mistaken; Griffith would never. I could see in his eyes, though, that he believed me, so I called him out on his bullshit. "I can see in your eyes that you believe me. I can see everything in everyone's eyes. You believe me; you just don't fucking want to." He shut up and stopped protesting. After a long silence that wasn't uncomfortable, he told me. "If you ever need to get away, where no one will know where you are, come to my back door. Knock three times. I will ask who it is, knock twice, and I will let you in. You can crash." I knew Richie didn't answer the door for most people, and I knew he didn't answer after dark. Richie had had a drug problem, and the demons came out to play at night, so he would basically lock himself in when the sun would go down. I understood. I told all my friends at school, Patty, Katy, Vicky, Dierdre, and Theresa. They all knew. I told anyone who would listen. Tick tock.

Griffith never stopped. I was made to go directly to his room on Friday nights. I faked sleep as he would dry hump my leg or ass. When he was done, I tried not to think of the filth he left behind. He would come over to visit me two or three times a week; he would stay until Grandma would tell him it was time to leave. Eleven pm when she would come upstairs to set up the coffee pot for the next day. Griffith would follow me downstairs to "Tuck me in," touching me everywhere and then un-tucking his shirt to hide the wet spot on his pants before leaving; the hot tears always came in silence. There was a volcano forming with the bomb in the pit of my stomach.

I found salvation in drugs more often. I had very little money, and selling small amounts of weed to high school kids wasn't enough for what I needed. I would, again, insert myself into groups of people that were getting high. Even when they would realize someone was taking their shit, they never thought it was me. Crack was my favorite. I loved it. I hated it. Coke was easier to hide and often easier to steal. You take what you can get.

I was breaking. I could feel a wall in my head tingling and cracking. Something was fighting its way out. I was on the phone with Brad when I did what I thought I would never do. The demon I carried locked away in a vault inside my mind kicked its way through and came smashing out.

Something was different with Brad that night; he kept asking what was wrong, why I was so quiet, and what was going on. I couldn't answer. The tears were slowly leaking, and I could barely control the full sobs that I knew were coming. This was one of the only two things I couldn't talk to him about. The other was relationships. We didn't discuss our love lives or sex lives with each other. I knew he was still with Marissa; as far as he knew, I had only been with him and Kyle. That topic was off-limits, and we knew it without saying it. It still hurt us both too much. I was pacing the living room at my Grandma's house, everyone was asleep except my grandmother, and she didn't care what I was doing.

I tried to just tell Brad I had to go, and he kept asking, "Brad, I can't, I pleaded with tears that I could no longer keep from my voice. "Yes, you can. You can tell me anything." Not this. Not the secret that would make him hate me. "Simone, you have always been able to tell me everything; it's you and me against the world, best friends forever" I lost it and let out a sobbing cry, "Its Griffith," There it was. The rest, of course not in detail, came out. That he had been touching me in the vilest ways since I was eleven years old. Brad was quiet, but I could feel his anger in the silence, and I knew it wasn't anger toward me.

I finally calmed down a little, and he told me, "I know. I have known for a while." I was utterly shocked. He knew and didn't hate me? He knew and wasn't disgusted? "Simone, I wanted to help. I wanted to make it stop. I wanted to save you, but I didn't know how. You hadn't told me, and I had no proof. I used to hope to come in from work and catch him." He sounded like he was crying, too. "What would you have done if you caught him?" I was genuinely curious. "I would have stabbed him." There was a long silence as I pictured Brad coming in a year earlier in his McDonald's uniform, walking into Griffith's room, and stabbing him. "Now, you've told me, and I can help. I can call CPS and the police. If you need more time before I call, I can do that. I can wait until you're ready." I asked him to wait; I couldn't deal with that again, not right now. I saw Brad and me lying on his floor. I felt his arms around me. I could smell him again for the first time in months. "You don't hate me?" I asked through my cries. "Why would I hate you? You did nothing wrong. He did," The last two words he spits out with the anger he tried to hold in. "I don't repulse you? You're not disgusted by me?" I asked with a desperate need to know. "I could never be repulsed or disgusted by you," he answered, and I could hear he was softly crying with me. I cried. I cried another ocean of tears, and he listened while I did so. There were only tears and the comfort of his breath. The words that we could never say hung in the silence. We both knew it. Before we got off the phone, he told me exactly how much he understood my pain. When he was a kid, someone had done similar things to him.

Fridays, I had to stay in Griffith's room, but I spent Saturdays with Drew. I should say I spent Saturdays under and on top of Drew. One Saturday, Griffith burst into Drew's room. We were fully dressed, halfway drunk, laughing, and playing Uno. Griffith looked dumbfounded and stomped out, leaving the door open. The next day, Drew put a lock on his door.

There was no escaping Griffith. There weren't enough drugs or alcohol on the planet. I had become numb to the candle wax. I started heating knives and holding the hot metal against my upper arms and thighs. Never long enough to leave a mark. Paper clips worked too. I started looking at knives and thought of cutting myself. Maybe it would have the same effect as burning. I tried it a couple of times and just couldn't do it. This was before I knew that cutting and self-harm was a thing that people did, well, people other than me. There was only one option left. I had to die. Tick tock.

I made a plan. I would take pills, a lot of pills, as many as I could get my hands on. I heard about people trying to kill themselves this way and failing because they would throw it all up. I figured if I spaced it out and didn't take them all at once, it would work. Tina had a shit load of over-the-counter medications, nothing lethal, but if you take enough of all of it together, it should work, right? I picked a day and was excited to follow through with it. I could finally be free. I even told a couple of friends what I intended to do. Katy and Vicky even asked me to call them if there were any problems.

At eight o'clock on the planned date, I climbed the two flights of stairs to the bathroom; I grabbed every pill I could find. Tylenol, Motrin, Aleve, Advil, some antacids, some old, expired antibiotics, and even Midol. I popped ten at random and went back downstairs. I stopped at the phone in the living room and called Katy to let her know I had started my mission. An hour later, I took ten more; half an hour later, I still felt nothing, so I ate ten more. I called Katy and let her know I was up to thirty; I would wait half an hour and take ten more. She told me to call her when I did it. When I called to let her know, she got mad and made me promise to stop, or she would tell her parents. I told her I would, but I didn't. I felt a little dizzy while I was watching TV in my room after fifty. I laid down and struggled to take twenty more. I dozed off for a little while; I woke up and took a handful. I felt the darkness coming. I was finally going to be at peace. I was finally going to be free. Relief was just over the horizon. Those were my last thoughts.

I woke up sometime later and ran the two flights of stairs to the bathroom. The amount of vomit was incredulous. It just kept coming. For the next several hours, I got sick every time I tried to move. How was I still getting sick? I guess I took them too quickly after all. I even failed at dying. Fucking failure.

As the sun was coming up, I started to get scared. I didn't want everyone to know what I had done. I stumbled to the living room phone and called Griffith. "Daddy, I tried to kill myself. I took a lot of pills. I can't stop getting sick. I need you to come and take me to the hospital." I hung up. I didn't think I needed to tell him not to tell anyone. He would know I did it because of him and just kept his mouth shut, right? Wrong.

I got sick several more times while I was waiting for him to get there. When he showed up, I was waiting at the front door. Tina popped up behind me and asked, "What is he doing here?" I ignored her and walked out the door. He was on his way toward me, and we passed each other as he went into the house. Why was he going in? I opened the passenger door and laid across the seat. My head was spinning. I was so tired. There was a hospital basically down the street; it would take him two minutes to drive me there. What was he doing, and why was he taking so long? I lifted my head and puked all over the floor of his truck. "Have a present, you fucker," I thought as I laid back down.

I was almost asleep when Griffith opened the door and pulled me out. He threw me over his shoulder and brought me back into the house. Griffith dropped me unceremoniously onto the hallway floor, sat down, and watched TV. Grandma was at the table; Tina was in the kitchen, slamming shit around. I didn't get hangovers, but I imagined this would be what one felt like. The three of them sat there talking about how stupid I was and asking each other why I would do such a thing. Griffith didn't say much, but he laughed at

119

their comments and interjected agreement at everything. Bianca was called and told; she didn't come. I ran back and forth to the bathroom, getting sick regularly. Of all the times I got sick, no one came to hold my hair; no one offered me any comfort. No Dr. was called. I was throwing up for three days.

Katy called after school every day. She was told by either Grandma or Tina that I was very sick and couldn't come to the phone. I was grounded from going to Griffith's that weekend, which was far from a punishment. He also didn't come over much that week. When I returned to school, I felt physically better than I had in a long time. I had no voice for over a week. Katy told me she had told our Social Studies teacher, Mr. B., that I had been absent because I tried to kill myself. If she did tell him, he never said anything about it. I did notice him looking at me a lot more, though.

Drew came to my house a few times. He fixed some things for my grandparents and helped Tina with her old computer. Tina put pants on when Drew came over. She blushed when he was over, and he flirted with her. I found it amusing. Drew had told me once that he didn't have relationships with women. He had women he hung out with, and he slept with all of them, but no actual relationships. One of his female friends was Lily; she was probably the largest woman I had ever seen in real life. Drew asked if we could have a threesome and include Lily. That was a hard no. I wasn't necessarily against the idea of a threesome, but not with her. His next move was to ask if we could take turns. He wanted to fuck one of us while the other watched and then have us switch. That was fine, but I was going first. The arrangements were made, and she wasn't happy about it.

Drew fucked me for hours while Lily watched. I caught her face a few times. Sometimes she turned on and masturbated. Sometimes I could see the hurt in her eyes, and all I thought was,

"Boo fucking who." She got angry and said she was leaving; I said no, it's fine, stay, and got out of his bed. I left his room naked, scooping up my clothes on the way. I went to the bathroom and peed one drop that burned like the fire of a million suns. I didn't go back to Drew's room. I was fine with being watched, it was even a turn-on, but I wasn't into watching. I know now that Lily was in love with Drew and would have done anything to make him happy, no matter how much she hurt herself.

On the phone not long after, Drew asked if we could have a threesome and invite Tina. I shot that down faster than the offer of Lily. Not only was she gross, but she was my aunt, absolutely not. Drew started calling Tina, and that was fine with me; if he fucked her, though, I would not fuck him again. Sharing a guy that you don't care about is one thing; sharing with family is another. If Brad and I had been able to have a relationship, I wouldn't have shared him with anyone. Drew was most certainly not Brad.

I started dating. Not anyone in particular. Not anyone from school. Just guys from where Griffith lived. A lot of them. I didn't have sex with any of them, but I made it known that I had boyfriends. During one escape from Griffith's bed, I made it known that all of my boyfriends knew, and they would beat him up. I drank but couldn't find darkness. I did find the dumpster with the homeless man. I brought him a six-pack, a pack of cigarettes, and twenty dollars. We never spoke, but we truly saw each other. I fell asleep there with him and again felt him making me a blanket out of newspaper. I trusted him; I knew he wouldn't hurt me.

I woke up in pain. Everything hurt, even my hair and nails. I woke up stuffed on the floor of Griffith's truck. I went in and surveyed the damage. There were bruises on my back, chest, stomach, and outer thighs. Someone had beat the shit out of me; I chose not to speculate. I never saw the homeless man again. It was no longer safe to go there. Someone had brought me back to Griffith's, and I suspected it was the monster himself.

I struggled in school, balancing my different lives. I started to have episodes where I couldn't breathe, and I felt like my chest was being crushed. Grandma took me to the Dr, where I was diagnosed with asthma. I was given an inhaler, a note for less strenuous gym, and a medical bus (I was a walker). I had already been a loser; now I was a loser who rode the short bus. Kierra was the only other kid on the bus with me. She reminded me of a hippy. Kierra was the kind of kid that just fit in everywhere. We became bus friends, but she would also talk to me if we saw each other in the halls.

I was surprised when she asked me one day if I had ever had sex; I told her I had, and she let me know she was thinking about it. "I have had orgasms before, you know, when I do it myself," she caught the change in my face, "What?" She asked, and I didn't say anything. "Simone? It is okay to talk about. Everyone does it. Even you." She gave me a playful shove; I shook my head and felt my face flush. "What? Really? You have had sex, but you never...? Wait, when you had sex, did you...you know?" My face grew hotter, and I shook my head again. "Simone! Have you had sex with more than one guy?" I hesitated and told her I had been with more than one guy and had had sex many times. "And you have never cum?" My face answered for me. "Well, I am not having sex then; I don't have a boyfriend right now anyway. But uhm, you should try doing it yourself." This had never occurred to me. It was one of the many things I was raised to believe was wrong. Girls didn't touch there. Ever. Unless it was to wash or wipe. Only boys did that.

I found other losers that let me sit with them at lunch. One boy, Jason, I already knew a little. Our mothers were friends. We became close, and we did like each other for a little while. It never went anywhere. He was my friend, and I didn't want to hurt him. I did, of course, flash him, and we held hands a couple of times while watching movies at his house. Jason was a decent human being; I probably could have loved him.

Griffith started dropping me in my hometown more often after my suicide attempt. I now had to keep that from Bianca, Tina, and Grandma. I often had nowhere to stay when I was there. I hung out with old friends during the day and walked all night. Nora snuck me into her grandmother's garage one cold night. I knew how much trouble she would be in if they found out I was there, so I made sure I was gone when the sun came up. My body was weak, and my brain was tired. I helped all of my friends with their problems. I gave advice on clothes, make-up, boys, girls, relationships, sex, and drugs. I focused on their problems and stuffed mine back into the vault they had slowly crept out of. The glue I used to seal it shut was weak, and I could steadily feel the demons trying to get out.

On weekends when I stayed with Griffith, my defiance grew. I would have a boy waiting when we got to his house; I would grab a beer and walk away. I came back late or early, depending on how you look at it. I often left with one boy and came back with another, but there were several in between. If I was back before I wanted to be, I would sit in the yard and drink all his beer. I smoked crack in his yard sometimes too, but I was careful. I didn't want Richie to know because I didn't want to fuck up his sobriety, and it would combine my separate lives in a way I couldn't accept. Coke had been causing nosebleeds that were scaring me. If only I could find Mary. If only Brad could hold me. If only Todd had shot me. If only I could find darkness. If only I could die. If only. Tick tock.

I scheduled boys to pick me up all over town. Each of them got two hours of my time. If they pissed me off, I would walk away and find another boy in front of them. None of these guys were my age. I would not give the time of day to anyone under sixteen, and I don't think I had an age limit; if I did, I never found it. If I knew Griffith was asleep, I would sometimes come back and sneak into Drew's room. Griffith never even knew I was there because he was used to me being gone all night. Drew and I would fuck until we passed out, sleeping naked and exposed just steps away from Griffith's door. When we woke up, we fucked all day. It began to burn when I peed more frequently.

Griffith surprised me one night when I was home. He brought me a present. It was the cutest fluffy brown puppy. Some lady he had done work for had given him the puppy as a tip and a thank you. Grandma made it clear the puppy couldn't stay; she had cats, I had school, and there was no way I could care for it. Griffith explained that it would be mine but stay at his house. I named her Teddy. I adored that dog. Animals make better friends than people.

I found that every year I would pick a teacher. A teacher that I declared was safe to tell if I ever needed to. That year I had picked two. Mr. Duke, my Algebra teacher, and Mr. B, my Social Studies teacher. Christmas came, and Griffith got me a new TV so I wouldn't have to watch Tina's soap operas. The next several nights, he took an extra-long time "tucking me in." That weekend before I could vanish into the streets, he hit me and made it clear I was to go nowhere. Drew had Lily over for the weekend. There was nowhere to run. While I was in the bathroom changing, the fucker hid my boots. I had been sleeping with those on every night that I had to be in his room for at least six months. I don't remember what happened at all. I woke up in his truck again. My clothes were torn, I had scrapes and bruises on my legs, and glass in my foot. I didn't question any of it as I plucked the glass from my foot and went to the bathroom to get myself together. This was his house. His house where I was a bitch, a drunk, a drug user, a punching bag, a piece of human garbage, and everyone's cum dumpster. His house where the tears stayed away or silent at the very least, where the attitude stayed strong, daring, and outright brazen, the house where you showed no fear and no pain.

Grandma's house, my home, was where I was mostly quiet. A place I could sleep without fear. Where I could sometimes laugh, but I still needed to hide. I had to hide the burning of my own flesh and the marks that others left behind as souvenirs.

At school was where the tears came, where I was bullied relentlessly. A place where kids are cruel just because they can be. But I could blame the tears on them and not the demons in my vault trying to break free. Tick tock.

Boys in the hallways had been touching me. I wasn't the only girl dealing with it. I blamed many of my never-ending tears on that. The school administration allowed me to leave classes early to avoid the problem. I burst into Spanish class with a few friends, crying hard. A junior who had failed the class, Craig, spoke to me for the first time. "Whose bothering you? Who is putting their hands on you? You tell me, and I will go beat the shit out of them right now." He offered kindly and seriously. "Oh yeah, Craig? You going to go beat the shit out of my stepfather for me?" The words burst from my mouth loudly. Craig hung his head, "I am sorry. I can't do that. I would if I could, though." The teacher wasn't in the room yet, but everyone that was there heard me. I never spoke to Craig again. Tick.

The streets of my hometown were my searching place. What was I searching for? I never knew. Myself? Someone like Todd? Someone like Todd with a gun? The place I belonged? Griffith was the one who said one night he thought I was seeking certitude. He was probably right.

Spring was coming, and I kept getting sick. I was always coughing and was struggling to breathe often. The gym teacher made us run the mile, even if we were supposed to be excused. I tried. I ran slowly but steadily as my lungs burned. He jogged alongside me, telling me to go faster. "You can do it, come on, I know you can," he encouraged as he jogged. I tried to tell him I couldn't. Frankie and his friends ran past me, making fun of me on their way. The tears started to flow again. The pain inside my head was breaking through, making the pain in my lungs seem like a tickle. The teacher's encouragement and the kids laughing sent an echo of anger through me. I looked at my gym teacher and yelled, "Fuck this and fuck you, too." The kids laughed, and the teacher told me to go to his office after class as he jogged away. I didn't go to his office; I knew better than to go to a private location with a male teacher. I did walk past his open door and tell him to go fuck himself, though.

I skipped class to smoke and drink in the bathroom often. If it ever got brought up, I would say I must have been with the school social worker, Mr. Steinfeld. Everyone knew I was in his office a lot, so it was believable; he would also go along with it if they ever asked him. Laurie, a popular girl, was also often smoking in the bathroom. We became bathroom friends. That was the only place she dared to speak to me. Laurie caught me drinking often, and she caught me doing coke. I offered to share. She tried my Jack and didn't like it; she declined the Coke. She told me once, "Everyone knows you are troubled or whatever. That's why you get away with talking to teachers the way you do. You should just tell someone whatever your problem is." I ignored her and had another drink.

Music was my escape. Rock and metal filled my mind with sounds that blocked out the scrapes at the wall in my head. Some bands had song lyrics that spoke to the broken child living in my soul. I don't hear music the way most people do; I feel it. I had blank tapes, and I recorded songs off the radio. Many of the songs Brad and I had listened to together were recorded. When I would play them, I would close my eyes and sing along. I could see us as we had been only a year before, dancing, laughing, singing, hugging. I didn't talk to him often anymore; I still missed him, needed him, and loved him. If I went really deep into my mind, I could almost feel his arms around me, almost smell him. Almost.

The burning pee is what finally got me taken to the Dr. It had been bad for days. One night though, I could barely move. I kept running to the bathroom, feeling like I was going to wet myself for one drop that would make me cry. Griffith was there and told Grandma he would take me to the hospital. YES! I screamed inside, but I said nothing. Grandma said no, she would call the Dr. In the morning and make an appointment. I fell to the floor, clutching my abdomen and crying.

The Dr. Diagnosed me with an upper and lower respiratory infection and a urinary tract infection. It would be the first of many. The nurse, Paula, came in and gave me information on how UTIs are caused, one way being rough sex. Drew was rough, and I never really wanted to. Paula started taking my blood and casually asked me if I was having sex, I told her no, but she knew I was. Paula asked again, and I just didn't answer. After my blood was drawn, she stuffed a handful of condoms into my pocket and told me if I was going to do it, to be safe. I eventually gave them to friends that were thinking of having sex. Paula also gave me her home phone number and told me to call her if I ever needed help. I called once, and I told her about Griffith; she said she had to go, she was getting ready to go on a date, and she also said she didn't know how to help me.

Do you know how it feels to love and hate someone at the same time? Not just dislike them, but pure unadulterated hate? That is how I felt about Griffith. I never knew my father. He and Bianca split up before I was a year old. When Brady was four, our father picked him up for a visit. Brady was back just a few minutes later, and he told

127

Bianca, "Daddy says he doesn't need me anymore." Brady never saw our father again. That is one of the only two memories that Brady has of him. Bianca had been with Griffith since I was three. I loved him as a father; I idolized him as a father. But I hated everything else about him. I hated his flannel shirts, dark blue work pants, voice, laugh, beard, and hands. More than anything, I hated his fucking eyes. The desire I could see there was killing me bit by bit. My time bomb had fizzled out or been locked away in my vault, and it was replaced by a volcano forming deep inside of me. It was threatening to erupt; I could feel that the fire had already started.

The Dr's office called a few days later. There was an issue with my blood work, and I needed to come in the next morning fasting. When the repeat labs came back, we needed to go in again. The results couldn't be given over the phone. I was hoping I was terminally ill.

We were not brought to a patient room but to the Dr's private office. It had to be something deadly. The universe was taking mercy on me, and the sweet salvation of death would soon take me away from everything. Or not. Instead, I was diagnosed as a type one diabetic. I needed to be hospitalized to get it under control and begin taking insulin. Not only was I not going to get the death I craved, but I would have to use needles, which led to thoughts of Todd and heroin. It was the only drug that scared me, I hadn't done it in a while, but I could still feel the power it had. Of course, it all had power over me, but that was one that could lead to A.I.D.S., which was where my real fear had always lied. Several of the places Todd had shot me up (and there were a couple of other people that did it for me) had gotten infected, leaving scars. Scars aren't track marks, though, and to this day, if a Dr asks me where the marks came from, I say, "I don't know; they've been there as long as I can remember."

I was in the hospital for a week. Griffith came the first day and was next to my bed when Bianca got there. She had told him not to come, they argued, and both left. I called Brad at Marissa's house "Simone?" Marissa asked; I didn't want to talk to her. "Yeah, hey, is Brad around?" I asked for him a second time. "Simone, Brad, and I broke up. He moved out. I don't know where he is." I cried another ocean. I tried to get the words out that I was in the hospital and asked if she could please find a way to get a message to him for me, but nothing came out. Nothing except a muttered "fucking bitch" that wasn't directed at her but at the situation. The tears didn't stop. I didn't speak to Brad for sixteen years.

They had me practice giving insulin shots on oranges. I outright refused to give myself shots until they told me I couldn't leave until I did it. After I got home, Bianca and Grandma decided I could no longer spend weekends at Griffith's house. Their justification was that it was dirty, which was true, and there were drug addicts, that had been true, but by this time, the only addict there was me. They didn't see that, though no one did.

In true teenager fashion, I had an epic tantrum. I screamed, cried, and threw things. I claimed because I wanted my dad, but that was a lie. I wanted my boyfriends, my real hometown friends, to keep fucking Drew, to keep drinking and getting high. I wanted the good parts of being there that I couldn't tell them about. I wanted the freedoms and addictions that they all chose not to see. They won, and I lost. I could still go, but after my morning insulin and I had to be back for the evening dose.

On my first Saturday back there, I was still suffering from UTI symptoms. Griffith had dropped me off there and went to work. Drew was on me at once, trying to get laid. I told him I couldn't and why he promised to be gentle. I still said no, so he talked me into watching a movie and playing cards. He would not stop pushing for sex no matter how many times I told him no. We did kiss a few

129

times. Drew picked me up and put me in his bed. "It is Saturday. I know what I get on Saturdays. You are mine on Saturdays," Drew said with a smile as he climbed on top of me, pulling my clothes off. I stopped protesting. I didn't even cry. This was, after all, my only purpose in life. I only existed for men to fuck whether I liked it or wanted it or not. Drew wasn't gentle.

After he was done, I went to the bathroom and saw he had left an exceptionally large hickey on my neck. I yelled at him for it, more playing around than serious. I could say it came from any number of boys closer to my own age. Drew stood and punched me in the stomach, "Use make-up and cover it," he ordered. He picked me up, put me back in his bed, and left several more across my tits before he fucked me again.

Bianca was taking me clothes shopping. I used make-up, covered the hickey, and went willingly. I am not girly in any way; I sweat a lot and did a lot more when I was a teenager. Dressing rooms in stores are exceptionally warm. I tried on outfit after outfit, with Bianca rejecting them all because I was just too fat. After yet another change, she came in to see how it looked and screeched, "Oh my God, what is that on your neck?!" I looked in the full-length mirror and saw that between the clothing changes and the heat, the makeup was gone. "Who did that to you?" She was shrieking and totally overreacting. "It's nothing, Ma. I was with my boyfriend yesterday, that's all." Then the string of questions came. She was irritating me, and I knew how to irritate her back.

"What boyfriend?"

"Well, I have a few. It could have been any of them." I told her with an evil grin.

"Very funny. Who is your boyfriend?"

"I was serious. I have six or seven boys I am dating. They all live near Griffith. Some of them go to school with Brady." That was mostly true; there were at least ten, and a lot of them were no longer in school.

"Oh yeah, how old are these boys?'

"Sixteen to eighteen." Again, this a partial truth; outside of Drew, they were sixteen to twenty-seven.

I thought her eyes were going to fall out of her head. I gave her a remarkably similar smile I gave to guys and said, "What is it, Ma? It's not like I am fucking around with guys who pick me up on the side of the road." My smile widened, "Or am I?" We left, and she took me back home; no clothes were bought. Grandma said the only problem she saw with it was that she read hickeys can cause cancer.

The next school day, I was in typing class (yes, those still existed in the nineties) when there was a "Psst! Psst!" from the table next to me. Emily was trying to get my attention. Another stuck-up girl that never spoke to me any other time. I looked at her, and she mouthed, "Your neck!" I touched it, and makeup came off my neck on my hand. After class, I headed to the bathroom, and Emily followed me. "Simone! Is that a hickey?" Obviously, you twit. "Yes," now I knew the questions would come. "I didn't know you had a boyfriend. Who is it?" I walked faster and ignored her; she caught up. "He doesn't live around here," I told her. "What school does he go to?" Emily was nosy. "I already told you he doesn't live around here. I am seeing a few boys that all live near my stepdad," I answered honestly. "Simone, that is a big hickey! Are you having sex?" I thought about pulling my shirt up and showing her the other ones, but I didn't do it. "Not with one of my boyfriends. I have sex with someone else."

Her jaw dropped. "What school does he go to?" Emily was as annoying as my mother. "He doesn't," I replied. "What do you mean? Why not?" The girl was dense. "He graduated. He's older. "My make-up was fixed, and I was headed back out the door. "How old is he?" I stopped dead in the hallway, and we stared at each other. "He is thirty-one." Emily didn't believe me and told the whole school that I had a hickey, and I gave it to myself with a vacuum. No matter how honest I was, no one ever believed me.

I became calmer after I stopped spending so much time at Harry's house. Griffith let me take alcohol home as long as I didn't get caught with it. I smoked Grandma's cigarettes in addition to whatever Griffith would buy me. I got my high in any way I could. I wasn't as angry or violent. Griffith didn't leave me alone. He still came cover several times a week and stayed until he was told to leave. His "tuck in's" were getting longer.

On nights, he didn't come to my house. He called. It had been a while since I talked to Brad, and I needed him. He had kept me calm and grounded. I missed him in ways that I cannot describe. In the weeks after I told him, every time we talked, he asked if I was ready for him to make the call. I did want him to; I just didn't know how to deal with the aftermath. If I had somewhere else to live or a different family, it would have been different. A normal family would have been there for me, supported me, believed me, taken my side and loved me. These people were the opposite. Brad had been the only comfort and safety ever.

It was late at night, and I was on the phone with Griffith. I was seeing him that night as a parent and not the monster he really was. "Friends come and go, Simone. I am sure he will call you when he can," Griffith's tone was both comfort and annoyance. "You don't get it," I blubbered. "You are only fifteen; you will have a lot of friends whom you will lose over the years," he said. "Yeah, I am fifteen, but you don't get it. I was fourteen when I fell in love with him," I said, almost choking on my tears. "I know you have feelings for him, but you guys are just friends," Griffith said with caring and compassion. "You still don't get it. I'm in love with him. Yeah, we were just friends, but **I am in love with him"**; the silence he gave made me feel good; in it, I could hear the pain of his broken heart.

My friends were all pushing me to tell, and some were getting bitchy about it, but not likc I blamed them. If I were the friend and I knew what they knew, I would have found a way to keep them safe, as I had done with Raynelle. Vicky told Katy she didn't want to talk to me anymore. I asked Katy why, and she told me Vicky said, "It's not that I don't like Simone, I do, but why does she always have to bug us with her problems," That hurt, and I wondered how many of my other friends felt the same way. I felt a burning in the pit of my soul.

I was in the school library with Katy and Patty; they told me I needed to tell. They said I couldn't keep going like this because I was going to wind up killing myself. They were right, but I didn't see that as a dreadful thing. "You said there were teachers you felt comfortable telling. You have three days to do it. Or I will," Katy said while looking me in the eye. She meant it, and I knew then that I needed to do it myself; the words had to come from my mouth; it would just be so much easier if I had somewhere else to go. Patty said she would go with me when I told her.

We went to Mr. B's classroom and found he was out sick. On the way to Mr. Duke's classroom, we stopped at every bathroom so I could smoke. I cried so much in the hallways that day. Laurie had been right about me being able to say whatever I wanted in that school. I frequently told teachers to fuck off or kiss my ass. I cut classes all the time, and I never hid it. Sometimes, I just needed to walk, so I would drop my stuff in my locker and just pace the hallways. Nothing was ever said. The teachers who had hall duty never asked me for a hall pass. This courtesy was extended to any friends while they were with me as well. If a bunch of girls got caught smoking in the bathroom, their parents or guardians were called, and they got detention. No one ever called my Grandma or Bianca. Only once did a substitute who didn't know me even make me go to the office.

I had been caught smoking and drinking. While being escorted to the office, I didn't put the bottle away. I drank on the way there. Mr. Holt entered the office looking defeated. "You want a shot?" I asked as I took another drink. "Simone, I just have one question before I call your grandmother and mother," he paused for impact, and I drank again. "Why?" he asked his pathetic question, and I drank. "Because the solution to every problem I have is in the bottom of this bottle," I picked up my backpack and let it fall open on his desk, "And if it isn't, it is in the bottom of one of these." I made sure he could clearly see the contents that didn't contain anything related to school. If he had searched it, he would have found a blackened knife and a few lighters as well. He never called my mother or grandmother.

Patty and I walked the halls as I cried, not silently; I had never cried so loud in my life. Tears ran from my eyes that I couldn't control, and snot dripped from my nose. We got to Mr. Duke's class; he was sitting at his desk grading papers. I sat in the back row with Patty next to me. I tried to speak, and I heard Mr. Duke asking what was wrong. I couldn't even look at him; I couldn't stop the tears; I wasn't strong enough to do this. The fire inside me intensified, I was burning inside, and I still felt a faint tick-tock.

"I came here to tell you something," the tears made me incoherent. Patty stood next to me and reached out to touch my back; I instinctively flinched away from her. "You can do this," she said, speaking softly. Mr. Duke asked the usual questions. Was it a classmate? Was it a friend? Was I in trouble? "It's about my stepfather," I finally blurted out the words that would start the conversation. I glanced up for a split second and saw he looked like he was going to cry, too. "Simone, is he hurting you?" The tears were clear in his voice. I couldn't answer him; I needed to run. I got up and told Patty, "I'm sorry, I can't." I ran from the room down the hall, around the corner, and ran some more. I ran the square hallways in tears until I found Katy. I told her how hard I tried and begged her not to say anything; I explained that I knew and understood I needed to do this in my own way. She agreed to keep her quiet a little longer.

Griffith was there that night; I said I was tired and going to bed early. He, of course, followed for his 'Tuck.' I gave him an attitude asking for the millionth time, "I think I am a little old for that, don't you?" He ignored me as he sat on my bed and began caressing my leg. Griffith's hand moved upward slowly, and I kicked at him, making it look like it was an accident, and I was trying to get comfortable. I rolled over angrily, putting my back to him. "When are you going to get a girlfriend?" I bitched. Griffith's hand still found its way to my crotch. "When you turn eighteen," he whispered in my ear. His tone was different from the other times he had said that, and it didn't have a questioning sound like it always had before. It was said as a fact. That is when I realized what he meant all the times he had said it before. He planned on me being his girlfriend. Griffith planned on *us* being together. I felt my eyes widen with the new understanding of the words he had been telling me for years; the tears rolled from my eyes silently onto my pillow. I knew that night it was him or me. I didn't want to live, but I would be damned if that mother fucker was going to take my life or take one more thing from me. I had no control over anything in my life; I never had. I decided that I would be the one who controlled how and when I died.

It was May 16, 1994; I awoke feeling better than I had in a long time. I woke up feeling strong. I threw on jeans and a long tie-dyed shirt that came to my knees; I was ready. I waited for study hall and asked for a pass to Mr. B's class claiming I had to get some makeup work. Mr. B was sitting at his desk working, I entered his room, and he was obviously happy to see me. He had nicknames for most of us; I can't use my real one here because it was based on my real name. I will just say he called me "S." He greeted me happily as I walked in, "Hey S, how are you doing?" I approached his desk; I was ready but unsure how to begin. We chatted as he caught up on paperwork from his sick day. Our conversation was about politics, and as it ended, he asked if I needed anything. "I came here today because I need to talk to you. I need to tell you something." I didn't waiver in my determination. "Okay, walk with me downstairs, and we will talk," he said while waiving in the direction of where he needed to go with a stack of folders. We talked about so much, yet so little, as we walked. He dropped stuff off in two offices and was headed to a third, his last stop. Mr. B stopped outside of that last office door; we stood across from each other in the hall. He was a large man with a military build and demeanor. "My point is S, if you need something, I am here for you. If you aren't ready to tell me whatever it is you came here to say, then you don't have to. I'm here for you whenever you are ready. If it is about those days you missed and the work that was due, I know I heard you took a bunch of pills, but I don't listen to rumors. Since I didn't hear from you, it didn't happen. You need to be ready to deal w-" I stopped him there; I heard what he was saying loud and clear. I also heard my heart telling me it was now or never, that if I didn't do this right now, I never would. I would end up Griffith's girlfriend. That. Was. Not. Happening. "Mr. B, I have to tell you what I came here to. I have to do it now. Today. Or I never will."

We stood there in the otherwise empty hallway facing each other. He, with his feet planted securely on the ground, tall, muscular, arms crossed at the wrists in front of him, self-confident in not only who he was but his place in the world. Me in my long shirt, unconfident, wavering stance, on wobbly legs and dangling arms that I didn't know what to do with. There was no sound at all, except for maybe whatever was inside me that was going to explode and erupt at the same time. His eyes looked at me with caring and concern; his eyes looked at me like a friend. I couldn't hold his gaze as I said the words; they darted from the ceiling to the floor to the wall and everything in between, only occasionally meeting with his. I didn't cry. "My stepfather is, and has been, for as long as I can remember, sexually molesting me." Our eyes met on my last word, and I saw his eyes change. They now looked at me with pity, and I saw anger. I hate that look. "And now I have to go," I turned, and I ran. I heard him calling me, "Wait! S!! Come back, and we can talk!" I didn't stop. I again ran the hallways and let the tears go burning my face like lava. The bell rang, and the hallways filled with kids; I ran around them, I ran through them. I ran until I couldn't see where I was going, and I crashed headfirst into a water fountain. Then I got up and walked instead.

It hadn't been long since I was approached by the two-vice principals, Mrs. Huffy and Mr. Cirillo. They kept their distance and asked me to come with them to the office. I agreed, somehow not realizing what they had wanted. As we walked, they both turned back and looked at me, and that is when I saw it. That look. It is the look people give when *they know.* "No," I whispered and backed up, "Not again." Mrs. Huffy reached back to grab my arm as I turned and ran again.

I again went to Mr. B's classroom. How could he talk to them, or anyone for that matter, without talking to me first? He was an immensely popular teacher, and there was a mob of kids talking to him outside of his door. Katy and I were at the back of the crowd, and I asked her to get his attention; she yelled for him, but he didn't hear her. I knew he would hear me, "Hey, Mr. B." I called from my spot in the back firmly. Mr. B looked up, and our eyes met at once. The look of pity was gone. He looked at me the same way he always had, the kindness, concern, and now anger reflected from his soul. The sea of kids parted as I walked through them into his classroom. I entered the room, and he closed the door behind us; this school didn't have locks on the doors, so he held it shut. I wasn't scared. I didn't need to be afraid of this man. I learned through his class how he felt about people disrespecting others, rape, and other assaults; he wasn't that type of man. I looked at him with fierce anger that he saw clearly. I told him off in ways that I didn't think he knew were possible. "S, you told me because you wanted help. You told me because you wanted and needed me to help you, and you knew before you did that I would have to go to the office with it," he said once I allowed him to speak. "Yeah. Yeah, I did, but I thought you would have had enough respect to talk to me first," I screamed in his face, flung the door open, and walked away as he continued to yell for me for the second time that day.

Mr. Steinfeld found me walking the halls and walked with me. He didn't look at me any differently than he always had. On one of our laps through the building, I stopped in my biology class to get the books I had dropped off earlier. "Uh, Simone, this is class time, and I didn't give you permission to go anywhere," said Mr. Lewis as I was walking away. "I didn't ask for your fucking permission. I don't need it. I will do what the fuck I want." The defiance was clear in every part of me; the class laughed. "You are going to fail my class. Your attitude isn't going to help matters." I left while giving him the one-finger salute. He was clearly still having a tantrum from the week before.

I had asked to go to the bathroom when he said no; I said, "Okay, I will just bleed all over your chair then." His face turned red, and

137

he continued teaching like I hadn't spoken. "You're embarrassed? Isn't this a biology class? A teen biology class. So, you, as the teacher, are aware that teen girls get periods and bleed? The blood comes out of their vaginas. I am a teen girl, and I have my period right now. You won't allow me to use the bathroom, so I will sit here and bleed in your chair. "I had interrupted with the best biology lesson the class got that year, and I saw Mr. Lewis turn redder than I knew was humanly possible. He tried to continue his lesson anyway, and I had gotten up and walked away, telling him to go fuck himself on my way out. I had learned that hurting a grown man's ego or limiting his control, is worse than hurting a teen girl's feelings.

Friends came and walked with Mr. Steinfeld and me on and off throughout the day; most of the day, it was just him and me, though. I told him many times that if my family was called, I wouldn't and couldn't go home. He just told me we would deal with that when the time came. When my body got tired, we sat in a big window in the second-floor hallway, talking. Classes were in session all around us; my absence didn't matter any more than my presence had. The conversation we had wasn't memorable, but he said something that sparked anger inside of me. I leaped from the window ledge and told him, "You are no better than anyone. I have every right to feel the things I do. I have every right to be angry. You don't know a fucking thing, so get the fuck down off your high horse and on the ground where you belong." I didn't notice that kids had begun to hang out of the classroom doors until I heard the clapping and laughter. I again walked, and he followed.

As the day went on, they allowed me to sit in an empty office in guidance, and Mr. Steinfeld stayed with me. I calmed down and told him I needed to talk to Mr. B and apologize, I had taken anger out on him, which he didn't deserve, and it wasn't meant for him. He arranged it but stayed in the room. I talked to the two of them as if they were my friends. They don't know it, but that is how I saw them. As friends. Two of the three best friends I ever had.

I apologized to Mr. B, and he told me there was no need, that I had every right to be angry, and that he wasn't mad at all. "You looked at me differently," I said to my feet. "S, what you saw in my eyes -" I cut him off, "Was pity. I hate that look." He paused before finishing his thought, "Yes, S, for a split second, you did see that. The rest of what you saw was anger. Not anger at you. Anger at him. He took from you. He stole who you are, your whole childhood, and changed who you were born to be. He disrespected you in the vilest, most evil, and most horrific ways. In a way that no child, no woman, no person, should ever be disrespected." I was quiet.

Mr. Steinfeld was called away for a call, and when he came back, I had a full-fledged panic attack. "The police called. They can't come today. No one has called your house yet. The police will be here tomorrow, and your family doesn't need to know anything until then," he said casually, like we were talking about the weather. I burst into a new wave of tears and told him Griffith was supposed to be picking me up and taking me to a movie that night. I was panicking and hysterical as both men tried to calm me.

Mr. B talked me into calling Griffith now while he wasn't home and leaving a message that I couldn't go tonight. The two men sat with me while I made the call. Griffith's voice on his machine sent me into another wave of hysteria. I blubbered into the machine about how sorry I was. Finally, I got out the words, "Daddy, I'm sorry. I can't go to the movies with you tonight; I can't see you. I didn't do this to hurt you. I did it because I didn't want to be hurt anymore." After I hung up, they both told me what a great job I had done; I could hear they meant it, but I didn't agree. Mr. B told me he was proud of me and that I gave him more of an explanation than was needed and more of an apology than he deserved. What stuck out was that he was proud of me. No one had ever been proud of me before.

The three of us sat and talked a while longer. We even laughed. I looked at Mr. Steinfeld and said, "But you knew. You knew and didn't help me." I expected him to deny it, but he didn't. "Yeah, I knew. It's my job to know. I couldn't help you. The law says I can't do anything unless you tell me or someone else." We all looked at our feet as I asked Mr. B, "Did you know too?" He looked me in the eye and answered honestly, "No, I didn't know. I knew you had something going on, something troubling in your home life. But I didn't know what it was." His free period was over, and he left to teach another class.

I went home that day filled with fear. I didn't talk to Kierra on the bus, not about boys, sex, orgasms, or masturbation. I just sat and listened to whatever was on fire within me. I didn't notice my nails were dug into my palms until I felt a trickle of blood. That was a good pain. It would accompany hot knives for years to come.
I laid in my bed as soon as I got home. If Tina or Grandma tried to talk to me, I just told them I didn't feel well, and they went away. The phone rang that night at nine pm. I ran for the kitchen to answer it, knowing it was Griffith but hoping I was wrong and it was Brad. I quickly fantasized it was Brad and that I could tell him I told him. Daydreaming that he would offer to let me live with him. If he did, I would go to school, I would get good grades, I would clean the house, and I would keep my feelings for him to myself. He could date and sleep with whomever he wanted to. I knew if I was with him, despite any feelings we had for each other, he would keep me safe. The memories of the safety he gave me were still my only comfort.

The fantasy was killed as I answered the phone, and Griffith's voice greeted me. He never got my message. Brady had played the machine; he told him I called and was so upset that he couldn't understand what I had said. Griffith started asking what I was so upset about. I told him I couldn't tell him; I shouldn't even be talking to him. I didn't cry. He wouldn't accept my answers, so I told him the same thing I had told his machine. "I didn't want to hurt you; I just didn't want to be hurt anymore." There was silence, but I knew he hadn't hung up. "Do you know what I did?" I asked. "Yeah, you told someone. You told someone what's been...uh, uh, what's been, uh, going on." His voice cracked, but there was no anger; hearing his words somehow filled me with relief. "Yes," I said in a sighing whisper. He said he wasn't mad and that no matter what happened, he would "Always be there for me, always be my dad, and always love me as a daughter."

I thought about just not going to school the next day. I could just load my backpack with whatever I may need and walk away. I didn't have anywhere to go, but that meant nothing to me. I had nothing against sleeping in the streets. I had done it far more often than I have written about in these pages. I don't know what made me get on that bus and go to school when what I really wanted to do was run.

Mr. Steinfeld met me at the front doors and explained how things were going to go. I was to go to my classes, and when the cops and CPS got there, someone would come to get me. It was late in the day; I was already in Algebra class when someone finally came. By then, I had hoped they just weren't coming; I had been hoping they were never coming. Mr. Duke stopped me in the corner of the classroom, "Simone? What you wanted to tell me that day, he does hurt you, doesn't he? Like touches you and stuff?" I gave a slight nod, and a tear rolled down my cheek. Our eyes met for a split second, and I saw in his eyes that someone had hurt him that way, too.

I walked slowly, in a fog of quicksand, to the office. "Hey, Simone. Do you remember me?" Asked a female when I entered the office. I didn't know who she was, her hair was slightly familiar, but that was it. "We met a few years ago. You were eleven. My name is Detective Lorenzo." I looked at her again; still too much make-up and the same peacock haircut. I don't remember most of what our conversation was or giving a formal statement, verbal or written. Detective Lorenzo asked me why I waited so long to come forward. She told me the previous case had still been open until a month prior. I told her that I had recanted my statement when I was eleven, and I thought the case was closed at that point. She told me there was no record of my recantation. I explained about me telling Bianca what I did and that she would have called and told them. Detective Lorenzo said Bianca had never called. I confronted her with what Bianca had told me she said. Because of what Griffith did to me, I was going to grow up and be a whore. Detective Lorenzo said she didn't say that. She said that a lot of young girls who are molested grow up and are promiscuous or prostitutes. Verbiage aside, that is the same fucking thing. I made it clear to everyone involved, in every conversation that day, that if they called my house, I would **NOT** go home.

I was sent to a group home, one of those places that no one is supposed to know is a group home, but everyone does. The next day, Grandma and Tina met me in a McDonald's parking lot; the family wasn't allowed on the property to give me some clothes and diabetic supplies. Tina begged me to come home. Grandma handed me my bag and said, "You did all this to be able to take your needles out of the house," and laughed. Her eyes revealed that she meant it. I didn't ever want to go back home. I wanted to be permanently placed somewhere. But my grandparents told the police I was welcome to come home. They assured everyone that Griffith would not be allowed there. The cops had no reason to keep me from going home since it was a safe place, so the group home said I couldn't stay. I was in the group home for three days.

The next few weeks would be filled with awful comments from everyone. Tina said that the last few weeks, she had felt weird when he was around, and him being near me made her uncomfortable. Grandma told Bianca that she had seen some of it and that I had started it. I confronted her, and she said she said it because it was true. I wanted and needed clarification. "When school was starting, you got new clothes. You tried on every outfit and showed them to him," she said with a laugh. I told her that he had told me to, and I didn't change in front of him. I changed behind a closed door. I am still baffled at how this was me doing anything wrong or inappropriate. Grandma also said I should have waited to tell until after Griffith had fixed her sprinkler system. Now she would have to pay someone to do it, "Since we can't have him here because of *you.*" Grandpa, who never really acknowledged my existence, told me that he did see things happening over his book. He also said, while running his fingers through his beard and with a smile on his face, that he grew his beard in admiration of Griffith. My voice screamed in my head, "Shave it off!" I said nothing, though, and he

142

didn't shave. Bianca said that the day she saw the hickey on my neck, she had thought he had done it. Then she told me that she had had a meeting at my school a few months prior, where they told her they "Suspected inappropriate behavior on behalf of the stepfather." That meeting happened when I was still staying at his house every weekend. Drew even said I should have waited to tell. Drew told me how Griffith had been planning a huge surprise sweet sixteen for me. All my friends from all of the schools I had been to would be invited; Griffith was giving me a car, and there was a small two-bedroom house on the back of Harry's property that was being fixed up to be mine. I tried to explain to him that I didn't want any of those things, but he didn't get it. I saw myself in the doorway of that house, with a dirty toddler at my feet and pregnant and a ring on my finger. Griffith, of course, being the husband and father. I didn't want any of those things. All I had ever actually wanted was a dad. I had wanted a family with two parents who loved me in the way parents love children. I didn't want to be loved by a parent the way you love your spouse.

I rarely talked to Drew after that; when I did, he would tell me how depressed Griffith was without me and how different he was. Drew talked to Tina frequently. I always knew when she was on the phone with him; she would blush and giggle like a teenager. Tina was mean to everyone; she called my grandparents worthless and useless, despite the fact that she had been mooching off of them her entire life. Tina was an overgrown child; she would make me play with Barbies with her. Once when she was making me play with her, I told her I had been fucking Drew for months. She didn't believe me and told me how he had been trying to get her into bed. I told her that when I had that UTI, it was when I was fucking him, and it was because he was so rough. She made me call him that Saturday while she listened to the extension. After we caught up, I said, "Hey, Drew, it's Saturday." He laughed and said, "Yeah, I know. You should be naked in my bed." I laughed too, knowing she was listening, and asked him, "Oh yeah? What would I be doing naked in your bed?" He had no idea the call was a setup and answered honestly, "Now you know on Saturdays your ass is mine, and we fuck all day. I was hoping to see you again. I love it when you are on top of me." I told him I had to go and hung up. Tina came downstairs crying and called him in front of me. She confronted him, and he denied it. Drew told her he and I were just friends, and he never touched me. Tina believed him, even though she had heard the truth just moments earlier out of his own mouth. I never talked to him again, but she did. I heard her end the conversation. At one point, I walked into her telling him she couldn't have sex with him; he must have asked why because the next thing she was, "Because you fucked my niece." I turned around to smile at the hurt I heard in her voice. They had all hurt me. My whole family had betrayed me. They had all known, seen, or suspected something, yet they chose to let me suffer. It was my turn to hurt them.

Brady continued coming over, usually once a week. I was uncomfortable around him. I knew he wouldn't try and do anything to me again, now that we both knew I could and would kill him. He lived with Griffith, though. Whenever we were alone, he would pass me notes, tell me messages, or give me gifts from Griffith. This did include alcohol.

The night of my big chorus concert, Brady came by before the show. My friends and some teachers knew I was worried that Griffith was going to show up. I was positive I had seen him driving around by the school and parked out front. Never in his own vehicle but in his father's or others that I knew he had access to. I also knew he had been parked outside of my grandparents' house. No one believed me; they all said I was just paranoid. Brady handed me a small box and a card from Griffith. In the box was a beautiful pair of earrings that I never wore. The card had several lines half-assed and crossed out. The crossed-out phrases included things like "I am sorry for the things I d-" and "I wish I could control my-" It was signed, "Love always, Daddy." I knew then that he would be there. I could feel it.

I had a solo part for the first time. It was only a few lines of a song, but it was a big deal for me. Just before my solo, the back door of the auditorium opened. The light that came in blinded me. I felt fear burning through me. But I sang. I sang my part perfectly. I kept trying to focus on who had come in that door, and I couldn't see well enough to tell. It was a large person, was all I could make out. I could feel his presence. After the song was over, the same person who had come in late left. I saw his silhouette as he left. There was no doubt in my mind it was him, but no one believed me.

Patel, a senior, asked me to go to prom with him as friends. We made arrangements to go with Sierra, who wasn't popular, and her friend Matt who was gay. A case manager I had through CPS paid to have my hair and nails done, and Bianca took me shopping for a dress. The prom was amazing. I danced and laughed. Mr. B was a chaperone; he was surprised to see me. Mr. B hugged me and told me I looked nice, and I knew for once it wasn't man code for "I want to fuck you." During the sit-down dinner portion of prom, I felt a hand on my thigh. It was Matt; I took him into the lobby and verbally assaulted him. Matt told me that Sierra had liked him, and he didn't want to hurt her feelings, so he told her he was gay. I told him off again.

Toward the end of the night, Mr. B approached me on the dance floor and asked Patel if he could cut in. A slow song started; we danced in the middle of the dance floor. I asked him if he was coming back the next year, he had been a long-term substitute for a teacher that needed to take a leave of absence. There were no definite answers, and he was waiting to hear about a contracted position. When my group of four was getting ready to leave, I went to find him and say goodbye. We hugged, and he whispered in my ear, "I really am so proud of you." I knew; I could see it in his eyes. I heard him tell another chaperone, "She is going to do great things." I never saw Mr. B again. I think he is the only person in my life who has ever been proud of me.

Sierra's parents had gotten us tickets to a comedy club in the city. I had been the youngest at the prom, so I was most certainly the youngest at the club. Our server let us know that sodas were unlimited and free of charge, and there was also a selection of drinks containing alcohol for six dollars each. She also made it known that we didn't need to show identification. I hadn't had a drink in over a week; I was sticking to the free soda. As the first comedian came on stage, Patel leaned in and whispered, "I will buy you one of those drinks if you have sex with me in the limo." I shook my head and showed no emotion. That was what I was worth to someone I thought was my friend. Six dollars.

I laughed along with everyone else, especially when the one guy did a whole set about teens there for prom. It was pointed out by Sierra that I was only fifteen, so there was a string of jokes about me being the baby. I was crying inside, though. Patel's words, his question, had shot another piece of me dead. I really did need a drink. I got home from the club not long before daylight. I told Grandma I had a great time, took off my dress and make-up, and got in bed. I didn't get up for three weeks unless I had no other choice. I never saw Patel, Matt, or Sierra again.

It was early June when I called Bianca and begged her for my father's number. I only knew the things I had been told about him. He cheated on and beat my mother. Brady's last memory of him, and the memory of being in a highchair, crying while our father choked our mother with a phone cord. She had been heavily pregnant with me at the time. He had written Brady and me each a letter when I was seven and included a picture of himself. Our father let us know he wanted to see us; Brady said no right away, and I was intimidated into saying no. He watched us getting off the school bus and took pictures of us when I was around ten. At almost sixteen, none of that mattered; I needed to meet my biological other half. I made it clear to Bianca that if she didn't give me his number, I would find a way to get it on my own, so she gave it to me, and I called immediately. "Hi, is Charles there?" I asked the woman who answered the phone, "No, he is at work. Can I take a message?" She replied cautiously. I asked if there was a better time to call, and I was told he slept all day and worked overnights. The woman, who had to have been his second wife, Anne, was getting hostile about me leaving my name and number so he could call me back. That is how I knew he hadn't been faithful to her either, and she thought I was one of his other women. The irony of his relationship was clear to me even as a teenager. He justified his affair with this woman when he left my

146

mother for her. He had felt bad for her because her husband, who was the father of her three kids, was beating her. I thought about just hanging up when my name came out in a whisper, "Simone."

She was relieved instantly and happy to hear from me. She told me how she always knew one day I would call. I heard all about how Charles would get depressed around my birthday because he had never had me in his life. I was told how he had a poster-sized picture of me as a baby in their room. Anne said I absolutely must come to meet him, and we set up the meeting for that Saturday. All I heard through the whole conversation was simple, "I was wanted."

Bianca brought me to Charles' house that sunny Saturday, bringing her new boyfriend Otto along for some kind of backup. When we got there, Anne escorted us around to the backyard, where Charles was waiting by the pool smoking. Bianca made it clear through her actions that she didn't want to leave me there; she stalled as long as she could, making small talk. The only valid question she had for him was, "Whom do you think she looks like?" He replied that I looked like her, and she disagreed. This was one of the few instances in my life that she was right. I could have been his twin. Charles asked us if we still talked to Griffith; Bianca gave me a look, and we both said no. She was then pushed to leave so we could get to know each other.

With Bianca gone, Charles and I sat at the table by the pool and got to know each other. He told me all about his life, his job, his travels, his stepkids, and his six-year-old son. Anne had tricked him into getting her pregnant when she knew their relationship was in trouble. I told him of my life, frequently correcting myself when I would refer to Griffith as "My dad." Charles told me I didn't need to do that, that he knew Griffith had raised me, and Bianca had told him throughout the years how Griffith was our father and not him. Bianca had begged me not to tell Charles about Griffith and what he had done. "No, Charles, he isn't my father," I reached over and snagged one of his cigarettes and lighter as I spoke. "Bianca made me promise not to say anything." I began as I saw we had the same mannerisms. Charles was slumped forward, looking at the ground, and both of our left legs bounced up and down. It was clear why she always hated when I did that; I smiled at all the times she backhanded me and told me to stop. "The reason we don't talk to Griffith anymore is because of what he did to me." I inhaled deeply as I took in his physical reaction. His body slumped hard as if he had been beaten. One tear fell from his face and hit the patio.

Charles felt guilty. He thought if he had been involved, it wouldn't have happened, or he would have picked up on it, and he would have been able to stop it. I didn't believe any of that, but it was nice to see he cared. The thought was comforting, but I already knew there was no knight in shining armor for me in any form. Not in a boy, a friend's loving arms, or even a father's. I also knew that Charles wasn't the one to blame. Bianca came back several times during the day, and she was sent away each time. Before her last return, he asked if I had any questions for him. I did, and he already knew what it was. Charles looked away as he leaned back and prepared himself for the question every abandoned kid has for their deadbeat parent. "I want to know what I did. What did I do as a little baby that you didn't want me? What was so horrible about me?" He hadn't prepared enough and slumped again, but there was no tear. "It wasn't you, Simone. I always wanted you. It was your mom. We didn't and couldn't get along. I'm sure you have heard stories about how I hit her. It's true. I'm not proud of it, but it did happen. She is the only woman I have ever hit; I am not ashamed of it; she pushed me, nagged me, and in those moments, she deserved it. Does that make sense?" It made more sense than he ever could have known. I was, after all, my father's daughter.

When we were leaving in the still hot, bright early evening, I turned to tell Charles it was nice to meet him, thinking I would never see him again, and I was greeted by his warm and loving embrace. He hugged me long and hard, then asked when he could see me again. I told him I would call; I didn't want to push a relationship that he didn't want. I didn't want to come off as clingy or needy. Bianca grilled me the whole way back to my grandparent's house; she eventually asked if I told him about Griffith. I lied. I felt it was my place to tell people what I wanted to about that when I wanted to. Bianca called Charles the next day and told him he didn't lie, and he told her I had already told him. She was mad at me for it. The truth was she wanted to tell him herself; that way, it could all be about her and how she was hurt. The truth was, it wasn't about her, and she didn't have a fucking clue what hurt was.

Sweet Nothing

Summer came, and I turned sixteen. On the morning of my sixteenth birthday, I woke up at six-twenty am. "That's funny; that is what time I was born," I had time to think before my mind had its first slip. I traveled backward in time in my head. There were tons of snaps of memory there. Dozens of images, flashes, and pictures appeared in my head. They were all quick, and many were indecipherable; the ones that were clear, though, were brutal. They were full of Griffith and several other men, most of whom I didn't recognize, touching me, violating me. In some of these flashes, I was as young as three. When it stopped, I said, "Happy fucking birthday to me," aloud and went back to sleep.

All of my friends forgot my birthday. I had spoken to and seen Charles over those few weeks. He had made it clear that he would not call me at my grandparents' house; he was convinced they hated him because of how his relationship with Bianca ended. They didn't hate him, though; hell, they didn't even hate Griffith after what he had done. Bianca took me to an amusement park for my birthday with her boyfriend Otto, naturally. He was immature and kind of goofy, but he was nice, and he never looked at me the way most men did. Bianca even called my favorite radio station and did a birthday shout-out. After dinner, we went to the beach to see the fireworks. Have you figured out when my birthday is yet?

I began to have violent nightmares where I would talk, scream and cry in my sleep. Grandma would hear me and come in trying to help. She talked to me and asked questions that I was capable of answering. She recorded it once, and the conversation was disturbing; it was worsened by the fact that I sounded like a small child. The recording was something like this;
"Where are you?"
"Shhhh, Daddy's coming.
"What is Daddy going to do when he gets there?"
"Daddy hurts me.
"Tell Mommy."

"No! Mommy can't know. Daddy says if mommy knows, she will die."

I remembered more all the time, usually in the form of a nightmare. I told Raynelle about these experiences, and her response was, "Bitch that has been happening for years. Brad used to talk to you until you would wake up." I needed more information; I didn't want Brad, of all people, to know the things that came back in my sleep. Raynelle couldn't remember anything I had said in my sleep. Just that Brad would talk to me, I would respond, I sounded like a little kid, and sometimes I would cry or appear to be being beaten.

I spent as much time as I could that summer with Charles and his family. Two of his three stepkids wanted nothing to do with me; they didn't look at or speak to me. The two of them felt I was there to steal him from them, but I had felt throughout my whole life they had stolen him from me. They also had their own father, who was very active in their lives. Charles and I spent countless hours on the phone; we went to dinner at Olive Garden, we went to a carnival, and we went to lunch at a greasy burger place. I was so ecstatic, too, to be loved by a parent as nothing more than their child; I ignored the fact that the burgers were from the same place I had first smoked crack just a few short years ago. I told Charles I thought Griffith was watching me; he believed me and started leaving a baseball bat in his vehicle. He assured me if he ever saw him, he would beat the shit out of him. No one else had believed me; Bianca even told Charles I was paranoid and crazy, but I wasn't. I could feel him.

I still had my second life, even though it wasn't as active. I would tell everyone I was going to the library, the park, or Dierdre's house, and I would instead get picked up by random guys. I gave away hand jobs and blowjobs freely; I did drugs any chance I got. It didn't matter what they were or who was offering. I blacked out and woke up in locations I had no recollection of going to. I would sometimes know when I came to that I had had sex. I would also know, based on the marks on my body, that I hadn't consented, and I knew just because I knew me. The school year was starting soon, as was the family court trial against both Griffith and Bianca.

Judge Rankin had ordered that I go to therapy, and that was fine; everyone knew I needed it, even me. The judge picked the therapist, and Bianca brought me to the weekend appointments. On one such therapy day, I decided to come clean with Bianca about a few things. She backed out of the driveway, and I told her I had three things to tell her, and she wasn't going to be happy about any of them; I told her she should probably pull over to avoid an accident. Shockingly she listened, "Okay, number one, I smoke. Two, Brad and I were just friends, and although we were not in a relationship, we were having sex. Three, Griffith wasn't the only one who did things to me. His father did too." With a dumbfounded expression, she began with, "You do not smoke." I pulled out my cigarettes and lighter, only to be greeted with, "Those could be anyone's; you are just holding them for someone." I stepped from her truck, lit one, and smoked half before she instructed me to put it out and get back in. She began driving at once and, on the way, asked, "How do you know about Griffith's father? You never said anything before." I tried explaining to her the flashbacks and nightmares; I made sure she knew that I hadn't always known, but she insisted that those things were not necessarily real and could just be imagination or dreams. "You repeatedly said that there was nothing going on with Brad; why did you lie about it? I don't get it." Again, I pointed out that she would have had him thrown in jail. It was her turn to surprise me; she told me she would not have. That she knew the feelings I had for him were real, and she would have allowed us to be together. If only she had told me that before I lost him. Bianca's main focus on the things I told her was that I smoked.

Charles and I watched movies in his basement; I had gone to his house for several Friday night pizza dinners. He had begun asking questions about Griffith, and once, just once, I told him a little bit of detail about what I believed to be the first time. The details were not graphic, just that I had been three and a half, I had been punished for something I did, Bianca had walked in, and I had been instructed to lie to her about what was happening. As I talked to him with my eyes closed, reliving this moment of my life, I cried like a toddler. I choked on my own tears, and Charles came to sit beside me; he rubbed my back and put a trash can next to me in case I got sick. It didn't happen, but when I gagged and heaved, he held my hair back just in case. I have never gone into that much detail with anyone since then.

My therapist, Jodi, was clearly incompetent. After several months of seeing her weekly, I asked her what my diagnosis was. She didn't have one and gestured to her DSM sitting on the bookshelf when I told her I could have diagnosed myself faster. I quickly skimmed the pages, deciding it would be fun to convince her that I had either multiple personality disorder or manic-depressive disorder (now called bipolar). I had never played with a woman's head before the way I had many men. I wondered how far I could push it and how much work it would take.

I spent my free time over the next few weeks researching multiple personality disorder, now renamed dissociative identity disorder. I convinced the queen of incompetence that that is what I had. I even kept a journal of writings to her from my other personalities and drew her a map of where they lived in my head. I named them for her, too. Shortly before the case against Griffth and Bianca, where they were both being charged with neglect and he was also being charged with endangering the welfare of a child, Judge Rankin scheduled a hearing to check on my progress. I wisely showed up sober; a breathalyzer was done as soon as I entered the building.

Jane from CPS, Amanda, my lawyer, and Jodi were all there. Amanda didn't listen to me at all; she was fighting that I, as a troubled teen, didn't belong at my grandparents' house. Jane was really nice, even though Bianca didn't like her, I did. She was calming. Jane spoke. First, she told the judge I was complying with all caseworkers and making progress in therapy. She had no recommendations. Amanda had nothing to say, which was typical; even when she said something, it meant nothing. Jodi was up next, where she proudly told the judge she had diagnosed me with multiple personality disorder. I smirked when she said it, and as she explained that my brain divided itself into alters to protect me from the abuse I suffered, I smiled knowingly.

Judge Rankin knew to pay attention to all of me, not just my words, but my face and body language, as they often said what my mouth didn't. "Simone, I see you have something to say; care to speak up?" She asked with a tone of experienced judicial wisdom. "I have no problems going to therapy; I do not deny I need it. But could I please see someone whose IQ is at least as high as mine?" If nothing else can be said about me, I am honest. "Elaborate," ordered the judge. I pulled out my notebook, detailing my library research and my written plan to convince Jodi I had multiple personality disorders, "I was bored, and she is incompetent," I concluded in my statement. Judge Rankin ruled that I could pick my own therapist, dismissing Jodi and her diagnosis. After that, I saw my mom's therapist, Joe, a few times. I connected with him better, but that isn't surprising; I tend to work better with men. He let me smoke in his office, shared his cigarettes with me when I didn't have any, and a few times even gave me a drink.

I would need to testify against Griffith on two separate days. There were three lawyers to question me, Bianca's, Griffith's, and the state's, which was also my own. During prep, I was told I couldn't bring up anything that happened before the second time I told or anything that I remembered through a flashback. Amanda asked me to detail some of the abuse. I gave a very basic description of his hands rubbing across my chest and back and him dry-humping me. On the stand, my testimony was that of minimal touching, which amounted to occasionally grazing me while he rubbed against me until ejaculation. Bianca's lawyer asked where Bianca had been during this, and I said she was asleep. But on the stand that day, I had a flash. The couch when I was eleven, not once but several times, Griffith suddenly stopping, his arms going limp around me, and one eye open just a sliver. I remembered following where that eye was looking, right over to the other couch, where Bianca's eyes were wide open. I didn't say anything on the stand, and I was done for the day. I left through the double doors of the courtroom, where I stumbled into a wall as soon as I heard the doors shut behind me. My head clunked off the wall, which brought me back to the courthouse. I ran to the bathroom to throw up. Violently.

154

Griffith, his lawyer, and Brady walked past me on their way out of the courthouse. None of them looked at me; it was like I didn't exist. The lawyer seemed pissed; Griffith's eyes were once again filled with anger, evil, and hate. "What she says happened isn't anything like what was actually there. It wasn't anything like what happened." Griffith said to his lawyer. Rage flared inside me; how dare he! He was right. It wasn't because what I described wasn't anything compared to what actually happened. What he had done was so much worse than what I had told that courtroom. I pushed off the wall, ready to fly out of the building and scream on the courthouse steps what had really been done to me. I was going to tell him in front of anyone within earshot all the ways he violated me, all the ways he had murdered me. The gentle hand and voice of Jane brought me back, "Simone, don't listen to him; it will be okay." I didn't run out of the doors, scream, cry, or even speak. It would show weakness if I gave in to the anger raging within.

Griffith had no character witnesses; he had been dating a woman. He started dating shortly after I was out of his life. She had a seven-year-old daughter. I remember being scared for that little girl whom I didn't know. I thought about just taking it all back to save her. I could take it, I was used to it, I could handle the pain, and I already knew how to cry silently. That little girl didn't deserve it. I did.

The next day it was Griffith's lawyer's turn; he had a different lawyer than the day before. I found out afterward that his original lawyer recused themselves because they felt he was guilty. I knew his lawyer would be the hardest on me. I thought I would be pushed for more detailed accounts of what happened that I would be pushed until I broke. I wasn't prepared. Nothing about Griffith was asked at all. "Simone, we heard things yesterday about Griffith, but today I want to know more about you."

"Simone, do you know a man named Brad Anjou?"

"Yes"

"Uh huh, and who is Mr. Anjou to you, Simone?" This lawyer wasn't even looking at me.

"He was my best friend." I didn't lie.

"He was your best friend? Anything else?" He tossed a file onto his table.

"If you are asking if I was having sex with him, the answer is yes, I was." I told the room confidently, "Uh huh, and how old were you when you started having sex with Mr. Anjou?"

"I was fourteen." I wasn't ashamed; I had had sex with a man I loved. "You were fourteen when you were having sex with Mr. Anjou? How old was Mr. Anjou?"

"Twenty-two," I was smug in my response and even smiled a little. "Simone, do you drink alcohol? Smoke cigarettes? Smoke marijuana?"

"Yes, yes, and yes," I didn't know Griffith knew about the weed; I only smoked at his house with Brad or when I was there alone...

"Simone, do you know a man named Drew Lupus?" He took a drink of water.

"Yes, I do."

"Simone, what is your relationship with Mr. Lupus?" This man still hadn't looked at me. My eyes followed him to avoid looking at Griffith.

"He was a friend, and if you are asking if I was having sex with him, too, the answer is yes." My brain got a little foggy, and I had to force myself not to think about the fact that Bianca was in the courtroom listening to this.

"How old were you, Simone, when you were having sex with Mr. Lupus?"

"I was fifteen," I was honest and calm; I even outwardly smiled.

"And how old was he?" The lawyer suddenly looked right at me, and I knew where this was going. Not only was he trying to turn it all around on me, but they could use this information to go after Brad and Drew. I was silent. He asked his question again, louder, his voice booming. I held my silence. "Judge Rankin, can you please instruct Miss Simone to answer how old Mr. Lupus was at the time they were having sex?" The judge turned toward me and asked gently, "Do you know how old he was?" I nodded. "Then you have to answer the question." I hesitated before addressing the judge, "I will, but I want to say something after this is over, if that is okay?" She nodded, and I looked back to the lawyer.

"How old was Mr. Lupus, Simone?" His voice was softer now, but we both knew what he was doing.

"He was thirty-one." I forced a blank expression. I couldn't show fear. Not here. Not now. Never in front of Griffith.
"Nothing further." Boomed the lawyer.

Judge Rankin looked at me with soft, caring eyes, "Simone, you had something to say. I think you have earned that right. Go ahead." I only had seconds to gather my thoughts and keep all emotion tucked away. "I want it to be known that all of the things I have done that are seen as bad by the court were done under Griffith's care and supervision. I was at his house when he provided me with unlimited alcohol and cigarettes. The two men in question also lived in the same house as him, and I was left alone with them for hours daily. Griffith's house is also where I was smoking marijuana. The sex I had with Brad and Drew was consensual. I never told Griffith about Drew, Brad, or the marijuana, so the fact that I was questioned about it means he knew and allowed it to happen, to continue while he was supposed to be a father taking care of me. I ask that no charges be pressed against Mr. Anjou or Mr. Lupus." Judge Rankin thought about it for a few moments in deafening silence. "I agree with Simone. These things happened as a direct result of negligence that wasn't her fault and not directly the other men's fault either. No charges will be brought against them. Simone, thank you. You may leave the room." As I stood in slow motion and stepped down, I saw a court officer tear up a few pieces of paper. I left through the same double doors. This time my head smacking the wall didn't help, and I fell, first on my knees and then on my face.

I was sitting on a bench in an unfamiliar hallway, surrounded by EMS personnel and smelling salts being waved in my face. Jane was holding an ice pack on my head; I panicked at once. "What happened? Holy shit, I collapsed. Holy fuck! Did he see me? Did he see me hit the floor?" I hyperventilated the words as a paper bag was put over my face to breathe into. "No, Simone, he didn't see you. You did great, though. I was really impressed." Jane said kindly, while Amanda nodded her agreement. "Judge Rankin was also impressed. The papers were already drawn up to arrest Brad and Drew when you gave your speech. You just saved them both jail time." I breathed heavily into the bag and thought of Brad. I had grown to see Drew as a predator in a way; it was something I was just having thoughts of, though, and not really on a conscious level. I knew I couldn't protect Brad without also protecting Drew. I didn't see Brad that way. He had brought me back to life when I didn't even know I was dead, and it was still the thought of his face, his smile, his voice, his smell, and his protective arms that gave me a little bit of life.

I wasn't allowed in the courtroom outside of giving my own testimony. Brady would be going in the next day and taking the stand, and I would be going back to school. Bianca told me things that were said in the room, even though she wasn't supposed to. Brady testified that he "Knew something happened, but he didn't know what." He still lived with Griffith; I thought it was big of him to be as honest as he was.

I started having flashbacks during class and was terrified I was going to cry or say something in front of everyone. Accommodations were made, and I was allowed to leave any and all classes, if needed, without permission. The empty office in guidance was still there, and it became mine. That is where I was to go if I felt a flashback coming, if they had started, or if I just otherwise felt I couldn't handle classes. I couldn't just walk the halls, which was my natural instinct, and my assignments were still due on time. The office, my office, had a desk, two chairs, and a phone. I was allowed to use the phone as I wanted as well. I often called Mr. Steinfeld since I had his direct extension just to have someone to talk to. Some of the school staff were more family to me than my own blood was.

Charles and I had grown close, we spoke several times a week, and sometimes I even called him dad. I tried to leave it up to him when I would call because I still didn't want to be pushy. I was doing well in school, even though I had failed biology the previous year. To this day, I say it was Mr. Lewis' fault because he couldn't handle the lesson I gave on teen girls getting periods. My new biology teacher was Mr. Bloom; he was another person that seemed to really see me. He was the only person that believed me when I said I saw Griffith outside of the school. Mr. Bloom casually ignored my frequent trips to the bathroom and the fact that I knew I smelled of whiskey when I returned and that I was suddenly very awake in class. He implied that he knew what was going on without ever saying.

In October, I had a nagging suspicion that I was pregnant. I asked a few friends if I could take a test at their house. They said no because of their parents, which I understood. I called Charles from the music teacher's office. I was going to confide in him and ask if I could take the test at his house. There was no reason for Bianca or anyone else to know unless it was positive.

I had woken Charles, and he was irritated but made it clear he would still listen. We teased each other often about being "out carousing" once we knew that we both had the same affliction for cheating. I stumbled over the words that I was possibly pregnant; I didn't mention the fact that I wasn't officially late yet but would be the next day. "Uh oh, Simone, have you been out carousing again? If you are going to do it, you need to be smart. If you had been smart and not stupid, you wouldn't be in this situation now," he said in a callous tone I hadn't heard before. I apologized for waking him; he asked that I call him after I got home from school. My best friend Theresa had heard the whole thing.

As soon as I walked in the door from school, I called Charles. "Hey, it's me," I said, hoping he was in a better mood. "You have a lot of nerve calling me! You gave one of your little friends my number and had her call me! I do not appreciate being called by someone I don't know! I certainly do not appreciate being called a dick by someone I don't know!" Charles screamed at me as I pretended to have no idea what he was talking about. "Oh, so one of your friends just happened to have my number and called me to tell me I'm a dick?" I hesitated, and then it hit me. "My planner has a phone book in it. My friend Theresa heard us on the phone earlier; she had said something about you being an asshole the way you talked to me. She must have gotten your number from my planner when I was in the lunch line," it was the only explanation I could think of. "You have my number written in your phone book? Why? Because you don't call me often enough that you have it memorized? You are nothing but a money-grubbing bitch like your mother. Do not ever call me again!" Charles slammed the phone down in my ear. I flopped onto the couch with no tears left to cry. I was shocked and hurt. Theresa had offered to do it, and I had left my planner so she could get his number.

I had plenty of tears the next day; Mr. Bloom noticed and asked to see me after class. I said nothing, so he brought me to the office. We sat next to each other, and he gave me honesty, "If you don't tell me what's wrong, then I have to tell Mr. Holt. It's him or me." No one liked Mr. Holt; he was just one of those adults that were unapproachable by kids. I stuttered through my sobs, "I just have a feeling that I'm pregnant." There was no hesitation on his part. "Go to your office. I will be back in twenty minutes." I did as I was told and saw him leave the school grounds. Mr. Bloom appeared less than twenty minutes later and escorted me to the bathroom. He kicked the smokers out with a firm "Get back to class," no detentions or calls home were issued that afternoon. "Go ahead; I will watch the door," he said as he handed me a paper bag with a two-pack of pregnancy tests. As I did one of the tests, I heard him outside the door, telling everyone they had to go to a different bathroom. No one was getting passed him. The test was negative. "Can you take the other one in the morning at home?" The answer was clear on my face. "I will meet you first thing in the morning when you get off the short bus," Mr. Bloom said with a smile and a nudge. I laughed and went to class, feeling a little relieved.

True to his word, he was at the door of the bus waiting. I was escorted to the bathroom at once while he again guarded the door. It was also negative. "Come on, let's go to your office," he said. For once the silence we sat in wasn't full of pain, anger, and awkwardness. "Simone, is it someone from school?" I didn't know how to answer that; I couldn't tell him the truth, that I hadn't knowingly had sex in over a year. I hadn't knowingly had sex since

Drew. So, I just told him no. He pulled another brown paper bag from his briefcase and handed it to me. It was full of condoms. "I am not judging. If you are going to do it, be safe. Don't do it because you feel like you have to. Sex is supposed to be a good thing for both people involved." I nodded in agreement, and we both went to our classes. I got my period that night.

I snuck out that night and met a guy named Keith. He seemed to be an average guy who had no problem going and getting liquor for a teenager. He didn't even want anything for doing it. As I drank, he produced a joint, "You get high, teenager?" I nodded, and he passed. When his joint was gone, mostly smoked by me, I gave him a hug and walked away. He followed, and we walked together in silence as I drank. Not far from my house, he pulled out some coke. That wasn't free, blow for blow, I guess. I almost got caught sneaking in. Keith became my new Todd. I never consented to anything, but he took what he wanted, so I took all the pain-killing self-destruction he gave. When my grandparents thought I was at a friend's house, the park, or the library, I was with Keith. I even got away with sneaking him in a few times. He discovered my like, my need for heat, and tried to burn his name into my upper arm. Friends saw my homemade bandaging and told Mr. Bloom. I told him it wasn't a big thing; I had done it to myself and would not do it again. He made sure I knew if I did, he would call home.

I wrote a poem that I really liked. It was about my life changing and things getting better. I slipped it under Mr. Steinfeld's door. I was called into his office after he read it and asked for an explanation. I gave him what he asked for, even though I had thought it was pretty self-explanatory, and he didn't take it that way. He took it as an intent to commit suicide. An ambulance was called, and I was dragged off, quite literally, to a mental hospital. Any kids that were in the classes in the front of the building got to witness as it took several grown men to chase me, hold on to me and strap me forcefully into the ambulance. They also got to see Mr. Holt get kicked in the balls. No one understood anything. I said I was being hurt; I had to be mistaken; I said I was doing better, but it meant I was suicidal; I tried to commit suicide, and I was told I had no reason to do that. I didn't like humans at all. That poem was later published in two different books of poetry.

The nut hut sucks; they strip search, thankfully not thoroughly when you are a kid. I was given the list of rules. No belts, no shoelaces, no loose strings, no tampons, "Wait, what the fuck do you mean no tampons?" The nurse tried not to laugh, "You could tie the strings together and make a noose and hang yourself," she informed me very professionally. "Do you understand how fucking stupid that is? How many tampon strings do you think it would take to make a noose? Not just a noose, but one strong enough to hang a fucking human with it?" She tried not to agree, but the slight smile on her face did it for her, "I don't make the rules; I just enforce them." The rules were endless, and there was a ton more if you were on suicidal observation (SO), which I was.

The girl's SO room was simple, four beds, a bathroom that stayed locked, and closet space that no one used. If you unpacked, it meant you were staying. I was the fourth member of the SO room; my roommates were Sharonda, Maritza, and Hailey. On my first night, Hailey snuck out of the girls' SO and into the boys. She fucked her boyfriend, snuck back in, told us all how great it was, and then loudly masturbated. All night. The sun was already clear in the sky when I threw my pillow at her, "Bitch shove a pickle up there or something; some of us would like a little sleep." She was offended by my words, but the other girls laughed. We were served lunch that afternoon, and everyone got a little cup of cucumber slices. The three of us stuck ours all together and presented our creation to Hailey as a nighttime offering. Hailey stood and slapped me. I laughed at her and told her honestly, "Try harder; you hit like a bitch," as I punched her in the face, breaking her nose.

After she got medical care, they had a mediation between the two of us. I was clear in my position, she hit me first, and if she could shut the fuck up at night, there would be no further problems. Hailey claimed she had done nothing wrong, but there were at least twenty witnesses that she had hit me first, and the other girls backed up my overnight complaint. Hailey agreed to be quieter. She again

162

snuck into the boy's SO, came back, and bragged about fucking all four of them, but her masturbation was quieter, and she finished up around four am.

Maritza found out her boyfriend was planning on dumping her. Someone, I will not name names, snuck in some acid. Maritza and I devised a plan to sneak into the bathroom and get high. Sharonda was crucial to this plan. She didn't get high on anything, but she supported the cause and would create a distraction. When you are on SO, you can't do anything without staff supervision. This includes using the bathroom, showering, and shaving. Anyone that was there longer than a few days was pretty hairy. Most of us would not shave with the staff watching, especially since some of the staff was male.

During group, which was the whole floor, not just the SO kids, Maritza started swearing she was Hilary Clinton, so I said I was Bill Clinton. In an attempt to get attention off of Maritza, who was trying to do headstands on the table, Sharonda screamed, "No! You are Kurt Cobain!" While pointing at me. I laughed, and Maritza ran to me, yelling, "I am Courtney Love! I love you!" They put us each in strait jackets and separate padded rooms for the night. They never bothered to drug test either of us. They said we were suffering from "Shared delusions." Adults will tell themselves anything they can to help themselves sleep at night.

I was numb when I got to the hospital. I had never experienced the feeling of happiness. I had different levels of depression, contentedness, and numbness. The closest I ever got to happiness was contentment, which is still true today. I had met with the psychiatrist before Maritza, and I got high. I knew how to deal with all of the staff and how to answer their questions. "Are you suicidal? Do you want to hurt yourself? Do you want to hurt others?" He had asked. I lied to each question and said no to everything. The real answers were, generally, yes, yes, this place makes me want to kill myself, some of them. I was released from the padded room and into a regular room with a bathroom I could use at will. I was questioned by the doctors again and told them what they wanted to hear; I was released from the hospital the next day. No one should ever attempt to analyze another person's words or art.

I had tried to call Charles many times both before and after my hospitalization. If he answered the phone, he hung up as soon as he heard my voice. Anne would talk to me if I called but did not put him on the phone. His stepkids would give him the phone, and then he would hang up. The man was as stubborn as I was. In time I gave up. He won.

I had kept in touch with several of my hometown friends. I called Tiffany to catch up, and she told me she had seen Kyle. She had his number, and he wanted me to call him. I called, thinking it had been two years and we could be friends again. Kyle wanted to get back together, we lived at opposite ends of Long Island, and neither of us drove, but I said yes. Regardless, things would be different two years later, right? Or was I just a glutton for punishment?

Kyle had signed up to join the army before we got back together, so we tried to spend as much time together as we could before he went off to boot camp. I wasn't allowed to go to him, but he took the train to visit me when he could. Our first time physically seeing each other, he asked me, "Did I ever tell you; you were my first?" Kyle asked with a laugh. "No, but I knew," it hadn't been hard to figure out. "How did you know?" He was still laughing but seemed a little embarrassed. "For one, you couldn't figure out how to get a condom on. For two, you sucked," my honesty is often considered problematic. We laughed, and he went on to tell me that he is now celibate until marriage, and his last girlfriend was a "whore" who had been with over one hundred fifty guys, so he was very sure he no longer "sucked."

Later that day, we were walking around in my grandfather's garden; we couldn't be seen from any windows and stopped to kiss. He sat in a patio chair, opened his pants, and pushed my head down. I obliged until he pulled me back up and turned me around. It happened so fast there was no time to respond. I was bent over, my pants were down, and he shoved his way in. My tears quietly watered a plant. Kyle still sucked, and I still bled when he was done. I didn't break up with Kyle after our garden sex. He knew by this

164

point that I had been abused sexually by Griffith. He also knew about things Brady had done, not what, just things. Kyle knew Brady still came to visit; he didn't know about the gifts and messages that were relayed from Griffith through Brady. No one did. Kyle started pushing me to run away; he said I could stay with his sister Krissy and her three kids. Kyle knew someone who would bring him to pick me up. I felt I needed to do what Kyle wanted. Why? Because I was trained to always do what men wanted.

I wrote notes to Grandma and Bianca that I was leaving, snuck my bag outside, and told Grandma I was going to the library. I walked away and didn't look back. My notes said I was uncomfortable around Brady, and he was their grandson; I knew he would always come around. It wasn't a lie; I was uncomfortable around him. It was more because of Griffith, though; even without the past gifts, he still lived with him and was still very loyal to him. Krissy was poor and could barely feed her kids. I felt bad being there. I contributed by babysitting so Krissy could work more hours. It didn't take a genius to know where I was, though, and Bianca called me there the first night.

Within a few days, Bianca came to see me. She confirmed that Kyle didn't actually live there. Krissy assured her there was no drinking, no drugs, and that Kyle had taken a vow of celibacy, so there would be no sex. I said nothing. Kyle had been staying there every night since I got there, and every night, he would come into my room and just shove it in. Bianca left me there but let me know CPS knew where I was and they may not allow me to stay there.
Kyle was a self-declared alcoholic and drug addict. He went to AA meetings, which were awful. Kyle said they helped him, but they only made him want to drink more. Krissy had a liquor cabinet, and there were always cold beers in the fridge. Krissy caught me sneaking drinks and told me she didn't care, just not to let Kyle know. Krissy also urged me to leave Kyle. She let me know his alcohol and drug problems were fictitious, which I already knew, and that he had been diagnosed repeatedly as a pathological liar. I was welcome to stay; she could get me a job where she worked, and we could work opposite shifts and take turns watching her kids. Kyle

would not allow me to work. I had to stay in the house unless he was going somewhere. I could only leave the house with him.

After a week there, I was asleep when Kyle came in and whipped me with his belt. Three hard strikes against my back, then my shorts were ripped off, and he got what he came for. When he was done, he asked, "Do you know why I whipped you?" I hadn't thought about it; no one ever had a reason before; I shook my head and continued withholding my tears. "Because it is your fault. That first night I was with you, my dad kicked me out because I was late. I wound up in a shelter; then you dumped me. I lost my family because of you, and you left me. I couldn't handle the pain of losing you, so I started using drugs and drinking. I became an addict, and all of it is your fault." I didn't respond. I knew he believed that all of his problems were my fault. I also knew it was all lies.

Krissy felt bad leaving me with her kids over forty hours a week and would give me some cash when she could. I used it all on alcohol. I drank in the bathroom at the AA meetings; no one knew, not even Kyle. People don't see what they don't want to see, and unlike Kyle, I was an alcoholic. It took years before I could admit that. A twenty-something guy at the meetings was interested in me; Kyle beat me for it. In true defiance and my self-destructive nature, I flirted with the guy in front of Kyle. So, he whipped me a few times. I deserved it.

Jane showed up with the cops after I was there for a few weeks. I was wanted that afternoon in court. Judge Rankin had been notified by Amanda that no one knew where I was, which was very much not true. My family wouldn't and hadn't lied when they were asked where I was. When I had gone to Krissy's, I had brought the dress I wore to prom; I didn't want anything to happen to it if I left it behind. I put it on to wear to court and, of course, wore my combat boots. I snuck a few drinks out of Kyle's view as I packed my stuff. Krissy was asking about keeping me and getting all of the information to become a foster parent, but I was told there would be no guarantee I would be placed with her.

While waiting for my turn in court, I was told I was being charged as a runaway. Judge Rankin passed me in the hallway, and moments later, a court officer was giving me a breathalyzer test because the judge believed I was drunk. I laughed because I knew I wasn't drunk. I blew a .08, though. I started to panic; I don't like to wait, especially if I can't walk. An older court officer named Bruce had been assigned to babysit me; he allowed me to pace a short hallway. I had seen Amanda once, just after the breathalyzer. She told me I was going to be placed in a treatment facility or juvenile detention. Neither of those options was valid. I needed to run.

Bruce was a nice guy, but I needed to figure out how to lose him. He talked about his wife and kids; he told me how sorry he was that such a nice kid was in so much trouble. Little did he know, I wasn't that nice of a kid. Bruce was pretty relaxed, but he also did his job well and was never more than a few steps away from me. I tried the bathroom window; it didn't open enough, and there was no way I could reach the ceiling to crawl through. I left the bathroom, hoping he had walked away a little, he hadn't, but I saw my way out. His shoelace was untied. "Be careful," I said while pointing it out.

Bruce got down on one knee to fix his shoelace; I mentally apologized for what I was about to do. I pulled my right leg all the way back and kicked as hard as I could, one trusty combat boot colliding with Bruce's face. For good measure and to give myself more time, I kicked him in the balls. As I ran down the first flight of stairs and rounded the corner, I yelled back, "I'm sorry!"

I hadn't had time to grab my bag, and I knew it would be searched; I had to get away fast, and there was nowhere to go. In that bag, they would find some clothes, a bottle of Jack, a crack stem, and a little bit of coke. I was a teenager in a fancy dress and combat boots in a town I didn't know. I stuck out way too much. My mom's, grandparents', Krissy's, and any friends I had were out of the question. If I was still in contact with Drew, I could have had him come get me. I could have hidden in his room, and no one ever would have known I was there. Being back in that house may have killed me, though. I didn't realize what I was doing when I stuck my thumb out, and a big delivery truck pulled over within seconds.

"Where are you headed?" asked the driver. "Anywhere but here. I can ride with you as long as you'll have me." I saw the look in his eyes as he scanned my body. The driver got a hand job, and I got ten miles. It was going to be dark soon, and I needed another ride before then. The next person to pick me up was a woman. She gave me twenty dollars, bought me a drive-thru dinner, and encouraged me to go home. Getting out of her car and slamming the door was when I realized I didn't have a home. I used ten dollars at the liquor store and ten to get high. I found my place to crash by a dumpster, where there were boxes, but no kind, quiet man.

I woke up to several people shouting, "Freeze! Don't move!" I opened my eyes to see I had overslept. The sun was bright and high in the sky; it must have been around noon. I lifted one hand to shield my eyes from the sun, and they yelled again. I had no reason to listen. What were they going to do? Shoot me? No one cared, especially not me. I sat, stood, stretched, yawned, and greeted them, "What's up, boys? Anyone have a drink? "One cop moved quickly, telling me to put my hands in the air; I did while laughing. As he cuffed me, I said, "Hmmm, big boy, better watch it, haven't you heard? I'm trouble; I might like that." I saw the car I was going to be placed in and Bruce standing next to it. Both eyes were beautiful shades of purple, his nose was broken, and I felt awful. Most of the people I hurt, attacked, and hit had deserved it. He hadn't. His eyes were not mad.

"Hey, do you guys think I can smoke first? I yelled and was greeted with laughter and shouts of "Bitch" and "Cunt." Bruce uncuffed me and cuffed me in the front. He lit me a cigarette, one of his, not mine. I leaned against the car, smoking, "Wow, Bruce, this is what, eight cops? Ten? For one little teenage girl?" He laughed, "You are one hell of a teenage girl," as he rubbed his face. "I'm sorry," I said quietly. "I know. You were scared and needed to go. I get it. Besides, I'm sure it is nothing compared to what has been done to you." I looked up at him to see he wasn't like most. He was in the rare group of people that saw me and saw through the bullshit I showed the rest of the world. Those were my people. I loved them all, and I still do.

I was put in juvenile detention for the night. I was charged as a runaway and with possession of drugs, paraphernalia, and assault. I was a quiet kid. I only caused trouble when scared or provoked. Three girls decided to talk shit and then hit me. I beat the shit out of all of them and was sent to my cell alone for the rest of the night. Juvenile's version of solitary. I liked it that way.

I was brought in handcuffs to court the next day. Two court officers were assigned to babysit me. Amanda, the child lawyer from hell, couldn't make it. Jane was there but not in the courtroom. Judge Rankin wasn't letting anyone in except the two of us and the officers. After we started our meeting, Bruce came in and said he didn't want to press charges. "Look at her, Judge. Really look at her. She is just a kid. Everything she is doing is because of whatever had been done to her." I laughed, a full belly laugh. "Nah. Bruce doesn't know what he is talking about. I do what I do because I can and because I'm a bitch." The judge ordered our hearing to be sealed, I went to AA and NA, and I was placed in a group home. I had already known they were seeking group home placement. Amanda had called the day before and let me know my grandparents had been deemed too old to care for me. In addition, Griffith was found guilty of neglect and endangering the welfare of a child. Bianca was fuming that the judge had told her openly, "I cannot prove that you knew anything, but if you didn't, you sure as hell should have." Judge Rankin continued on to tell me, "If you do what you are supposed to at the group home, all of the charges will go away." Jane met me in the hallway with my backpack, sans drugs and alcohol. That is when she told me where the group home was. I was going home. I was being placed in my hometown.

The Next Chapter

My first night in the group home was questionable. They didn't want to take me because I was diabetic, and they didn't want syringes on the property. I rarely took my insulin anyway. It was agreed that I could stay the night, but Jane would take me to the Dr the next morning. If insulin were necessary, I couldn't stay. Jane came and brought me two packs of cigarettes, another secret I have kept all these years. I was brought to Nassau County Medical Center, a hospital with a horrible reputation, and given a five-hour glucose tolerance test. The result was the doctor's claim was inconclusive. She said that I did need insulin, but such a small amount that going without for a little while wouldn't do much damage. The Dr said whatever needed to be said to ensure I had a place at this home. I was almost seventeen and only the state's problem for another year. I was able to stay; my glucometer and glucose tabs were locked away in a closet with all the other kid's meds, plus our cigarettes which we had to ask for every time we wanted one. Smoking wasn't allowed between ten pm and seven am; the smoking area was the back deck only. If staff determined you were smoking too much, they were withheld for a little while. The cook lowered the carbs in my meals where he could and picked up a sugar-free drink mix. He was reprimanded for doing so as it wasn't in the budget. He continued buying it with his own money.

The second week Jane brought me back to the same hospital; I needed to have a court-ordered physical examination to check for signs of sexual abuse. I expressed dismay at this immediately; it had been almost two years; what evidence would there be? Jane and I argued about this, but it was ordered, and she couldn't go against it. "It's been two fucking years. They will be able to tell I'm not a virgin, and that is it!" She knew I was right; her face and body language showed her agreement. She did her job and left me with the female Dr and two nurses.

The Dr explained they were going to take pictures of my body and any scars I had, do a full body exam, and lastly, there was going to be an internal exam. I was shown what instruments were going to be used. The initial exam was awkward; it would be for anyone. Having strangers see you naked is never fun, and the pictures were making me panic. It was causing the flashbacks to start again. I did as I was told, laying on the table, scooting down, lower, lower, lower. Open my legs, wider, wider, wider. Then there was no air. I tried to get up, "You aren't going to find any evidence anyway. This is stupid. It's been two years." The two female nurses appeared at my shoulders and eased me back onto the table. All three women assured me, "Just relax. It won't hurt." When you have lived the life I have, being forced to have an exam like this is just one more rape.

The Dr got the speculum inside me. They had lied. It hurt like a mother fucker. I was telling them it hurt and trying to get away. They couldn't restrain me on their own, so the Dr called for help. Several medical personnel, both male and female, came in to help. Some held me down; some forced my legs open and held them that way. I screamed in pain and heard one of the doctors say, "She's having a panic attack. She says it hurts, but it doesn't." It wasn't her body, and she didn't know what I felt. The door had been left open, and I was still trying to get away. The last two things I saw were Jane's face in the waiting room and the puddle of blood on the floor. A female voice yelled, "She's hemorrhaging!" Then there was darkness.

I don't know how long I was unconscious. I woke up in a different room and had been admitted. I never got the full report. I was a minor which apparently meant I had no say in my own body and had no right to know anything about it. The only things I heard were hushed whispers about "repeated vaginal and cervical trauma." I could have told them that without the hell they put me through. Fucking idiots.

I was well-liked in the group home by both staff and kids. I didn't cause trouble. I had no reason to. The kids were all troubled, none of us for the same reasons or in the same ways, but that didn't matter. We, for the most part, never discussed why we were there; some of the kids felt more comfortable discussing their situations with others. I wasn't a sharer. I was still dating Kyle, but he had gone off to boot camp. He called when he could, sent letters regularly, and always included money.

The group home staff was cool. They took us out to the movies, bowling, the public pool, movie nights at the house, the arcade, etc. I spent my seventeenth birthday there. The cook even made me a cake. It was against policy, but they allowed Bianca to take me out for the day. The two of us went for lunch and walked around the touristy town. We stopped at a palm reader who told me I was with my true love. She said I was going to be with him forever and I would be pregnant by the end of the year. She was half wrong, which also meant she was half right.

I was sitting in my room alone with a book when Kerri, my favorite staff personnel, came in and asked to talk. They had made plans to take us to the movies that night, and the rest of the kids voted on seeing A Time to Kill. Kerri wanted to clear the movie choice with me first and said if I was uncomfortable with it, we would see or do something else. I had never heard of the movie and knew nothing about it; I didn't want to disappoint the other kids, so I said it was fine.

For those who have not seen it, it involves the graphic rape of a child. While I had gotten exceptionally good at controlling the daytime flashbacks, the nightmares were still coming regularly. During the day, if they started or I felt them coming, I could dig my nails into any part of my flesh; a little pain was all it took to keep me in the present moment. Heat still worked best, but it wasn't readily available. I went to bed the night of the movie, not realizing how much it had affected me. One of the other girls heard me crying and talking in my sleep; it was intense and scared her, so she went to get the staff. When I have these nightmares, I can hear everything around me. If people talk to me, I respond. What no one is prepared for, though, is that when these nightmares happen, I sound like a small child. If, in my dream, I am beaten, my unconscious body responds as I take the beating the same way I did at the time of the initial assault. I can be talked awake by hearing people's voices and them asking enough questions for me to understand that whatever is going on isn't happening right now.

Kerri and Megan had been getting ready to leave for the night, which would have just left Ethan there. He would have been scared to do what Kerri and Megan did. They talked me awake the same way my grandmother and Brad had. It took a while, and by the time they succeeded, I had wedged myself between the bed and the wall, hit the window, which broke it, and I had no shirt on.

As Kerri helped me get my shirt back on, Meagan grabbed blankets. The two of them walked me out to the sliding door overlooking the deck. That night the rules were broken, and accommodations were made. Ethan unlocked the door, retrieved my cigarettes, and handed me the whole pack. I was told to smoke right where I sat, in the house, and blow it out the sliding door, and I could smoke as much as I wanted. Kerri lectured me for saying going to that movie was fine and more for saying I was fine when we got back. It happened several more nights, only now Ethan knew what to do. I was given free rein at night. If I didn't want to sleep, I was allowed to sit and use the living room TV, and I could go smoke on the front porch where I couldn't be seen by the other kids.

I did break the rules there, but I never got caught. I was remarkably close with Stephanie. She was dating Darius, and I had a flirtatious thing going on with Foster. Stephanie's cousin Jory was also there. I had kissed Foster at the pool under the water and flashed him. Darius and Foster were supposed to sneak out of their window one night and into ours. At the last minute, Foster chickened out, so Jory came instead. Martha was the third girl in our room, no one liked her, but Jory said he would fuck around with her anyway, just to have something to do. I was in the bunk above Martha, and Stephanie was in the single bed across the room. With no guy to fool around with, I was going to go to sleep when I heard Jory from below me, "Sorry, I can't do this." His head popped up over my bed rail, "Simone, you want to fuck around? I won't tell Foster." I was bored and shrugged; he climbed up. Jory whispered in my ear that he hadn't done anything with her, only leaned in to kiss her, but she smelled so bad he couldn't do it. We really didn't do anything. We talked. He got a hand job, that's all. Nothing. The boys snuck back to their room before the next bed check. Martha was so pissed that in the morning, she told on us. All of us denied it and were believed. Five against one.

Summer was half over, and I was waiting to see what fate had in store for me. The policy was that no one could stay longer than ninety days. My ninety days would be up the third week of September. The staff and people directly in charge of the house were meeting with the board of directors to see if I could just stay. I was doing well. I was going to AA weekly and hadn't had a drink in two months, there were no NA meetings nearby, but I was drug-free too. For the first time since I was eleven or earlier, I was completely clean and sober. I was ushered away when the directors came in with the board's decision. I eavesdropped from a hallway; the request was denied. Despite a letter from every staff member and one from myself, they said no, I couldn't stay. I was to start the school year there with my old friends, my losers, my outcasts, and after three weeks, I would be transferred, and the transfers would continue every three months until I turned eighteen. I knew what I needed to do. It was time to run.

Joanna wanted to go too, so we made plans, each packed a bag and met in my room at 1 am. I was dressed slutty; she wasn't. I should have prepared her for how we would have to travel; I often forgot that these people I hung out with were just kids. I would just have to do the work for both of us. Joanna had some money that her parents had given her during visitation. I didn't; all my money came in the mail and was locked up by the staff. Joanna gave me money to get cigarettes, and we were gone.

Some people stopped, realized we were kids and kept going. At fourteen, I could pass for a twenty-something; at seventeen, everyone saw me as a kid. We got a couple of short rides from middle-aged women who felt bad for us, but we needed to get further, faster. I needed a guy to pull over. A late twenty's cute guy stopped, and I tried flirting. He said he wasn't interested in fucking

174

kids, which I had never heard before. He was about to drive away, but he was the best option we had had in hours. Flirting hadn't worked, even when I hiked my skirt up, so I went for the next best thing. If he didn't want to fuck a kid, he would want to help a kid. I cried. I cried like my life depended on it. In less than a minute, we were in his car, and he was pulling away.

Joanna was headed to the train station; she had a family she could go to. He dropped her off there, and when I hugged her goodbye, she slipped some cash into my pocket. Joanna disappeared into the growing crowd on the train platform, and I never saw her again. The guy asked where I was headed and said he wasn't going that far but would get me as close as he could. He had worked at a local hospital and knew there were a couple of runaways from a group home, one in need of medical attention as a diabetic. Diabetes, they pretended, didn't exist any other time. He didn't ask if we were those kids, so I didn't volunteer any information.

Only the first specks of sunlight were coming through the night sky when we encountered a problem. There was a roadblock, and they were checking every car. I told my kind driver to tell them I was his niece, I was visiting for a couple of weeks, and quickly laid my head on the window. I appeared to be asleep by the time they tapped on his window. The flashlight was bright as the cop asked, "Who is the girl?" There was a brief hesitation before the driver said, "That's my niece, Raven. I am watching her while my sister is on her honeymoon; she got married last night." The cop came around and tapped my window; when I didn't move, he opened the door; I hung limply for a few seconds and then acted groggy. "What is your name, miss?" He asked with the flashlight too close to my face. "Raven and I are tired," I said as I rubbed my eyes to block the light. "Who is that?" the cop asked as he gestured toward my good Samaritan. I blinked slightly in his direction and said, "My uncle." The cop waived us through. I had no idea if they were looking for me; if they were, it didn't seem that they had pictures, plus they would be looking for two girls, not one.

We drove until the sun was bright in the morning sky before stopping for breakfast at a diner. After we ate, he offered me some money, which I declined, reminding him that my friend had given me twenty dollars before she left. As he put a fifty in my pocket, he asked me to please not hitchhike, he gave me a hug, and I was off again. I made a quick stop for more cigarettes and Jack; sobriety wasn't for me.

I was picked up by many people, mostly men and mostly assholes. Only two are worth mentioning specifically. The first one was an older guy in a hippie van. I got nervous right before getting in and tried to say no instead. He pushed, and I obeyed. We talked; I told him where I was going; he wanted to stop and eat at his house; I said no, just drop me off. He gave me a drink, and I woke up on his couch. His young adult daughter was there, cooking lunch. The two of them offered to let me stay. No one would find me, whatever I was running from would disappear, and I would be safe. It was a cozy little apartment, and they were nice, but I got a vibe of evil from them both. I acted excited to finally have a place to go but snuck out at my first opportunity. I knew the look in their eyes and knew they were not what they seemed to be.

The next was a truck driver. He was all eyes and hands from the second I got in. He asked, before the door was closed, what I was giving him for the ride, and told me that for the right price, he would take me wherever I wanted to go. I gave him flirty eyes and a half smile as I let my shirt sleeve fall off my shoulder and tossed my hair, "Well, what do you want?" He reached to touch me, and right before he made contact, "By the way, I'm only seventeen." He gave no verbal answer, but his hand going down the front of my shirt told me all I needed to know. I moaned like I enjoyed his touch. As he drove, he opened his pants and commanded me, "Suck it." I did, but he wasn't like Joey. I let him make a mess all over himself. We drove a little while, and his hand slid up my thigh, headed toward my crotch. That wasn't up for trade or something I was willing to give. I told him no, and he told me to get out, in the middle of the highway, without stopping. I laughed at him, and he tried to push me. This fucker was crazier than me, and not in a good way.

This was a man, and if I knew anything in the world, it was how to deal with men, especially perverts. I told him I had just meant not while we were driving, that he needed to find somewhere to pull over, so we could take our time and enjoy it. "That way, I can get in your lap and give you the ride of your life, Sir." He didn't believe me, "You tryin' ta play with me, little girl? I don' like bein' played with. Before you play games, you might ought to look behind the seat." I glanced and saw guns. I didn't react and showed no fear. Our eyes met, "I will kill you if you don't gimme some of that sweet pussy. Now show me sumthin', so I know yo' serious." I saw the truth in his eyes. His truth. He was planning to kill me no matter what he got. He had probably been planning to kill me since I got in his truck. I guess I should have stayed with the hippie man.

I smiled and played the role I knew so well. Slowly I turned to face him, putting my back against the passenger door. "You think I would play with you?" I put my feet up on the seat and opened my legs just enough that he could see, "The only thing I like to play with is myself," I opened a button on my already low-cut shirt. I lowered one hand into my shirt, and the other went between my legs. He now knew Simone's secret...I wasn't wearing any underwear. The bozo lost his load in his pants as I pretended to enjoy myself. I felt the turn as he pulled off the road and slowed down. I was increasingly irritated that this jackass had an unlimited supply of hard-ons to go with his collection of guns.

At that moment, I decided to just die. I would piss him off and get him to shoot me before he could fuck me. "He might do me after I am dead, but at least I won't have to feel it," I had time to think as he turned off the truck, removed the key, threw it on the dash, and it rolled off onto the floor. At the next moment, I decided to live. It was my life, and no one could take it but me. I had no plan and no time to think of one. He leaned toward me, and I placed my left boot-clad foot seductively on his shoulder but pushed him back. I felt the doors handle with my right hand. I pulled the handle and felt the soft click as it released; I smashed my right foot into his face and pushed myself backward out of the truck. I almost fell before jumping down onto the ground. I ran, looking back once, where I saw him spitting blood and teeth out of the passenger door. I ran as fast as I could to the closest suburbia. He would be looking for me on the highway, and his big truck would have been very noticeable trying to get down the streets of the suburbs.

It's easy not to be noticed in the suburbs. Everything is the same. The houses, the cars, the well-manicured lawns, everything blends in, even me. I naturally have no sense of direction, and I get lost in neighborhoods like that easily. I was getting worried when a middle-aged jogger approached me. He greeted me with a friendly smile and good morning. I kept walking, and he jogged alongside me, eventually striking up a conversation. We stopped in the road talking for about half an hour when he gestured to his house, "Come on in. I'll make you breakfast, and then I'll give you a ride." We were walking toward the house when I saw a uniform hanging in the back of his car. "You know, I think I should just keep walking and try and find my friends," I said, backing away slowly. He followed my gaze and looked at his feet. "You don't recognize me, do you? Picture the uniform on me. You know I'm not going to hurt you. I'll make you breakfast and take you back to the group home." I pictured him in the uniform as he suggested. Bruce. "Shit. Look, I never wanted to hurt you. I needed to get away; you know that I need to go now too. I really am sorry!" I started moving more quickly. "I do know that. It's why I spoke to the judge; please, just let me help you," Bruce said as my fast walk turned into a jog. I heard him calling for me in the distance. Bruce was a good man; if he had offered to take me in, I would have said yes.

I got increasingly more lost as I wandered through the streets that were designed to be a puzzle. I was also lost in thought as I heard a quiet car pull up beside me. "Hey, miss!" A young man's voice called; I glanced and saw it was a cop. I walked, and he followed alongside me in his car; we had a back-and-forth round of question and answer.
"Miss, what is your name?"
"I don't remember."
"How old are you?"
"Eighteen."

178

"Where are you going?"

"Not here."

"Where are you coming from?"

"Nowhere."

He was getting irritated and got out of the car. "Look, I'm looking for a couple of runaways. They ran away from a group home. You wouldn't be one of them, would you?" At least he finally asked his real question. "No, I already told you; I'm eighteen." He was losing his patience, but I didn't care. "What's your name?" He asked with a sigh. "I already told you I don't remember." He was boring me. "Just give me a name so I can verify you aren't one of them." The cop said with an eye roll. I crossed my arms and gave him a fake name, not totally fake; it just wasn't mine (sorry, Sophie). He got in his car and verified it wasn't the name of either runaway. "Have a nice day," he said with a smile as he drove away and made a left.

Suburbia, where all roads link back together, and if you can't find the main road, you are stuck. I had a false sense of security as I walked on, most likely going in circles, but I hadn't seen Bruce's house or the cop again. It happened in an instant. A hand grabbed the back of my shirt and my backpack, and I was dragged backward. We got to a car; I was turned and thrown face-first onto the hood. My backpack was yanked off, and I was handcuffed. The cop went to his car and produced a piece of paper that he shoved in my face; it was a picture of me with the word "Runaway" across the bottom. I told him it wasn't me and to get his eyes checked. He smacked my head into the hood of the car; I called him a pussy, and he kicked me in the back of the leg. Fucking cop.

After some back-and-forth banter with the cop, I was clearly the one with the wit and sarcasm; I admitted who I was, why I left, and why I wasn't going back. I was put in the front passenger seat and cuffed to the dash. "Is this really necessary?" I asked with a laugh. "With what I have heard about you, yes. Yes, it is." We drove back toward the group home. He stopped at a take-out place, went in and grabbed us some food, and brought me a diet soda. While he was inside, he had me cuffed to the steering wheel. I also had to eat and drink like that. As we drove, he calmed down, "Look, if we get there and they say you are free to go, I will drive you wherever you want." I agreed; I was seventeen, and they couldn't legally keep me.

While he was inside the group home, which was a while, I was again handcuffed to the wheel. When he came out, he was in a much better mood, and he released me right away. "They said they understand why you left and why you don't want to stay. You are welcome to, though, and you are also welcomed to leave." A deal is a deal; I turned to get back in his car, and he held the door shut and smiled. "Don't make me handcuff you to a tree." I looked at him with anger, "You said-" he cut me off, "They said if you leave, they can't give you any of your diabetic supplies. I am not comfortable taking you anywhere without that." I was a teenager. I stomped my foot and screeched. My diabetes never mattered to anyone except when it was convenient for them.

I stormed through the front door, filled with a fiery rage they hadn't seen before. They explained their standpoint, and I explained mine. They agreed with me that the decision that was made was unfair and even cruel. I understood them, and they understood me. The staff all wandered off, letting me know I could stay or go, whatever I decided was best. Ethan was still there and had been hovering quietly; he gestured for me to follow him. He unlocked the supply closet and gave me my glucose tabs, glucometer, cigarettes, and some of the money I had. He locked the door and asked, "Can I hug you?" I hugged him, and he told me, "You are one of the strongest people I have ever known. Good luck." I left again through the front door instead of the window.

I successfully hitchhiked to Krissy's house. She had already known I was on my way. CPS had let her know to expect me. They all knew I had been headed to her house; it was just a matter of when I would arrive. Krissy already had my bed made up, her kids were excited to see me, and I was happy to be there. Jane and her band of cops showed up the next day; Krissy hadn't been able to afford to get her house foster kid ready. They would not allow me to stay, but they did find me a foster home. It wasn't far from my grandparents' house, and I would be able to stay in the same high school I had been going to. It was technically in a different school district, but they had been granted temporary approval for me to stay in my old school as long as transportation was provided by someone else. I was going willingly, but they cuffed me, just in case. Judge Rankin wanted to see me before I went to the new foster home.

I entered the courtroom for what seemed to be the hundredth time. It was empty except for the judge and me. "Simone, I want to talk to you. This conversation is off the record. Just listen. Can you do that without that famous sarcasm of yours?" It was true; I had often been compared to Darlene Connor from Roseanne or Wednesday Addams from The Addams Family. I silently agreed. "You aren't a bad kid. I suspect you're involved in a bit more than a little drinking and occasional drug experimentation. You're usually very careful not to drink before coming to my courtroom. I respect that. I have not had you drug tested because I do not think that is what you need. I think your behavior is you lashing out at all those who have hurt you, those who have wronged you. You take it out on yourself because it is easier to control what you do to yourself, and you feel you deserve to be punished for what others have done to you. You are better than this; you are very smart; I am placing you in this foster home. If you do anything crazy, I will start drug testing you weekly and put you in juvenile detention. Use the strength you have to destroy the ones who hurt you, not yourself." I left without a word.

I went to the foster home without complaint or violence. Delilah was my new foster mother, she had an adult biological daughter who was going off to college and two adopted grown kids who lived in rooms in the basement. I had my own room, which was the only place in the house I was allowed to smoke. There was a door in my room that led to three other options. Go to the left, and it was the basement stairs, straight, and there was a door to the kitchen, and right was a door to the outside. Who the fuck, with any common sense, would give a kid, a teenager, a bedroom with a door to the outside?

Kyle got back from boot camp and took the train to see me twice before being sent away again. Both times he complained about my weight, and he gave me two different diet plans, complete with workouts. He also forced himself on me, in me, several times during each visit. I held my breath and tears each time as he grunted away until he finished. Each time, I bled. If I had to describe the physical sensation of having sex with Kyle, it would be simple. Imagine inserting a baseball bat covered in razor blades and then pouring rubbing alcohol into your vagina. Along with the forced sex, he still hit me, belittled me, he continued to blame me for his father disowning him and his fictitious addictions. He left a bottle of booze and a carton of cigarettes every time he left. Why did I stay with him? I have searched my heart for the answer to that question for years. It came down to two things, I didn't want to hurt him, and I deserved it.

I was determined to do well in school that year. If I could just focus on having one life, I could pull it off. Delilah gave me an allowance of seven dollars a week. For this money, I needed to feed her fourteen cats, clean their litter box daily, feed the two dogs, and let the dogs out twice a day. I discovered quickly that she didn't provide basic hygiene items, including shampoo, tampons, body wash, or conditioner. There wasn't any edible food because I wasn't allowed to cook. I asked Delilah how I was supposed to afford the items she would not provide for seven dollars a week. She looked me up and down, her eyes landing on my chest, and said, "I'm sure you'll figure something out. I got a job instead. I rode my old black and purple mountain bike to and from work the last few weeks of summer. Once school started, I would ride that bike to Theresa's every morning, get a ride the last half a mile to school, and then reverse it in the afternoon. I rode twelve to twenty miles a day. I didn't look for trouble, but it found me. On my third night at work, Keith came in for a pick-up order. I had been mostly sober, completely sober, when I was in the group home. I had drank a lot when I ran away, and I had used crack and coke more times than I care to admit, but I hadn't touched heroin. The truth? I don't think I

182

had been completely sober since I was eleven years old, except when I was in that group home.

When I went to leave work, I found Keith waiting by my bike. He gave me the classic "Hey stranger, haven't seen you in a while." I smiled and told him, "Yeah, I disappeared. It is what I do. You don't really see me now either." He was faster than me and grabbed my arm before I could ride off; his grip was strong enough to jerk me back and bruise me. "I got what you need, though, babe. It's free." He shook his hand, and the white rocks danced like dice. We all have our weaknesses.

This became an after-work activity. I want to clarify I never knowingly and consensually had sexual intercourse for drugs. I do not mean that in the way that Bill Clinton never had sexual relations with that woman. I have put enough in these pages that I am brutally honest about others and myself; I have no reason to start lying now. Hand jobs and blow jobs were different; I was one hundred percent willing to do those things for a high. Before long, I had to perform these "favors" for Keith's friends as well. I was using it often enough that when Keith didn't come to me, I went looking. I would bring groups of seven or eight guys back to Delilah's house. She worked all day, cooked and ate dinner at home, and then went to her boyfriend's until six am, when she would come back and get ready for work. She rarely poked her head into my room, but I made sure everyone was gone before she got there, just in case. I knew I could only hide one person under my bed.

By mid-September, I was spiraling again. Juggling school, homework, a part-time job, friends, and drug addiction was difficult. I awoke one morning with the first cracks of sunlight on my face. The guys were gone. There was coke, straws, rolled dollar bills, baggies, foil, and empty bottles everywhere. On top of that, my pants were open, and my shirt was gone. I almost tripped on an empty Vodka bottle when I got up; my whole body hurt. I made my way to the full-length mirror that came with the room, and I hated it. This was new; there was a sock tied around my arm and a needle hanging out of my vein. I knew at that moment that I was done. I

183

cleaned my room and showered before Delilah got home. On my way to Theresa's house, I got rid of all the drugs and alcohol in a dumpster behind the store Bianca worked for.

My morning classes were not even over yet, and I felt like I was going to die. I walked out of class, which no one questioned, and went to Mr. Bloom's class. He wasn't my teacher anymore, but in my heart, he was my friend. "Simone! Nice to see you!" His booming voice greeted me before I was even through the doorway. I pointed at his trash can, and he met me with it not a moment too soon. He said nothing to me; he told his class what pages to work on and went to his supply closet. Mr. Bloom walked me to his window, helped me lay down, covered me with a blanket, pointed his fan at me, and brought the trash can. He patted my shoulder and went back to his class, "Class! This is a former student. She isn't feeling well. She is going to be here for the next few days. Act like she isn't there." His lesson proceeded; he had a deep, loud voice. It was agonizingly painful any time he spoke; a kid coughed, laughed, a chair scraped against the floor, and the bells. Whoever decided there should be loud bells in school is a criminal. When the school day ended, Mr. Bloom told me, "See you when you get here in the morning. Good job today."

I was grateful when I got back to Delilah's that I only worked part-time and was off the next several days. I locked the back door and the back door to my room and got in bed. I spent the night having hot and cold flashes simultaneously, running for the bathroom and ignoring the few taps I heard at the back door. I left for Theresa's extra early and was halfway there when I realized my shirt was covered in puke. I went back, showered, and left again, stopping to get sick several times. Theresa's dad, Sidney, offered to just take me home because I looked so bad.

Mr. Bloom wasn't waiting for me when I got there; I just went to his classroom. He was working at his desk; I walked past him without a word and curled up in my window bed that was still there. Thankfully the trash had been emptied. This is how I spent the rest of the school week. At least by then, the bathroom runs had mostly stopped, and the hot/cold flashes had decreased. It was the weekend, my body hurt, and I knew how to make it stop. I laid in bed staring at the door that led to the outside. I wanted to go out that door, I wanted to find drugs, and I didn't care what kind. My eyes fell on the mirror.

I always hated mirrors. I thought they were creepy when I was a kid. As I got older, by around ten, I understood I was ugly, throwing in my weight and crooked teeth, and I avoided mirrors as much as possible. I stood on legs that wobbled like Jell-o, my feet felt like they were covered in glass, and the bones in my legs felt like they were made of toothpicks. I made my way slowly to the mirror. I saw myself the way I had the morning I knew I was done; I stepped back and saw myself in reality. I looked hard at every feature, at everything I loathed. I saw that, somehow, my pants were falling; I lifted them, and they fell. I ran to the bathroom and stepped on the scale. I had lost thirty pounds in around six weeks. A fat girl like me should have been happy about it, but not the way it happened. I went back and looked in the mirror one more time, and I saw Mary. I got back in bed and looked at the wall. The knocks had stopped when Delilah's grown son had gone out and yelled, "She got taken away and put somewhere else. Stop knocking and don't come back." He went passed my door to the bathroom, and I yelled thank you, he yelled no problem; that was the longest conversation I ever had with him; I wish I could tell you that I never did drugs again. That would be a lie. It was, though, the last time I did heroin.

I kept my head down and did nothing to call attention to the fact that I was still around. I applied for various internships. They were mostly in both news and Tv journalism. It didn't matter if all I did was get people coffee. I needed to do something that I enjoyed. I needed to be something more than the complete fucking disaster that I had turned into.

Friends and Relationships

I was with Dierdre and Theresa a lot; we were like sisters. They were both straight-edge, which is what I needed to surround myself with. I was sticking to weed and cigarettes until the night of the Pink Floyd laser light show. The three of us and their friend Phil were going together. I knew Phil, but we weren't close enough to call him a friend. He knew there had been rumors about me being involved in drugs and asked me to hook him up with some acid before the show. I set it up, and he shared. Theresa knew immediately that we were on something and wasn't amused. She was anti-everything. She lectured me but had no words or anger for Phil. It was all my fault; I was the bad one. I always needed to disappoint someone. I never did acid again.

The fall weather was in full swing, and Dierdre wanted to go to the carnival. She invited me to go with her, and it sounded trouble-free; how much trouble could I really get into at a carnival? We both met guys, I hooked up with Gene, and she hooked up with Egon. Egon was a tall goofy white kid; Gene was a sexy Dominican man. Dierdre was eighteen and a virgin, which I had nothing but respect for. When the carnival ended for the night, the four of us went to her car to make out. Gene and I got the back seat. Things were going faster and further than I wanted, and I tried slowing him down when his hand started to slide down my pants. He was pushy, and after a while, I just stopped resisting. It wasn't like I was going to be able to fuck him in the back of her tiny car. Well, I would, but I could always use the excuse that Dierdre and Egon were there to get out of it.

I was topless in the back seat, with his hand in my pants and his dick in my hand, when Dierdre poked me in the leg and asked, "Do you have any condoms?" I didn't, and neither did Gene, but I had some at Delilah's. I shouldn't have said that aloud. Dierdre knew how easy it was to sneak in and out of that house, so the four of us wound up in my room, piled into my twin-sized bed.

As things were progressing to a level, I was uncomfortable with, for both myself and Dierdre, I jumped up and said I was going to get a drink. I was hoping Dierdre would have followed me; I didn't want her first time to be with some random asshole she had just met. There was no reason to throw away the time she had waited; she wanted it to be with someone she cared about and was in a relationship with. She wasn't going to have that with Egon. She didn't take the hint and stayed in my room.

Gene met me by my bedroom door and started kissing me again. His hand went up my shirt, and I told him we needed to go back to my room. Delilah wasn't there, but either of her adult kids could come up to use the only bathroom at any time. "You don't want to go in there. They are busy and asked me to get out." Gene told me while pulling my shirt up. I cracked the door open and saw they were all over each other, and the condoms were out on the bed. "Shit," I muttered as I closed the door. Gene held up a condom, "I snagged one for us," he said with a smile as he led me to the bathroom.

Before the door was even closed, his pants were down. "Gene, you seem like a nice guy," I told him with a smile. "I am, baby, you will see. I want to be with you. I think you're one." I rolled my eyes, I am sure a lot of girls fall for that line, but I am not one of them. "Gene, I have a boyfriend. His name is Kyle, and he is in the army," I had been meaning to dump Kyle, but it was hard when we never talked. Call me old fashioned, but I always believed things like that should be done in person, and at that time, the only way we had to communicate was through letters. Gene stopped kissing me and pinched my nipple hard. "So, you just slutting around with me then? Playing until your boyfriend gets back?" I tried to push his hand away, but that made him pinch harder, which turned into pinching while pulling. "Gene, stop! That fucking hurts!" I screeched at him. He slammed his hand over my mouth and pushed me backward, "Shut up. You wanted to play, so we can play." His hard, forced kiss replaced his hand as he raised me onto the sink. Both hands went to the crotch of my pants, and I felt them tear open in my soul. With one quick thrust, he accomplished his mission, and in five more, he was done. "You were a great, babe. That was fucking amazing," he said as he pulled up his pants. I pulled my shirt down and tried to straighten my ripped pants. Deirdre and Egon were coming out of my room as we were coming out of the bathroom. "Hey, Egon needs to go, and it is four, so I'll drive them back and see you tomorrow." Gene kissed me and told me he hoped to see me again. This happened in 1996, and it took me until 2022 to realize there was no way Dierdre didn't hear my screams.

I showered in burning hot water. No matter how much I showered, I was never clean. I got in bed wearing my huge pale pink Baja sweatshirt and stared at the door that could take me away to a world where I didn't have to feel. I curled my body into my Baja; it could have fit two of me. I wanted to live inside of it forever. I let go and cried loudly. The voice came from inside me, but it was Griffith's, "Shut up, you little bitch, only the weak cry." I was gripped by a panic so hard that it dried my tears and stopped the blood in my veins from flowing at once. I don't know how long I stared at the wall wide-eyed in terror before sleep took me in its evil nightmare-filled grip.

I woke up in the late morning to the phone ringing; it was Theresa. "Bitch get dressed. I am picking you up. You are spending the day with Ray and me." I liked her and her boyfriend, Ray, but I didn't want to go anywhere. When they got there, I was outside smoking. My Baja covered me from my knees to the top of my head, including my face. The three of us went to her basement room when we got back to her house. I curled up on the love seat and continued to hide and not speak. They knew something was wrong and tried throughout the day to get me to talk. Theresa had gone upstairs to the bathroom, and Ray sat next to me, rubbing my back. His voice was comforting as he told me over and over that, I could tell them anything. "I got fucked last night, and I really didn't want to. I fucking said no." Ray rubbed my back until Theresa came back; I heard him whisper to her, "I think she was raped," he said with gentle concern. Her response was simple and killed me more than the sex had, "Again?!" The two of them came and sat with me; we talked as I hid in my hood. She tried to show compassion and sympathy, but her true feelings were what came through my darkening cloud. "How do you get yourself into these situations? This happens because of the situations you put yourself in."There was a bad storm, and the power had gone out. I heard them fucking around, and he whispered, "We can't. Simone needs us-" she interrupted her whispered response, "She'll be okay. It's dark, and she will never know." Then I heard them fucking. I thought they were done when I walked up the stairs to leave. Theresa's mom, Marie, stopped me, "Simone, where are you going? The storm is bad." My face was still covered; I told her I wasn't feeling well and was leaving. "You aren't walking. It's ten miles. Sidney, get Theresa and Ray, then drive Simone home." I attempted to protest, and she didn't have it.

Sidney yelled downstairs for the two of them to come upstairs so they could take me home, which was good because it turned out they were not done. Theresa sat in the front with her dad, who had really been a dad to all her friends too. She gave me nasty looks the whole way, which took longer than it should have. There were trees and power lines that had been knocked down, roads were flooded, and Sidney had to stop and get cigarettes. Ray slid closer to me and held me during the ride. When we pulled up at Delilah's house, Ray got out and walked me to the door; Theresa had protested, "I'm sure she can get to the door herself," but he ignored her. We got to the door, and he saw my face for the first time that day, "Simone, you know it is okay to cry, right? If you want to go to the cops, I will go with you. Theresa would, too." I looked into his eyes and saw that he hurt for me. It wasn't pity; it was pain. He hugged me tight and left.

In my room that night, with the door closed and the light off, curled in my Baja, I tried to cry. There was nothing. I felt pain, but I felt nothing. I dreamt that night. I dreamt of Griffith. I dreamt of a childhood that I barely remembered and was better off forgetting. My brain was putting more pieces together, and I didn't like it. My dreams showed me his hands covering my mouth at four, five, and six years old. They showed me his enormous body, crushing my tiny one. I saw and felt his hand stroking my back as he growled, "Shut up, little bitch, only the weak cry." I saw the months and weeks

189

before I told the first time. I woke up startled at the daylight and the sound of the phone ringing. It was Dierdre; she wanted me to go with her to pick up "The guys" and then meet up with Theresa and Ray. I told her I decided I didn't like Gene and didn't want to see him. She said that was fine; we would just pick up Egon. I was relieved to find out she hadn't had sex with him and agreed to go with her to pick him up.

We sat and waited for Egon; I brought condoms for her, just in case, but told her not to; he wasn't going to be a boyfriend. Egon appeared, walking toward the car...with Gene. That's when Dierdre confessed that she hadn't had a way to call him back and let him know Gene wasn't invited. She got out and pulled Egon away to tell him, but he said, "If Gene doesn't go, neither do I," and they both got in. Theresa was right; I always got myself into these situations. The four of us got to our destination, The Club, where we all hung out. Theresa and Ray were already there. Alcohol was served but not to kids, and the staff did know how old I was. I slipped a guy money for some drinks, and he was happy to oblige. I blew Gene off.

Theresa and Dierdre both kept telling me how much Gene really liked me and that I should just give him a chance. I hadn't told Theresa that it had been him, there was no reason to, and Dierdre, I believed knew nothing. I flirted with every guy there, I smoked, I snuck drinks, but every time I turned around, Gene was there, I told him I didn't want to talk to him and to fuck off, but he wouldn't go away.

I escaped to the bathroom, but when I came out, he was there blocking the hallway. "Get the fuck out of my way. I will scream." I told him with certainty that I would, in fact, scream. "Look, babe, I just want to talk. I want to apologize for the other night." What had I just heard? A guy, a man, a human in possession of a penis, wanted to admit and acknowledge wrongdoing? This made my anger and my certainty waver. "Can we just go outside? I want to explain, and I want to apologize properly." He had backed up, and we were in full view of everyone at The Club. Theresa and Dierdre had pulled me away and told me again to just talk to him because "He's a really nice guy." Gene came back over to me after he knew they had talked to me, "It is really loud in here; I just want to go somewhere and talk." There it was, and at the moment, I didn't hear it. "Go somewhere."

I went outside with him; we walked as we talked; I am not capable of staying still and talking. Or staying still and thinking, I pace, I walk, even now. We walked down the highway a little as he told me, "You are such a good kisser; I couldn't stop." Gene stopped walking when we were by the small grassy hill. I stopped with him and continued to listen, "I lost it when I thought you were just using me to play with." Gene said as he sat in the grass; I sat as well. "You are just so beautiful; I couldn't help myself," Gene said as his hand touched my thigh. "When a guy gets that worked up, we can't just stop." All I heard through all his words were, "It is all your fault."

Gene started to kiss my neck, then slid his hand down my chest. I pulled away, and he pulled me back and shoved me onto the ground. His kiss was hard against my lips, and his grip on my arms was fierce. He straddled me and pinned my shoulders to the ground. "See, babe, you can't just get guys all worked up like this; pull your pants down." I tried to get away instead, but he pushed me harder, and his grip got tighter, "Your way or mine," he told me. I did as I was told. His head hung over my shoulder; he held my hands without trouble the whole time. He lasted longer than he had the first time. I tried to hold in tears, but I couldn't. I turned my head, my face buried by the long grass, and cried. There was no way he didn't know. When he was done, we pulled our pants up, I dried my tears, and he tried to kiss me. I punched him in the face and told him, "If you ever talk to me again or touch me again, I will fucking kill you," through clenched teeth. I went back to The Club and told no one. There was no point; it was my fault; I put myself in that position and got what I deserved.

The carnival moved, and Deirdre wanted to go, and Theresa wanted to also; I joined them because it was expected of me to go. I was filled with anger and vengeance. The carnival's new spot was

Griffith's old town, where I was once jailbait. I had heard Griffith moved, but just being there fueled my rage. The three of us walked the lot, me in front. I wore all black, make-up and hair done, my shirt low, and I took in all the attention. I flirted with every guy in Gene's field of vision. When I walked past him, he looked, but he didn't speak. That was good for him because I really do think I would have killed him.

My eyes met with a cute guy; I saw his lust at once as I pushed my hair back and acted uninterested. "Hey! Hey! You want to play?" The guy asked. "Nope, I never win anyway, and I'm broke." He started up a conversation as my friends waited. "Are you dating Gene?" He suddenly asked. I laughed and told him no; Gene was an asshole who didn't know how to keep his hands to himself. "If you aren't dating him, are you dating anyone else here? Cause you are cute." I didn't lie, he asked if I was dating anyone there, and Kyle wasn't there, so I told him I wasn't. He asked me to meet him in half an hour. I did, and he gave me a big stuffed dog. He said he bought it from his boss, told me his name was Jake, and asked for my number. Jake called the next day; he told me it was the last carnival of the season and wanted me to come back and see him. I went back and found out he had set Gene up for stealing; Gene had been fired, and Egon left with him. I was later questioned by Jake's boss Kenny about the stuffed dog he had given me. Kenny said Jake had stolen it, not bought it, Kenny told Jake he had to pay for it, and the situation was resolved.

I asked Jake how old he was; he was twenty-four. He told me he wasn't into kids, and it was eighteen and up for him. I leaned against a pole and said, "Oh? Well, I'm seventeen." His eyes scanned me up and down, "Okay, seventeen and up then." I found out that night that I had a new reputation, which came with the name lot lizard. It is the same for carnival lots as it is for trucker lots. It is a girl who hangs around and fucks different guys at every spot. I heard about it from Gary, who ran the bumper cars. Gary had heard it from Gene before he was fired. Gene had told Gary I "wanted it rough and couldn't handle it once I got it." The fire inside of me ignited, and I stormed off the lot.

Theresa and Diedre followed me. I walked in the direction of Harry's house. I walked in the middle of the road between the cars. I screamed and yelled. I flirted with danger and death until I was in front of that house. I stared at the house with its dark windows and secrets. I took in its ominous presence. My eyes moved to Griffith's old window; I jumped back, startled as I saw the ghost of myself looking down; a ghost of Griffith was there, too, standing behind mine. I looked toward Brad and Drew's room. I saw the ghosts of Brad and me dancing to our music, one of me sitting by the window with a candle, the two of us sharing our secret love on his floor, and the ghost of me in Drew's bed. My eyes fell to the lower windows, and I saw my dead self everywhere. I saw the pieces of my soul that had been ripped out and continued to be tortured. The pieces I had left behind.

I told Theresa and Dierdre to wait there, that I had left something in the barn that I needed. I knew how to get in and out of the yard better than anyone. I didn't know if anyone lived there besides Harry, and I didn't care. I knew I had stashed a bottle of Jack in there, and I felt it would still be there. The ghost eyes, mostly mine, followed me through the yard, and more appeared. There I was in a cage in the yard; there I was in a ghost truck and car. I made my way to the barn, and after some digging, I found what was mine. A beautiful, unopened bottle of my best friend. I turned and almost ran directly into a ghost of Mary, showing me her track marks with a smile. I opened the bottle and drank, feeling the warmth take control. It gave me more strength, more power, and more rage. "Fuck you, you stupid bitch," I said to both myself and Mary's ghost. She was gone. I went back to my friends, and as we were leaving, I looked toward Griffith's window again. I looked at that girl, the one who was the deadest. I spilled half a shot of Jack in the yard and thought, "This is for you, kid," as I walked away. I went to Richie's, knocked three times, heard him ask, "Who is it?" and knocked twice. Richie saw me on the other side of that door, and his huge arms enveloped me in a giant stinky bear hug. We were invited in and sat at his table, I knew he was uncomfortable with my friends there, but I also knew we weren't staying long. "What have you heard?" I asked, knowing he couldn't lie to me. "Griffith said right after he moved out that he couldn't do a job with me for a week because he had court." I drank. "I asked him what he had court for, and he said traffic tickets. I didn't say anything, but I thought, yeah, more like for fucking your daughter." Richie offered us beers; my friends declined, and I didn't. "See, Richie, I told you, you believed me." I drank and smiled; Richie laughed nervously. He offered me a place to crash; he made sure I knew I could stay as long as I needed and that no one would look for me there. I did decline those offers, and my friends and I left. I never saw Richie or that house again.

By the time we got back to the carnival, I was drunk. Jake said he would call me that night, he did and when we were getting off the phone he said, "I love you," I responded, "I love you, too." I didn't love him, but what did it matter? It was just words and words meant nothing. We made plans to meet the next night at closing in front of the Ferris Wheel. He was helping take the wheel down when I got there, but he saw me. That man could see me a million miles away. Jake climbed down, told me he loved me and kissed me. There were no butterflies, but there was a tingle. I didn't love him, but I did like him.

When the carnival went to close for the year, Jake stayed behind. Dierdre and Theresa took me to see him, and he wanted me to go with him to his mom's. He said she lived near Poughkeepsie. I didn't know him well enough. I felt responsible for him, though. He had stayed there because of me, to be with me. My friends didn't like him and wouldn't leave me there with him. I took him back to Delilah's. If she came and checked on me in the morning, he would fit under my bed.

Jake and I stayed up all night; we had sex all night. Jake explored every part of me with every part of him. Thankfully, Jake didn't bite things that shouldn't be bitten. He seemed to care if I enjoyed it, so I faked it...a lot. Jake was my first consensual experience since Drew. If Drew even counted as consensual. I hadn't always said no, but he definitely took advantage of the situation I was in, and there was a lot of manipulation. There was pressure and force toward the end of our sexual relationship, but I had initially seen the earlier part

194

as willing. As I have grown older, I think he was just as much of a predator as Griffith was.

Jake had just slid under my bed when Delilah came into my room, "I'll drive you to school today; it's too cold." She had never offered me a ride anywhere. Jake and I snuck into the bathroom and showered together. I told Delilah I had a ride; Theresa's dad had paid for a taxi. Jake had called the taxi while Delilah was in the shower. I tried to get Jake a day pass so he could stay at school with me. They wouldn't allow it because I didn't have a parent or guardian note stating that he was a relative. I told him what time I had lunch and that I would meet him outside. I was surprised when I went to meet him, and he was there; I hadn't realized until writing this that a part of me had been hoping he would have left.

After I was done with school, we went back to Delilah's. I had been up on adrenaline for two days. It had been a lot easier with coke. Jake said he would leave so I could get some sleep and went out the back door. He was supposed to come back after dark. I had a lit cigarette in my hand, over an ashtray that was on my stomach, when Delilah came in and told me some guy was in the back yard looking for me. She said it was the same guy I had left with in the taxi that morning. I had just dozed off. It hadn't even been a half an hour. I needed to sleep. I smoked and tried to lay back down. I heard Delilah, and her grown kids talking about me at the table. Her son didn't like my music, her daughter didn't like that I showered so much, she didn't like that I would not eat her cooking, or my clothes, I was too big to be wearing what I did...Bianca bought my clothes, and everything fit or was too big. Delilah got a clothing allowance for me, but she used it to buy clothes for her grown kids.

I got up, smoked a cigarette, and packed a bag. A few changes of clothes, my walk man, and a couple of tapes, and I was done. I was so tired. I was tired of everyone and tired of running. I would never be good enough for anyone, and nothing I did would ever be right. I finished my cigarette and smoked another. They were still talking about me. Delilah's boyfriend was the only one who had anything nice to say. He had never seen a foster kid do homework before or get all A's. I hadn't been good enough for my own family; of course, these strangers who were paid to take me would not accept me either. I grabbed my stuff and walked out to where they were eating. "I am not coming back," I said to no one in particular. Only Delilah responded, "Good." It was time to go again. Time to run.

Just Disappear

Jake wasn't in the yard, so I walked to the train station. He had been talking about taking the train to his mom's all day. I couldn't find him. I had no backup plan. I started to panic, which led to crying. People tried to help. I told a woman I was running away from foster care, and I couldn't find my boyfriend. She tried to take me back to the foster home, but I couldn't go back there. She kept saying she would take me "home", but I didn't have one; I hadn't in three years. Then there he was. Jake came from nowhere at all. I ran to him, and he caught me as I hugged him. He already had two tickets. There was nothing Jake and I would not do. That included various sexual acts on the train. There was fondling, feeling, a blow job, a sixty-nine, and just a good old-fashioned fuck. Public sex was a thrill, just like doing anything forbidden or frowned upon was. It was an addiction and self-destructive at the same time. In between sex acts, Jake told me about his family. He had two sisters, Carissa and Sharon. Carissa had a four-year-old son. Sharon had a two-year-old son. Jake said he didn't really like either of them but that Sharon was crazy. They rented a four-bedroom house. His mother was Helen; she lived in an apartment next to his sisters, she was a corrections officer, and Jake had a warrant for his arrest. He didn't know if she would let us stay or for how long, but she had money and would help us.

It was very late when we got to Helen's. She told Jake right away that he could only stay a few days. She didn't pay attention to my presence and told us there were towels in the bathroom and food in the fridge. We had a bedroom, but there was no bed. At least there was a roof; I had slept in far worse places. We had sex for the next three days. We ran out of the bedroom wrapped in sheets to get in the shower, where we didn't get clean, he sprinted naked to the kitchen for drinks, or we stumbled aimlessly to the bathroom to pee, and that was it. The sex wasn't bad, but the female orgasm was still a myth to me.

On the fourth day, we got dressed, and Jake asked Helen for money. She gave him enough for milk and cigarettes but told him I

197

had to stay. After he left, I headed for the bedroom, but Helen stopped me, "Nope. Sit." I did. "How old are you? How much do you know about Jake?" I lied about my age like Jake had told me to and told her I was twenty-one. "You aren't twenty-one. Please tell me you are at least eighteen. What has Jake told you? Has he told you I am a corrections officer? Has he told you he has an arrest warrant? Has he told you that the warrant is because he stole my credit cards, ran up over ten thousand dollars in debt, and stole my car?" The only reply I had was, "I am twenty-one." Jake was taking too long; if I had known where I was at all, I would have just walked away. I didn't worry about money. I knew hitchhiking was a valid option as long as I knew where I was and which direction to go. I wanted to be near Poughkeepsie. It was where Brad had moved to Griffith's from, and maybe he was there. Maybe we could find each other. Not so we could be together, but so I wouldn't be so alone. So I could be safe again.

Helen grilled me some more. Nothing she said phased me, and she saw that. "Okay, you answer my questions honestly, and I will tell you something about Jake that I am sure he didn't tell you. Deal?" I nodded, this could be fun, but I already knew her first question. "How old are you?" A deal is a deal. "Seventeen," she sighed, "That isn't too bad; please tell me it is almost your birthday?" I didn't answer. "Oh, I forgot it is my turn. Did Jake tell you he has a drug problem?" The big fat NO was written on my face. "When is your birthday?" She asked again. "July," it was only late October, and she cringed. "He is addicted to crack. He will do just about anything, but he is a crackhead." The apartment door opened.

Helen commanded Jake to sit, "She is seventeen, Jake. Barely seventeen. Her parents will be looking for her. Has either of you called your parents to let them know you are okay? Or where are you? One of you better answer." I was better under pressure than Jake was, or he was scared of his mom because he told her everything. Yes, he knew I was barely seventeen. I didn't have parents, my mom didn't have custody, I was a runaway from foster care, and no, we hadn't called anyone. She ordered that I call someone and let them know I was safe. I called Bianca. I told her I was in upstate New York with my boyfriend, and everything was fine. Helen wasn't happy that she had Jake there with a warrant and now a runaway from foster care. I wasn't happy that I had committed the ultimate human mistake; I didn't see his addiction because I didn't want to. The coke use was now pretty clear; I knew he hadn't done crack around me; I would have smelled it.

The next day we took the bus to the mall. On the way there, I asked him about his addiction. He half admitted it; he said he liked drugs, especially crack, but he wasn't addicted. I knew that line; I had used it myself. I was honest with him, "Jake, I haven't been clean long. I can't be around it. It's drugs or me. Let me know now because I can hitchhike back and find a place to crash." There was no hesitation, "You." It was a lie, and we both knew it.

We walked the streets of Poughkeepsie; he ran into a friend, and they shook hands. It was no ordinary handshake. A block away, Jake opened the foil, "Fuck, it's powder. That isn't what I wanted," he licked it and tossed it on the ground, where I picked it up. Street rules applied; Jake insisted that I walk on the inside; if I had been closer to the road, it would have meant he was selling me. I didn't give a shit, but I used street rules to my advantage. I stayed on the inside, and two steps beside him, walking and snorting the coke he had thrown away. It was the last time I did coke.

We went to an adult store where the owner wouldn't let me in the back with him. He had been fined for having prostitutes in the back room. Jake explained, "She isn't a whore; she's my girl." It didn't matter; I waited outside until he was done. Jake came out upset. I didn't ask why; I didn't care. Jake was starting to feel like background noise. He told me that the owner had threatened him, Jake was told he needed to be back there at 8 pm and give him a blow job, or he would be killed. The solution seemed simple to me; we just wouldn't be around. It wouldn't be hard to be back at his mom's place by then. It was still early.

We walked all day. Sometimes something would look familiar, but not enough that I could place whether or not we had already been there. It was dark and getting cold; we walked on. I didn't think about it then, but Jake was very careful to walk me underneath all of the store signs. We had really just been walking in many different circles. "Okay, a friend in here owes me money. I'll be back out in twenty or thirty minutes. Just wait here, okay?" I sat on the side walk against the building, waiting. A woman came out of the neighboring store and was locking up. "Do you need help? Are you homeless? I can take you to the shelter." She had kind eyes and a soothing voice. "No, I'm just waiting for my boyfriend," I nodded toward the door he had gone into. "Your boyfriend is in the sex shop?" She asked with a raised eyebrow. I stood and walked to the road, looking at the sign above the store.

Jake emerged from the sex shop laughing. He tried to hold my hand, and I snatched it away from him. "I can't hold my girls' hand?" He pouted, "No," I replied angrily. "Why not?" He looked sad. "Because I don't know where your hand has been." He tried to kiss me, and I shoved him. "Why can't I kiss you?" Jake asked. "Because mother fucker, I don't know where the fuck your mouth has been either." We got on the train headed for Helen's; he was pouty and angry. "What the fuck, right do you have to be pissed? You are the one who just sucked some guy's dick! "I wasn't quiet. "Yeah, okay, I sucked some guy's dick to get us money to get back to my mom's house. We would have been stuck on the streets, and I didn't want you to have to go through that. It was the only way I could get us back. I did it for you, and you're mad at me." I stared at my reflection in the train window. I saw one tear trickle down my cheek and swiped it away with annoyance. It was my fault; everything in the fucking world was my fault. I was hurt; maybe Jake was more than just background noise. By the time we got back to Helen's, I had allowed him to hold my hand. The next day we were back in Poughkeepsie. We went to one of his friends' apartments, whereas the only girl, I, was given the only chair. The group of them sat around, marveling at how much crack they had. I sat and watched them, angry, fascinated, disgusted, needing. "Hey, Jake?" He came and knelt beside me, "That promise you made me yesterday? Forget it." I took it from his hands, lit and inhaled the sweet taste of self-loathing.

We were leaving the crack house when something happened. Something was wrong. I couldn't breathe, and my heart was beating so fast, in the wrong spot. My heartbeat was in my throat and my head; it was everywhere except where it was supposed to be. I felt my eyes roll in my head, and my body fell back; I got out one word, "Hospital." Jake carried me out into the cool air and kept trying to make me walk. My heart would not return to normal, I couldn't speak, my eyes kept rolling in my head, and my knees kept giving out. Then I was falling, someone was catching me, and I was floating. Flying.

I woke up several times in an old house. There were homeless people everywhere. "Shhh, sleep," a woman said as I was covered with a blanket. Each time I awoke, I felt a little better. Sometimes, it was daylight; at others, there was darkness. When I was able to sit up and speak, I asked the room, "How long have I been here?" The same woman replied, "Three days. He left you here, you know. He does come back and check on you once a day, but he did leave you. You can stay. If you want." Mother fucking asshole left me to die where I would never be found. Rage again filled my soul, and as it burned, I felt another piece of me die.

When Jake came back, I left with him; several of the people in the house told me not to go with him, but I didn't listen. I wasn't sure if I was going with him to stay or just to tell him my opinion of him and what he did. As we got to the street, I started yelling at him, "You left me to fucking die. Alone. Fuck you. Fire shot from my eyes, "I didn't leave you alone; I left you with them. I couldn't take you to the hospital. I have a warrant; You think I should have gotten arrested?" I thought he should have been hit by a fucking truck, honestly. Jake and I talked and yelled back and forth, not caring who had heard us. The road was for foot traffic, even though it was wide enough for cars. It was surrounded by apartment buildings, A window popped open above us, and a guy in drag yelled down, "Don't listen to him, honey! He is no good!" More windows popped open along the street, with more voices saying the same thing; most of them also yelled offers for me to stay with them, and they would take care of me. When I look back on this memory, I see my soul leaving my body and running to them, just like it had when I was eleven at my school. But I walked on with Jake. Now I can tell you honestly; I have not smoked crack since then. Jake and I missed the last train back to Helen's; he took me to his friend Wayne's. Wayne was a very large, soft-spoken chef. He made us dinner and gave us his guest room for the night. As usual, we had sex all night; a few times, I caught Wayne watching through the cracked doorway. In the morning, Wayne said there were towels in the bathroom and asked to talk to Jake while I showered. There were fresh homemade waffles for breakfast. It wasn't until after we left that Jake told me Wayne's feelings were hurt. "You know he was watching us last night, right?" I smiled and nodded; I enjoyed being watched. "Wayne is gay. He used to pay me for sex. I was a male prostitute. He fell in love with me. I didn't like it; I just did it for the money." There were no words in 1996, and there are none now.

We stayed at Wayne's one more time. This time there was no dinner, but the invitation to make ourselves sandwiches if we wanted to. I saw and felt him watching us again; only I felt hurt in his heart. It killed the thrill for me. In the morning, we were ordered to shower alone and offered cereal for breakfast. Jake told me on our way to the train Wayne said he was welcome back anytime, but I wasn't. He told Jake it hurt too much to see him with someone else. I understood. That night Jake got us matching rings and asked me to marry him. I said yes, I guess I would need to get around to breaking up with Kyle.

Another day walking the streets of Poughkeepsie, the place was pretty to drive through. Or even walk through. If you looked too close, though, moved too slow, or paused after dark, you could see the sinister things that hid there. Jake waived to a friend who was passing, the friend stopped, and they had a quiet conversation. Jake ran back to me and told me his friend Jeff needed help moving some things. I didn't have time to respond. "Go to the diner across the street. Get a hot chocolate. I'll be back in an hour." He put two dollars in quarters in my hand and was gone before I could say a word. I waited there for him, in front of the sex shop, for two hours. The same woman at the neighboring store saw and talked to me. She bought me lunch and offered to help. I just sat. It was dark when I walked to the payphone on the highway; I called a crisis line in the city. I had called them many times before. I explained that my boyfriend had left me on the side of the road hours earlier, that sometimes I said no to sex, and he didn't listen, the drugs and how he had left me, everything. They told me it was abuse, and I clarified that he hadn't hit me, so he wasn't abusive. The call center operator said if I gave my location, they would come to get me, and I would have a warm, safe place to stay. Several times I thought about walking out into the highway in front of a truck. I knew I would feel pain for a second, and then everything would be over. I couldn't bring myself to do it. The nine-line operator almost convinced me Jake's behavior was abusive, and I was about to give my location. But Jake appeared in front of me like magic. "I have to go; my boyfriend is here. I'll talk to you when I can, Mom; love you, bye." We slept on the streets that night. He had left with Jeff at about noon, it was after eleven o'clock, and we had missed the last train.

We were at Helen's for three weeks. She shipped us off to Florida on a Greyhound. Carnivals ran year-round there, and Jake knew he could get work. More often than not, on the bus, I sat in his lap, and we 'talked about the first thing that popped up.' We arrived in Miami, where Jake got his coat stolen in a drug deal. We got to Daytona Beach, where I saw the clearest water ever. Some guy offered us a ride and cash if we went to a timeshare meeting and pretended to be interested. We were convincing enough that he drove us to Jake's grandmother's house and gave us fifty dollars.

Agnes lived in a condominium village with all elderly people. Her condo was three bedrooms, so we had our own room and bathroom. There was a community pool that was never used; the elderly people said it was too cold. We had more non-stop sex. In our room, the pool, the pool bathroom, his grandmothers' entire condo when she went out, her car, wherever and whenever he wanted. If I told him no, he did it anyway or nagged me until I said fine, just do it.

After two weeks, Agnes was done. She dropped us off at a carnival with a "good luck." Jake had experience and got work right away, he got paid daily, and the first thing he bought was a pregnancy test. It was positive, he was elated, and I wasn't. It took me a few days to find work. Thanksgiving there was depressing; it was too warm for a late fall holiday. I started bleeding badly, and we went to the hospital. It was triplets, and I lost all three; I was both devastated and relieved. Jake continued using crack and lying about it; I got pregnant again; it was twins, and I lost them both.

We lived underneath the super slide, which is called the possum belly. It was dry, which was all that mattered to me. There was another couple that lived under there with us. We divided the space in two with a sheet. They had sex almost as much as we did. They approached us and asked to partner swap, but we said no. Their next offer was group sex, no swapping, just openly having sex with no divider. That we agreed to, Jake and I were definitely both cool with being watched. The other couple split up because the guy said he was in love with me.

We moved on to another carnival where we had a bunk room. They aren't big, but a roof, heat, air conditioning, and a small place to store stuff were a lot better than what we had had. I got a job working a game, which I wasn't good at. It requires being social, which I'm not. I am awkward, and I don't trust or like people. The guy in the next bunk room was also on crack, and I listened to his lighter flicking all night. It drove me insane. It made me seethe with anger because I craved what I was now scared to have.

Jake asked one night, "Have you ever been eaten till you cum?" I told him no and omitted the fact that I had never cum at all. Ever. He made it his mission to make it happen that night. Three hours. It took three hours. I had my very first orgasm while listening to that fucking lighter flicking. I saw a small red light in our shared heater; I was about to ask Jake what it was when I fell asleep. I slept with no dreams. The female orgasm had more than one benefit.

Only days later, I found out what the red light was. I overheard some guys talking about me and the bunkhouse orgasm. I confronted them and was told the guy with the calloused thumb had been charging people to see a tape of Jake and me. I went and told Jake about it first; he thought it was funny. Then I went to my lighter-flicking neighbor and demanded the tape. Only after I threatened to burn his face off on a flat-top grill. I threw a new lighter at him and kicked him in the balls on my way out. I heard rumors that he had made copies of the tape and that they still existed. I doubt it, though. I got sick, had horrible abdominal pain, and I couldn't hold anything down. Jake took me to the hospital, where they thought I had appendicitis. They ran tests, which only showed very high blood sugar. The Dr came in and said, "Well, it isn't your appendix. I have a question before we begin treatment, though. Your blood sugar is 758. How are you not in a coma? I threw up again and said, "You're the fucking Dr, you tell me. Give me a fucking insulin drip so I can leave." I hadn't taken insulin in months and was in diabetic ketoacidosis (DKA), which is deadly. I signed myself out against medical advice a few hours later once I stopped getting sick.

Jake and I were both fired. We went back to Agnes' condo. When I got pregnant again, she put us on a Greyhound back in New York. Jake was waiting for our bags at the Greyhound terminal in the city; I was walking around when I turned around and saw my own face on a missing person's flyer. Endangered Runaway. I took it and walked around looking for more; it was the only one. I stopped at a payphone and called the number. I told them it was a mistake; they said I had been reported missing almost two months ago. "I'm not missing. I know exactly where I am," I hung up, worried that the call would be traced. We spent the next few days sleeping in the subway and Grand Central Station.

Helen said we could stay as long as we helped her move next door. Sharon, the crazy sister, had moved out, leaving Clarissa unable to pay all the bills alone. Helen was moving in to help. Christmas came, and I don't remember anything about it. I don't even remember where we were. Helen was worried about getting caught with Jake at her place; she would lose her job. So, she put us in a hotel for a few weeks. Where I lost another set of twins. When the money for the hotel ran out, Helen got us some blankets and warm clothes and asked me where she should drop us off. She gave me some money without Jake knowing about it.

I went home. I used some of the money she gave me to buy a tent and a tarp. We walked past my old house, where I had grown up. We walked to the dead end, over the guardrail, through the power lines, and into the woods. Not far from the tree where Kyle and I had first had sex three years earlier, we laid down the tarp and pitched the tent. This would be home now. Jake and I lived there for months. There were plenty of places to keep warm. There was the library, grocery stores, White Castle, an almost abandoned mall, and an OTB. I also still had friends there. Several of their parents would let us stay for a day and feed us while we were there.

It turned out I had an intuition for horses. Jake would place small bets on the ones I had a feeling about, and we would always win something. We could always find a little money. You would be surprised how many people threw away scratch-off tickets that were small winners. Those two dollars to twenty-dollar tickets add up. Returning bottles and cans got us five cents each. Jake was also not shy about panhandling; I couldn't do it. We won enough on a horse race for an all-you-can-eat dinner for two and a pack of cigarettes. I wasn't used to eating regularly and threw it all up. One of the card and gift stores we checked the trash can at had a pizza place next door. They double-bagged a whole pizza and put it in the top of the can with a note, "for the homeless couple." The kid that took the trash out at 7-11 arranged to double bag the food, drop it in the dumpster, and Jake went right behind him and took it. They threw out a LOT of food. A kid I had gone to school with worked at McDonald's in Walmart. He would slip us food that was "leftover" at the end of the night. That is the only McDonald's I have ever seen that sold hot dogs. I would buy a hot dog for a dollar, eat half, pull a piece of my own hair out, and put it in the bun. I got a second hot dog free every time. A woman who worked at Walmart would leave a meal for us outside the front doors once a week. Bianca had come and visited a few times. Once, she demanded to see the tent. After we showed it to her, she gave us a cooler she had in her truck filled with food, and she bought us a second tarp to put over the tent. A security guard at the mall brought us to his house to spend the night a few times. The mall bathroom was single occupancy and big; I was able to wash my hair daily in the sink and take a "whore bath" for the rest of me. We mostly survived on the kindness of strangers during that time. The kindness of strangers has always touched my heart and soul. To this day, I think of them often and appreciate them every day. They are what still give me a little faith in humanity.

Jake had gone to panhandle somewhere, and I was sitting alone in the mall. A twenty-something guy started talking to me. He told me he was in college and trying to get into a fraternity. I told him I was seventeen, homeless, and possibly pregnant. "So, uh, I have to do something to get into this fraternity. I don't mean to disrespect you in any way; I really don't. But, uhm, I am supposed to jerk off in front of a random stranger. I will pay you five bucks if you watch me jerk off." I escorted him to the bathrooms. I stood just outside the alcove, and he stood in the women's room doorway, using the liquid hand soap to lube up. There was a payphone next to me, so I called Bianca, collect, while I watched the stranger jerk off, and collected my five dollars. I didn't lie to Jake about how I got the money; he thought it was funny. I used a dollar to get a pregnancy test; as always, he was happy about the positive, and I wasn't. It was almost time for the carnival to start again, the one I had met him at. At least I would know where I was since they did almost exclusively Long Island locations.

While I was on the phone with Bianca, she told me I had a date to testify before the grand jury. She was going to pick me up the day before, so I could have clean clothes and a real shower. Jake had tried to dye my hair with Kool-Aid, and he had cut it badly when I found the missing person poster. I told Bianca I would need my hair fixed. Tina was capable, so off went almost all of my hair. Grandma said I could stay the night, but Jake couldn't. He wouldn't let me leave without him, and I was worried about leaving him. He had been clean and sober the whole time we had been staying there; I worried if I wasn't around, even for a night, that sobriety would be gone too. I told Bianca I had arranged for him to stay with my friend Grant; after we got to my grandparents' house, I said Grant's parents had changed their minds. The truth was, Grant, was supposed to ask his parents and chickened out. Grandma wasn't happy about Jake being there. She let him sleep in the basement and locked the sliding door so he couldn't get into the rest of the house. It was warm, and there was a bathroom. It was better than outside. With my new haircut, I looked like I was twelve walking into the courtroom. I hadn't seen my lawyer, Amanda, since the family court trial ended over a year earlier. She was at the courthouse when I went before the grand jury. She didn't speak to me or even acknowledge my presence. Walking into that room was horrifying. There was a pile of strangers and the assistant district attorney. I sat across from all of these people, people that needed to hear details of my life that I didn't share with anyone. The ADA asked questions, and I answered honestly; thankfully, nothing he asked required graphic detail. I was dizzy, nauseated, and just wanted to run. Halfway through my testimony, one of the jurors asked me to repeat everything because she hadn't been able to hear me. I choked back vomit and tears and repeated everything. Only louder. When it was over, Bianca drove us back to the woods. I had a miscarriage again and blamed it on the stress of the trial. By the way, Griffith was indicted, and we would be going to criminal court sometime.

By the time the carnival started, I was pregnant again. Each time I had conceived, I was on birth control. Apparently, it had the reverse effect on me. While I hadn't been happy about any of the pregnancies, I had been increasingly devastated by each loss. The months that Jake and I spent homeless in the woods together were when I was the happiest with him. He was an amazing guy when he was sober. I had grown to love him.

I liked this carnival, a lot of the people who worked there already knew me from the previous year. I got a job working in the cotton candy trailer with Lettie. When the season started, we were the only two girls working there. Jake worked for a private game owner, so he didn't qualify for a bunk room. I worked for one of the show owners, but only employees that ran rides qualified for the bunk

208

rooms. We had our tent, though, and could usually set it up under the back of the funhouse to keep it dry. It wasn't always possible; no one's sleeping quarters were supposed to be visible to the customers. When I was local to Dierdre and Theresa, they came to visit, and Bianca did too. She brought her new boyfriend, Gavin. I really liked him. He was good to Bianca, which was a plus. She deserved to be happy. I made two hundred and fifty dollars a week in cash. It may not sound like a lot, but it was the nineties, and I had no expenses or bills.

I was the favorite of a lot of the guys that worked there. Many saw me as a little sister and tried to protect me. Especially Johnny; he was my favorite. Johnny was also a crack addict, but he was able to have separate lives as I had done. He never let me see that side of him, and he kept it from me as much as he could. At one spot where our tent was in an open area, Jake had disappeared, and there was a storm. We had put a small padlock on the tent because a lot of people who worked there had sticky fingers. Before Jake left, he didn't unlock the tent, and he had the only key. Not only was it raining, but it was chilly. I sat in the cold rain in the dark on a cinder block outside of the tent, waiting for Jake. Johnny got dropped off and saw me in the headlights as his ride backed out.

"Baby girl, why are you sitting out here?" He asked as his eyes fell on the padlock. "That mother fucker out there smoking that shit?" My denial kicked in, "He's clean," but my voice cracked. "Righhht, come on," he said as he walked me toward the bunkhouse. Johnny unlocked his door and pulled off my wet jacket, and hung it on the inside of his door. "Baby girl, I know you need to believe that. I also know you know; you are lying to yourself. You need to get rid of that mother fucker. You're too good for him. I'm going back out. There's my TV and a ton of tapes, watch what you want. Lay down, sleep. But lay with your head over at this end," he gestured to the left end of the bed, "That way, when he comes in, you can hear me beat his ass." He left me the key and closed the door. I hadn't been asleep long when I heard something outside. I realized quickly that it was, in fact, Johnny beating Jake's ass. I was almost asleep again when Johnny came in. "Baby girl, come put your head on the pillow;

I don't want to put my feet in your face." I was so tired I could barely move; Johnny moved me, then laid beside me. "Baby girl, I hope you know I wouldn't ever hurt you. I am not a perv like most of these assholes. I won't lay a hand on you. You need sleep tonight, just stay here and sleep." I curled up on my side and felt him curl around me; his big arms slid around me. I breathed him in, taking a little of his life to save my own. Johnny was safe. He never touched me.

There was a boy that worked there, who wasn't much older than me, Angel. He shared the fun house private bunk with Gary, who ran the bumper cars, and Ashely (yes, a guy), who ran the fun house. Angel had a problem with touching me; I told Jake many times, but he never seemed to care, and he never did anything about it. Every time I was near him, he would grab my tits or slap my ass. I was good friends with both Gary and Ashley, Gary was also dating Dierdre, so I was around Angel a lot. I got tired of it, and when he did it again, I slapped him, "If you touch me again, I will break your fucking arm." Angel didn't listen, and just days later, as I went past him, he slapped my ass. I caught his arm and twisted it behind him. I kept twisting and pushing his arm up with the force of adrenaline I didn't know I had. I slammed his arm up; the break was audible. I stood over him, yelling at him that I had warned him to stop touching me. Angel stood, and with his other hand, he punched me in the stomach.

The show had two owners. Billy and Bobby. Sometimes for smaller locations, they split the show up and did two spots at the same time. Jake got sent to Billy's spot to help set up while I stayed to set up the cotton candy trailer for Bobby. Bobby was who I actually worked for. Jake didn't have to go since he didn't work for either of them. He would help them out for extra money. I asked him to stay because I had been having a lot of pain since Angel hit me, but he wouldn't stay. Another girl, Zoey, had been hired, and we became close. She stayed close while Jake was gone. I went to the bathroom (everyone loves porta-potties, right?), and when I came out, Zoey ran to my side wide-eyed, "Don't look down, Simone." I tried anyway and almost fell over. Someone called an ambulance, and Zoey rode with me. I had a sonogram and saw my baby. It was my first moment of excitement about being pregnant. The tech said, "This baby is dead." I tried to tell him he was wrong. I could see my baby. Again, he said, "Yep, but it's dead." I pointed out the baby's head telling him to look; I could clearly see my baby on the screen. The guy was just a dick, "Yep, but the baby is dead. It isn't moving, and its chest is caved in." I tried to come off the table and kill him. Security was called, and Zoey explained the situation to them. A female tech came in and confirmed, via external and internal sonograms, that the baby was gone. She said it in a much more humane way. It was explained to me that the baby wasn't passing properly, and I would need to have a D and C. I was crying when I was put to sleep, and I was crying when I woke up. The hospital paid for a taxi for Zoey and me to get back to the carnival.

The taxi was arriving at the same time as Jake and Johnny were coming back from the other spot. I fell onto Jake crying. "He killed my baby. When Angel hit me, he killed my baby." Jake said nothing; he actually shoved me off of him. Johnny carried me, in my blood-soaked clothes, to his bunk room. Once I had calmed a little bit, he asked me what had happened with Angel. I told him as I laid on his bed with my head in his lap. He rubbed my head and occasionally wiped my tears with his shirt. I slept.

That night Jake insisted on having sex, no matter how many times I told him no. I was in mental and physical pain; sex was the last thing I wanted. He wouldn't stop, and he got what he wanted, as all men in my life that wanted me had done. I wandered around the lot like a zombie; Johnny came to check on me every chance he could. On the third day, he found me sitting alone with a crack stem in front of me and some crack in my hand. He knocked the glass stem onto the ground, stepped on it, and held his large hand out for the crack. I gave it to him; he threw it in the oil waste. "Baby girl, I'm going off to Billy's spot tonight. Angel is there. I'll get him for you. You are going to be okay. Don't go down this road again." Johnny lifted me up, hugging me in his big, strong, safe arms, and I swear he felt me breathing in some of his life. Johnny kissed the top of my head and walked away, wiping tears from his face. He didn't

211

look back. I heard later that night how Johnny had beaten Angel. Beat him literally off the carnival lot, into the street, and told him not to ever come back. I never saw Johnny again.

Everyone there tried to get me to leave Jake. They all said he was no good; I was too good for him, and I needed to go back to my family. I didn't have a family. I didn't have anyone. Lettie and her boyfriend Jimmy owned a camper that they drove to each spot. They said I could move in with them. They even offered to give me the bedroom and take the living room if I would just leave Jake. I didn't. I wouldn't.

The biggest perk of working the cotton candy trailer is that if there are leftovers, we could take them. Jake, Gary, Ashley, and I were potheads. We smoked weed for hours after the show closed at night and had wake and bake most mornings. I brought the munchies, so I got weed for free. Jake had run off somewhere; I didn't know or care where right after work one night. So, the guys and I were smoking without him in Gary and Ashley's bunk. The door flew open, and there stood my boss Bobby and Jake's boss Kenny. Bobby stared at me, "Where is he? Where is Jake?" He demanded, "Fucked if I know." Bobby and Kenny ordered and demanded I tell them where Jake was, but I really had no idea. Bobby asked me to come outside, he was a very large man, and next to him, I felt like a toddler. "Simone, I know you care about him. You were good for him, but you can't fix him. He has really fucked up this time, and I need to find him. You know he's on that shit again if-" I cut him off, "He's not. We smoke weed, and that's it." Bobby's eyes softened, and I vaguely heard Kenny "Keep telling yourself that, sweetheart," from behind me where he was pacing. Bobby put his hand on my shoulder, "I know you need to believe that right now, to save yourself, I guess, but you know in your heart, he isn't clean anymore. He was for a while, and it was because of you; he isn't going to change, though. You cannot fix him. If you see him, send him to me." He walked away with Kenny, and I went back to getting high.

212

Gary told me I could take his bed, so I wouldn't have to be alone in the tent, and he took Angel's. Gary bragged about having a different girl at every spot; the only one who hadn't put out yet was Dierdre, who was still a virgin. Gary flirted with me once in a while, nothing serious, just his hand on my thigh and a look. He never pushed or did anything that I was uncomfortable with, he knew it wasn't going to happen, and I knew he wouldn't force me. I woke up that night to Jake pulling my pants off and trying to shove himself inside me. He saw I was awake and simply said relax. There was no point in fighting. I just laid there until he was finished and went back to sleep. I heard him leave as I closed my eyes.

I was at work the next day when he popped his head into the trailer window. "We need to go. Now. I packed what I could, go to the office, and get your last pay; hurry up; we need to leave." Lettie had been sick for weeks; she was in the hospital and wasn't expected to make it. They had hired a new girl, Janice, to help me out. I hated her; she was a cunt who was trying to take my job. She had intentionally shot a ball of hot sugar out of the spinner at me; it hit me in the eye. She hadn't been there long, and I felt bad leaving Bobby, but I had to do what Jake said.

I went to the office, where Bobby was sitting in the window; I told him I was leaving and needed my last pay. His wife, Cathy, told me to come inside. They both pleaded with me to stay. They would give me a bunk room, and if none were available, they would pay for my hotel room in every spot. I would not have to share a room, and all my expenses would be paid; they would even raise my pay by one hundred dollars a week. All I had to do was, "Just leave Jake! Just leave Jake! Just leave Jake!" I looked up at Cathy and told her, "I can't. I love him." Bobby passed Cathy an envelope and walked away with his head hung low; Cathy handed it to me, taking my hand in hers, "You can always come back anytime you want," they said in unison from opposite ends of the office. I never looked back and never saw any of them again. The show went out of business at some point. Tax evasion. I never asked Jake about what had happened, what he had done, or why we had to leave in such a hurry. I knew he would just lie. I did love him, but I loved the people I worked with and for, too. They had become my family. If I had asked, and he had lied, I would have left him and gone back to them. I always suspected he stole, and not just a stuffed dog from Kenny, but money and a lot of it, from all of them.

Jake and I got near my old foster home; he wanted me to see if we could still sneak into my old room from the back door. Jake said if we were quiet, no one would ever know we were there. I wouldn't do that; I did have boundaries. The envelope Cathy had given me contained three weeks' pay. There was a sleazy no-tell motel not far away. I got us a room for a week. The first night, he again would not leave me alone for sex; I told him I didn't want to at least a hundred times. I was exhausted both emotionally and physically, and I just didn't want to. The sex wasn't worth the energy of faking multiple orgasms; it had still only happened that one time. Jake insisted I was cheating on him with Gary, and that's why I wouldn't give him what he "needed." I pointed out how insane that was, and he rebuked with, "If you are only mine, if your pussy is only mine, and no one has touched it, then you will fuck me. If you won't, it's because you know I will be able to tell if someone else has had you," so I did. My newest pregnancy was conceived in room twenty-five of that no-tell motel. Which one? I'll never tell.

We were homeless in a few more places. We stayed at Grand Central Station and rode the subway all night. Our tent was gone, and after a week, Jake said we could go to Yonkers, where he had grown up. He did have friends there, and we hung out with them sometimes. Only during the day, and Jake was never allowed in any of their houses. Like everyone else, they all told me to leave him. Several told me I could stay with them, and they wouldn't let him know where I was. They said after he got tired of looking for me, he would disappear, and they could help me get work and my own place. I didn't listen, and we lived under a bridge in Yonkers. Jake's old friend Kelly was there a lot. I didn't like her, she obviously liked Jake, and I could almost feel the heroin running through her veins.

Helen wouldn't let us stay, no matter how hard Jake begged. She did come and take us to the ferry and send us away to an island. Jake

214

had been there before; he said he could find work there since tourist season was coming. The island was full of hotels that employed mostly college kids from late spring to early fall. The hotels housed the temporary employees either in cabins or basement rooms. Jake said the only problem was that men and women couldn't sleep in the same location. We would work during the day, see each other at night and sleep separately. His former employer wasn't a full-time resident and hadn't come to open his business yet. Jake broke into one of the cabins, and we moved in. The water was off, so there was no shower, and the toilet didn't flush, but it was a roof. Jake left me there often to go look for work. I was sick and asleep when the year-round security guy came in and threatened me, I never saw his face, but I did hear him. "Be out in forty-eight hours, or the boss is pressing charges. I don't know who you are, but I know your man, and he isn't welcome here." Jake didn't seem to be welcome anywhere.

It was supposedly illegal to be homeless on the island. I researched it years later; I found that it isn't entirely true. It is frowned upon, to say the least, and if you are caught, they will charge you with anything they can to get you off the island. It was a tourist location for rich people. Rich people on vacation do not want to see homeless people. We were there and homeless anyway; rarely did we follow the rules. There was a big hill where a hotel had once been; it burned down, and they never rebuilt. There was a huge hole in the ground where the foundation had once been. That's where we lived, using a charred piece of plywood to make a tent to shield us from the hot sun and rain. Jake got a job with Louie painting houses. He knew I had been having trouble finding work and gave me money for lunch a few times a week. I spent a lot of time on the beach the first week. After burning bad enough that I couldn't move, I found the library. I read *Kiss, the Girls* in one day. It is the only *Patterson* book I have ever liked. The movie didn't do it justice. Jake started drinking while we were there; there wasn't access to a lot of drugs. There was a lot of coke, but it was the tourists that had it, not the locals. Drugs had made him lie, manipulate and steal; alcohol made him violent. Some guy introduced himself to us as Stan; Jake lied about his name. Stan swore he knew Jake from somewhere; Jake insisted he didn't and ushered me away. Later he told me that Stan was a cop in Poughkeepsie, where Jake still had an active warrant. Jake became distant; he didn't want to be around me; he just wanted to hang out with the local teenagers. That distance turned into violence as he accused me of sleeping with a fifteen-year-old local boy. For the first time since we had been together, he hit me; unlike most, he aimed for my face. Suddenly he said I was cheating on him with every guy on the island, locals and tourists. I found a rusty old knife in our "home" and began trying to slice my wrists with it. I got a little deeper every day. The only people I spoke to were the other secretly homeless people I had befriended. I would never have slept with any of them; they were just my friends. I also never would have had anything to do with a teenager. I was seventeen, and even eighteen-year-olds were out of the question for me.

He drank more; the distance became greater, and the beatings became daily. One night as we fought under our plywood, he broke up with me. I had never been dumped before; men didn't leave me; I left them; I didn't know how to respond or react to this. I pressed my abdomen against his back and said, "What about the baby?" I hadn't taken a test, but in the motel, I had the thought of, "You just got me pregnant." I wasn't even late yet, but a part of me knew. Jake slammed his back into me, telling me, "There is no baby in there." He slept; I didn't. I stayed for days, being treated like human garbage. It is what I was and what I deserved. I was beaten before he went to work and after he got back, sometimes in between if we saw each other. The breaking point – Jake hit me with a two-by-four. It crashed across my back, but he had intended to hit my stomach. I ducked to protect the baby I was certain was there.

The next morning, I walked into the police station. It was a tiny island with just two or three cops. "You have a man on the island with a warrant for his arrest. I will tell you everything you want to know if you get me the fuck off this island and somewhere to go when I get there," The cop agreed. I told him everything. The next morning, I left on a ferry without saying goodbye to Jake. There was a car there waiting to take me to a youth shelter in the Hamptons. Yes, you read it right, the Hamptons.

The director Calvin did my intake; he was a decent guy. He was also in a relationship with another guy who worked there. At the end of the intake, he asked if there was anything else he should know about me. "Yes, there is about a one percent chance that I am not pregnant." I was sent via public bus the next day to a clinic for a pregnancy test. It was positive. I called Bianca from the waiting room while she was at work. We caught up, and she said she was going to go if there was nothing important going on. "Okay, Ma, I will talk to you later. Oh, by the way, I'm due in February," I told her. "What do you mean due in February? Due for what?" Bianca seemed genuinely confused. "It is June, ma, and I am due in February. Do the math," I told her with an attitude. "Why do you have to play games? Why can't you just come out and say whatever it is-" She was screeching in my ear. "Ma! It is June. I am due in February. I'm pregnant." I heard her fall and hit a wall. I hung up. She was dense sometimes. I hadn't told her of the previous pregnancies; this one felt different. I took the bus to social services as I had been instructed to do. They had no place to put me; they sent me back to the youth shelter.

Bianca called me there that night, screaming I was lying about the pregnancy and demanding proof. The staff faxed her my letter of confirmation; I gave her Louie's number and asked her to call him, so he could let Jake know. Jake called me after he heard; he was again ecstatic, and just like that, we were back together. Toni was the only female staff member. We became close, and she implied that I could stay with her. She never said it because it was against the rules, and she could lose her job. After I turned eighteen, though, nothing could be said about it. Jake called daily, begging me to come back. The state found placement for me, and it was back at Delilah's. I was worried if I had a baby while in foster care, they would take the baby, so I refused. I couldn't stay at the shelter since I had other places to go. Back to Jake, or back to Delilah's. My dumbass chose Jake.

I got back on the ferry with my heavy duffle bag and set off to get back to the island. I hadn't heard from him in two nights, but he had been using Louie's phone to call; the long distance was

217

expensive. A stranger saw me struggling with my bag and offered me a ride. I was dropped off where the homeless people hid. I had been close to Ziggy; he treated me like a human. Ziggy had been born on the island; he had been badly burned in a fire, leaving him severely scarred. I saw him sitting in his usual spot and sat next to him. We quietly watched the water, taking in each other's peaceful silences. "Why are you back here? You got out. You aren't supposed to come back once you get out." He had never told me to leave Jake or said anything bad about him; I knew how he felt, though. "We got back together. I'm pregnant, and we're going to be a family. Where is he?" Ziggy's head fell. "I wish you had called Louie before you came back. Honey, Jake is gone. Some cops from Poughkeepsie picked him up on some old warrant." I knew he had been picked up because of me. I had told them *everything* about Jake. "Well, let's see what I can do to get kicked off the island this time," I said with a laugh. Ziggy opened his wallet and handed me a hundred-dollar bill. "Get you and that baby somewhere safe. I know you want a family, but family isn't always what's best, and family isn't always about blood. Besides, you are too good for that BOY you're with." I was dumbfounded. Ziggy's wallet was so full it didn't close, and it was all hundred-dollar bills. "Ziggy! Dude! You have all that money! Why are you homeless?" He laughed. "Because that is the way *my* life is supposed to go, honey. *You* have a different story to tell. Pack away your demons and tell your story when you are ready. Now, get out of here before you miss the last ferry." I walked away, vowing to pay Ziggy back while he was telling me not to.

I was hitchhiking back to the ferry; a car had just stopped when the cop pulled up behind it. "I heard you were back. I threw you off once. Get off my island." He followed me to the ferry and waited to make sure I got on it. I never got to pay Ziggy back. It's hard to send money when there isn't an address. I have never been back to the island. I strongly believe Ziggy died long ago. Ziggy, if there is any chance you are alive and reading this, I last saw you in June 1997. I put my demons away; I locked them up tight. They have been trying to escape lately, so here I am, So here I am in June 2022, twenty-five years later, telling my story. You were right; blood isn't always family. You were my family.

I wound up back in the youth shelter, and from there, I was sent to the first group home that I had ever been in. There was no place that would take a seventeen-year-old pregnant, diabetic, long-term. I hadn't taken insulin since I was in Florida. The state didn't care that I didn't see a Dr or take insulin until they needed an excuse as to why I couldn't be placed somewhere. Helen reached out and took me in. As soon as I got there, she had me apply for food stamps, medical, and cash assistance. Social services required I get a letter from Jake stating he was the father of the baby. When he called, I explained the letter they wanted from him, and he asked, "Am I?" I was livid and let it be known. Jake proceeded to accuse me of cheating on him with every boy that was on the island from thirteen to sixty, especially brothers that were fourteen and fifteen. I most certainly had no interest in kids my age, let alone younger ones. I watched Carissa and Sharon's kids in exchange for staying until I got a job; it didn't take long. I interviewed at McDonald's; they told me to come back after I had the baby; pregnancy was a liability. I interviewed at Arthur Treacher's; the manager didn't care that I was pregnant. He said he would give me a job if I came in for a second interview and showed a little more skin. I got an interview at a grocery store and didn't tell them I was pregnant until I was in orientation and already had the job. It was part-time, and the minimum wage was five dollars and fifteen cents an hour. I was a cashier, but I picked up extra shifts in every department. I usually worked forty hours despite my part-time status.

I had turned eighteen. In my teen years, I had been called a lot of things. Flasher, jailbait, lot lizard, runaway, alcoholic, addict, and many others. What really would have summed up all those things was – I was the girl moms warned their teen sons about. It was all about to change, though. I was about to enter motherhood.

Barely Legal

My pregnancy care was through a clinic, yes, like the nasty ones you see on TV. At my first appointment, the Dr yelled at me because I had already gained ten pounds, and I was only supposed to gain twenty through the whole pregnancy. I asked about my diabetes, and they told me high sugar was normal during pregnancy. I wasn't given insulin and was told to just test my sugar once in a while at different times. This is actually completely false, and they could have killed my baby by not providing proper care. I didn't know that, though, and had no way of finding out. At eleven weeks, I developed hyperemesis gravidarum (HG), which is like morning sickness on steroids. When I went back to the Dr for my next appointment. I was yelled at for losing fifteen pounds. That Dr would have gotten along well with Bianca, I never could do anything right in her eyes either.

At twelve weeks, Helen and Carissa tried to talk me into having an abortion. I was young and considered myself pro-life. I was more of a situationist. I was one of those idiots that said it was okay in cases of rape, incest, or medical problems. Technically the baby I was pregnant with was conceived through rape, but I wouldn't admit that to myself, let alone other people. Bianca had been pushing for abortion also. Carissa and Helen almost convinced me to do it. I told them I would talk to Jake about it when he called; I felt he had a right to make that decision with me. Helen said, "No, Jake isn't here. He isn't a part of this. You are the one that is dealing with all of it and will have to deal with the rest of the pregnancy and after the birth. In this situation, Jake isn't even real right now. You are the one who is real" My hand fell to my abdomen, "If I am real and my baby is attached to me, then my baby is real too." I went to my room, and nothing else was said about it.

Don had been hired at the same time as I was. As I was bagging groceries, he walked over and asked how I liked the new job. My response was, "It sucks, dick," which was my response to everything those days. Don noticed, and it sparked his interest in whether or not I sucked dick. We started seeing each other very casually. Stopping at Burger King or McDonald's on break or after work was the extent of it. Don was always broke, and I always paid. He invited me over to his friend Myron's in Poughkeepsie so we could hang out and get to know each other. I agreed; Myron was cool; his place was a bedroom with no door and a half bathroom also with no door. He shared a kitchen and shower with his landlord Chris who lived on the main floor. Myron made us dinner; it was fabulous. I lost track of time and missed the last train back to Helen's. I left her a message and stayed at Myron's with Don. Nothing happened. I napped in a chair, and no one touched anyone else.

As I started spending more time with Don, I asked Jake's mom and sisters not to tell him. I made sure they knew it was very casual. I didn't want Jake to know unless it became serious. They agreed that he didn't need to know and shouldn't know. I brought Don back to Helen's after work because they all wanted to meet him. No one was home, Carissa and Helen had both been called into work and Sharon, who was also pregnant, went back to her apartment because she wasn't feeling well. Don and I started kissing, "Hey, you know how you always say everything sucks, dick? It got me thinking, do you? I bet you do, and I bet you do it really good too." Don had wiped it out, and I felt obligated, so I did. He was done in under five minutes, and like most men, he could only shoot once. Which meant I was done, too, even though I got nothing out of it. I would have liked a bit of attention; pregnancy hormones are brutal.

Don and Myron wanted the third-floor apartment but couldn't afford it on their own. They started asking if I would be their roommate. I checked out the apartment and it was nice. I told them I would think about it. I missed the train home two more times that month and Helen said I couldn't go back and forth. Either I lived with her, or I didn't. Jake was medicated in jail it made him more moody than any street drug did. One minute we were fine, and he wanted to be with me. The next I was a slut, bitch, whore and I should die. Carissa and I became friends. She told me if she had been with Jake, she would have turned him in for the warrant. The words "I did" slipped out. She approved and told me not to ever tell anyone else, that the rest of her family wouldn't understand.

Don and I had sex. It wasn't planned; it was one of those situations where it "Just happens." It shouldn't even count since he was about the size of my pinky finger, and no there was no orgasm. Jake called right as I was waking up one morning. On my way to the phone, Carissa tipped me off that Sharon had told him I was seeing someone. I didn't know what to expect when I got on the phone. Jake seemed like his normal self. I was getting ready to hand the phone back to his mom, "Oh yeah, by the way. My sister says you have a new boyfriend? Is that true?" He was calm. "Not exactly, no. I am seeing someone. It isn't serious. We are just getting to know each other I guess." Silence. "Well then why the FUCK are you still at my mom's house? You're dating and I'm sure fucking another guy, while YOU are at MY mom's house?!" Not so calm. I tried telling him it wasn't like that at all. His mom didn't care if I was dating someone else, she had been pushing me to leave Jake since day one and was happy there was someone else. "Get the fuck out of my mom's house!" Jake screamed, in case I hadn't gotten the point, and hung up. I talked to Helen and clarified that she didn't want me to stay with Jake, was happy there was someone else and didn't care if I stayed. I moved out a few days later. I didn't want Jake thinking I was using his family, and after the way he screamed at me, it just felt wrong to be there. I hadn't been told that the apartment, the whole house, was roach infested.

I have a severe bug phobia. I cannot even look at a picture of a bug, or a drawing for that matter. I was also not told that Chris was on crack. My bedroom was above his living room, when he would get high the smell would come right into my room. On those nights I would close the smell in and sleep on the couch. Since being pregnant the smell just made me sick. Don and Myron were often short their share of the rent, the electric, and the phone bills. They never had money for food. I could barely eat because I was so sick all the time. The food was all bought by me though, and they would eat it all saving nothing for me on the rare occasion I could keep something down. I got a mini fridge for my room and kept my WIC cereal and milk in it. I would have something to eat, and it would not have roaches in it. I was so desperate to eat, that sometimes I just put the trash can next to me and throw up after every couple bites.

Don took the train with me to go visit my family. We could only stay for a day though and the visit was kind of rushed. There was a restaurant I wanted to go to. I couldn't remember how to get there so I called Bianca and asked for directions. She brought up Don by asking, "What even is he?" He heard her but didn't know what she meant. "He'ss a human, ma. What else would he be?" I knew what she meant. "You know what I mean. Like background, what even is he?" She asked again. "Well first, he is human. Other than that, he's black and Puerto Rican." I heard her disappointment in her silence. I had been raised that interracial dating, mixing in any way, was wrong. I had known since fourth grade that that was wrong, when I had a huge crush on a black boy. Bianca had never met or even seen most of the guys I had dated, she had no idea that most were not white.

Bianca's disappointment was even clearer when she came to see me at my new apartmentwhen she met Myron. Myron, who told her what a thoughtful, caring, wonderful, respectful daughter she had, also happened to be a dark-skinned Jamaican man, in his early forties, with dreads to his ass and a Barry Manilow voice. I could hear the anger in her boiling blood as she tried to play nice. She called me that night, and I got lectured about how races mixing in any way was wrong. People of different races shouldn't be living together, not even as roommates. She also didn't believe I was capable of being just friends with a person who owned a penis. Bianca thought I had sex with any and every man who ever looked at me or even said hi. She was at the end of one of her speeches, "Oh my God, what would people think?" There was only one response to that. "Oh, I don't know ma, that I am not a racist asshole? That I treat people as people?" She shut up and didn't bring it up again.

Don and I had a sex life, bad sex whenever he wanted whether I wanted it or not. He wanted anal, I didn't, my previous experience if you recall wasn't pleasant. Don pressured me until I gave in. It wasn't nearly as bad with something...so small. It was still the wrong hole though. After he got it once, he wanted it all the time. Whether I did or not. Other than sex, we didn't see each other unless it was at work. I was okay with that.

Don frequently talked about a guy named Fraizer. They had some kind of feud, supposedly every girlfriend Don had cheated on him with Fraizer. I got home from work around midnight most days. About two weeks before Thanksgiving, I got home, and Don wasn't there. Myron was cooking and some guy I didn't know was sitting on the couch. My room smelled like crack, so I closed the door and went to the living room. Myron came in and started telling me some fake story about how Don had hitchhiked with a trucker into the city, to see his baby's mom, after he found out his kid was in the hospital. Don would still sleep with his baby's mom when he was in the city, but he had nothing to do with his child. I also knew he was still sleeping with his ex-girlfriend Shari. She didn't live far from us. I laughed at Myron, "Myron, I know he's still fucking Shari. I don't care, if he's with her just say so." Both Myron and the stranger stared at me wide eyed. The stranger spoke, "You know your man, is out fucking his ex? And you don't care?" He asked incredulously. "He isn't my man. We're just seeing each other. We never said we were in a relationship or exclusive. Besides, he's just keeping me warm until my actual man, with an actual dick, gets out of jail." There it was the truth spoken aloud that even I didn't know until I said it.

The three of us hung out, watched Tv and talked. The Stranger and I flirted; Myron pretended not to notice. I went to the bathroom, when I came back, Myron was in the kitchen again, the Stranger gently stopped me, "If you really feel that way, you should get even. Kiss me." I did, I heard Myron behind me "Oh shit. I don't see a thing. I am going back to the kitchen to finish making my food." When he popped his head back in, we were no longer kissing.

Myron sat on the couch; the Stranger sat me in his lap, we kissed some more. No tingle, but he was an incredible kisser. Myron's voice interrupted, "Don's going to be pissed. I won't tell him, but he'll find out. Fraizer strikes again." I pulled away from the Strangers kiss, but stayed in his lap, "You're Fraizer?" He nodded, I

224

smiled. Even better. We went back to kissing, and a little touching. "Do you have a condom?" I whispered in his ear while he kissed my neck. In one swift move he pulled one out of his pocket while still kissing me. "Myron, can you do me a favor and go smell my room?" He did and said the coast was clear, Chris must have gone to his room.

We walked to my room still attached at the lips, clothes started coming off before the door was closed. This man was actually turning me on, it isn't hard to do, but most men don't care enough to take the two minutes and try. Maybe it would be the night I had my second orgasm. We got in my bed, he put the condom on. Just as my legs parted, I was struck by severe abdominal cramping, that brought tears to my eyes. I asked him to wait, just a minute, while I got in a different position or something. He knew I was pregnant, it had come up in conversation, before we kissed. Instead of stopping, he just shoved it in. The pain increased as he pounded away. I hit him, clawed him, punched him, pushed him, pulled his hair, he would not stop until he was finished. After he was done and getting dressed, he made the stupidest joke ever, "Baby you got any black in you?" I didn't reply. "After that, you might have as much black in you as I do." The pain stopped shortly after he left.

There was no way I could deny that was happened with Fraizer was rape, like I had done and still do, with many others. No one else needed to know about it though. I put myself in that position, it was my fault. Fraizer made sure it got back to Don within days that he "Fucked his new girl." Don slammed in the door after work, I was washing all of our work clothes by hand in the sink. "Bitch, did you fuck Fraizer?" He snapped at me.

"Yup sure did." I would have so it was a half lie. "When?' He asked as he threw his coat on the floor. "The other night when you were fucking Shari." I was angry about all of it. Don punched the wall, called me a "Cheating slut" and walked into our room. "I'm the cheating slut? How the fuck was I cheating, when we aren't even together? We are supposed to be just seeing each other. Which means we are BOTH free to see, date, and FUCK anyone we want.

You have been fucking your ex-girlfriend and your baby mom, but I'm the slut? Fuck you. You were just here to keep my bed warm until my real man gets out of jail." That time I meant to say it. Tears rolled down his face as I walked away. Don came up behind me and hit me in the kidney. I didn't say anything.

Fraizer kept calling, I kept ignoring the phone. I got out of the shower one night and heard his voice in the living room. I gathered my clothes, went to my room and closed the door. My room was huge, the closet was the size of a small room. Don was moving his stuff and a twin bed into the closet, since we were now, "Split up." He said I would need the space in the bedroom for me and the baby. I heard the three men talking, I wished I could leave, but I wasn't even opening the door. Don opened it though, rolled his eyes at me and went to his closet. He left my door open. Myron went through the kitchen to his own room and closed the door. I had heard Fraizer had tattooed the names of every girl he slept with on his arms. I opened the apartment door, "Before you go, let me see your arms." He took off his coat and shirt, both arms and part of his back had many names, a list of conquests. "If you ever, put my name on your body, I will fucking kill you. Get the fuck out." He left; I locked the door.

The day before Thanksgiving he kept calling, Don wanted me to answer it and I wouldn't. Don called Fraizer told him I was home and invited him over. As soon as Fraizer got there, Don went in my room, closed and locked the door. Myron was asleep in his room on the other side of the apartment. I was trapped and this wasn't a position I had put myself in. I didn't even have shoes on, they were now locked in my room. I had to pay rent anyway, so I walked downstairs, leaving my apartment door open, and knocked on Chris' door. Chris invited me in, I sat on his couch, and we talked for a few. I gave him his money. "Anyway, uh, Simone, I know you're pregnant, so I don't want to do it in front of you, but I've got this rock I really want to smoke, unless you want some?" I declined the offer and left. I still craved it, but I would not do that to my baby, and the smell was horrid. I went outside on to the front porch; it was covered in snow and ice. I wouldn't be able to walk anywhere without shoes. I figured Fraizer was gone anyway.

My door was wide open the way I had left it. Asshole could have closed the door, I thought as I walked through it. The door slammed behind me. I jumped, and turned around to see him behind me, his coat and shirt were on the floor. He tried to kiss me, I shoved him backwards where he fell onto the couch. I figured my best option was to get to Myron's room. Fraizer moved fast, he grabbed my arm, I slapped him across the face. I was about to slap him again, he grabbed my hand, pulled me close against him and whispered in my ear, "I like that." As he tried again to kiss me, I turned my head. Fraizer pulled me to the couch, pinned my legs down as he straddled me. His kiss fell on my neck, his hands opened my pants, he leaned up and opened his own. Fraizer knew how to move in a way that I was always pinned down, but he could still move freely. He laid me down and pulled off my pants, put on a condom, all without taking the pressure of his body off of mine. My arms remained free, I again, hit, punched, and clawed. I got his chest, arms and face, but I could see in his eyes, that he hadn't lied about liking it. As he pushed into me, I grabbed his ponytail and pulled out two handfuls of hair. He kept going, the more I fought the more turned on he got. When he was done and dressed, he said "Now I know you have as much black in you as I do," with a smile. I told him if he ever came back, talked to me or came near me again, I would tell the world what had really happened.

Don didn't open my door until the next morning. He had all kinds of nasty comments and questions about if I got the dick I had wanted. Myron was starting Thanksgiving dinner; Don and I were taking a taxi to work to pick up our paychecks. I changed and put on my comfortable Baja; even pregnant I could still fit at least two of me in it. Don's childish comments continued, all I could do was ignore him, and use my hood to cover the tears that slowly ran from my eyes. It had been two hours and he wasn't giving up. I spun around to face him, "You don't even know what the fuck happened, okay, just shut the fuck up." He bent down into my face "Yeah, I do. You fucked him!" I met his yell and raised it, "No, the fuck I didn't! Not ever! You don't get it, just go away!" I sat on the couch and curled back into my Baja. Myron was at the table listening, taking

227

in every word. "Explain it to me then. If you didn't fuck him, explain it to me," Don said calmly, almost caring.

I didn't want to say it. That meant admitting it. The last time I had admitted to non-consensual sex, I was blamed for it and that had been my best friend. Hell, most of the times I had sex with Don it wasn't consensual, and at least half the time when I had sex with Jake. If I hadn't been pregnant at that moment, I would have killed myself. "Yeah, you can't say anything because you're just another cheating slut!" he said as he stood and walked into my room. I jumped up and screamed "No the FUCK I'm NOT!!!" My hood had fallen, and the tears were visible, neither of them had ever seen me cry. Myron whispered to Don, I only heard "Saying she didn't want it." They both looked at me, Don's eyes softened, Myron's filled with anger. "Is that what you're saying? That you didn't want it?" Don asked softly.

I cried. I fell to my knees and let the river flow. Both men approached to offer comfort, I instinctively flinched away from their touch. I pushed Don away as I stood. "He raped me the first time. I tried to avoid him. I tried to keep him away. But your stupid fucking ass set me up to get raped again last night! Just leave me the fuck alone!" I cried on Myron's shoulder, while Don sat on the couch looking like the dumbass he was. Happy Thanksgiving.

Fraizer stopped by once after that. Don and Myron blocked the door so he couldn't see me. They told him they knew what he did and not to come near me again. I saw him around a few times, he would cross the street to get away from me. As far as I know he never got my name added to his list. I met many other girls he had been with. Most just said "That boy has a nice dick," with lust in their eyes. Two told me he had raped them; both had been Don's girlfriends at the time. I am willing to bet a lot of his conquests didn't want it.

Don's ex-girlfriend, Shari lost her place. I said she could stay. The two of them were on the couch screwing around, I was sitting in my room with the door open. I heard him tell her to stop because

228

I was right there. I clarified again that I didn't care, and we weren't together. We had really just been roommates, that were having sex. We weren't having sex anymore. Myron came in and jumped in my bed, 'We don't want to leave Simone out, she needs attention too, "I laid with him, and we cuddled for a while. I wasn't interested in him, he wasn't interested in me, but we were both lonely. I reached down his pants, "Mm girl, what are you going to do with that thing when it pops all the way up?" It was too late for that, it already was. So, I blew him, no neither of us bothered to close the door. Don was pissed at both of us for it, everyone knew it even though he never said anything.

The next night, Don and Shari both slept in my bed with me. Don got the middle. He flip flopped between which one of us he was facing. When he was facing me, I was jerking him off, I was quite sure he was getting the same from Shari when he faced her. He finished with me, I knew damn well the boy was one and done. I took it as a win. I didn't want him. I didn't like him as anything but a friend, and even that was questionable. We all have our petty moments.

I was cleaning my room, there were built in bookshelves along one wall. I was going through papers that had started to stack up. Some were medical, and I wasn't paying attention to the name. This paperwork couldn't be right. I read it over and over, not matter how many times I read it; it didn't change. "STD screening Herpes positive, Hepatitis B positive." This didn't make any sense. I had been tested for everything under the sun when I went to my first prenatal checkup. Everything was negative. Finally, my eyes focused and fell on the name. Don.

I walked to the clinic as fast as I could, the receptionist greeted me, "Simone, I don't think you have an appointment today?" There was a nurse next to her, I put the papers in her face and pointed. She noticed the name immediately, "Simone, this isn't you?" I caught my breathe. "No, it's the guy I have been fucking the last few months." I was brought back, and they did a screening for everything, but I would have to wait for results. When Don came through the apartment door, I punched him in the face, hard enough that he fell down the stairs. When he was able to get up and walk back up the stairs, I did it again. He was smart enough to not come back up, he asked what he did, and I threw the papers down to him. I locked him out. Yes, I had made the choice to have sex with him in the beginning. He should have told me though. I would have chosen differently if I had known.

It was a cold wet rainy December night in 1997. My bus stop was several blocks away from my apartment. I started walking with the eerie feeling that I was being watched. I had come to accept this feeling as a part of who I was, though. A car pulled up next to me, "Get in, I'll give you a ride," said the large man behind the steering wheel. I thanked him but declined. He followed me and kept pushing me to get in. I agreed, and he asked that I take my coat off first so his interior wouldn't get wet. "You're pregnant," he said once the coat was off. I felt this man couldn't know the truth, "No, I'm not." His eyes were glued to my abdomen, "I can clearly see. You're pregnant." He persisted. "I recently had a miscarriage. It'll take a few days to go down. "I hated the way the lie felt and tasted in my mouth. Lying about my baby dying was painful but it seemed important that he not know.

I got in and he drove. The man offered me twenty dollars for a blow job. I said no. He offered several more times and each time he was told no. As he pulled up in front of my place and I started to get out he softly said, "Good girl." I walked up the porch steps and into the main door of the house when it hit me. I hadn't told him where I lived. I didn't find out until years later, but that man's name was Kendall Francois. In February 1998, just two months after he gave me a ride home, he was arrested. He was a serial killer. The bodies of several prostitutes were found in his home. I knew one of them, she had gotten high with Jake and me.

A small group of girls I worked with threw me a baby shower. They let it slip that a larger group would be throwing one after the birth, just in case something went wrong. Bianca got engaged to Gavin. He was there to talk to when I needed an ear, too. He was

230

diagnosed with cancer and then wasn't so great to Bianca anymore. Myron, Don and I got a Christmas tree, it was decorated with four ornaments. They were a gift from one of my managers, Winnie the Pooh and friends, baby edition. Myron started to realize how hard things were for me, or at least started showing that he knew. He would frequently come get me and we would sit in his room having deep conversations about everything and nothing all at once. He was like Ziggy, family. It was almost Christmas and Jake would be getting out soon.

I will never understand why inmates are released at midnight, but that's where I was on Christmas eve. There were a handful of us waiting for our friends and family. It was mostly middle-aged women waiting for their kids. When Jake came out, he came right to me, but a guy that had been waiting went to him. I had no idea that he also had a secret boyfriend. Jake said he didn't know if I was really going to come, so he had a backup plan. The three of us walked around for a while. Jake kept ignoring the boyfriend and sticking his tongue down my throat. The boyfriend got annoyed, left and never called Jake again. We went back to my apartment where I just wanted to sleep. I was still suffering through HG, I had been hospitalized for dehydration a few times, I had been sent in for pre-term labor a few times, and I then had a stomach virus. I had already been violently vomiting at least hourly, on this night I was lucky if it was only twice an hour. Jake had other things in mind. He had been in jail for a whole six months and *needed* to get laid. "Go call your boyfriend then," I said as I rolled over and threw up again. As I was getting sick, he slid the back of my pants down and shoved it in. That only made me throw up more, and no, he didn't stop until he was done. The next day we went to the hospital. I was given fluids, and a prescription for a suppository to make me stop puking. An oral medication would have been pointless since I couldn't hold anything down. Back at my apartment, Jake handed it to me, "Nope, I will just keep barfing. Nothing is going in my ass." Jake did it anyway while I was getting sick, and somehow turned it into something sexual, and again fucked me while I was getting sick. I turned my head and threw up on him.

"So how pregnant were you when you had sex with Don?" Jake asked a few days later. "I don't know, five months I guess." He thought. "So, it isn't really my baby. Not just mine anyway. The baby is part his. Get a DNA test done. The baby will have three sets of DNA, yours, mine, and Don's" I was about to tell him that that isn't how any of this works, and explain basic biology to him, when Myron came in and told me there was an ADA on the phone. The ADA told me it was time to move forward with the criminal case against Griffith. He would be tried in two different counties and was facing up to twenty-five years in each. My heart thumped with fear, happiness and relief. My hand fell to my growing baby. "I'm sorry. I was pregnant when I went before the grand jury, I had a miscarriage from the stress. I am pregnant again. I need to have my baby first. I will call as soon as I'm ready." I hung up and he didn't call back.

Bianca had been pushing me to give the baby up for adoption, ever since it was too late for an abortion. Gavin was getting me baby stuff. Bianca got diapers, wipes, washcloths, and a few other things. Gavin had brought all that, a car seat, an antique crib, highchair and more. Bianca knew a couple that wanted to adopt and had their hopes up about getting my baby. She was also pushing me to marry Jake before the baby came. My grandparents were pushing for the marriage too. I got bullied into agreeing to the marriage. Bianca and Gavin paid for everything, rings, license, justice of the peace, said they would cook the food and make a cake. Gavin was still battling cancer, but he was only a dick to Bianca.

Jake went to Helen's three days before we were supposed to leave. He didn't come back. I called Bianca to let her know. She sounded sympathetic and said if I wanted to come along for a visit, that was fine. I told her I would, but I had some things to take care of first, and I would be on a later train. I went to some of the places where I knew Jake hung out, and I found one place where he had been only hours earlier. He had stolen a TV and a few other things from his friend's apartment. Before that, he had been stuck in a K hole. I have done Special K before and do not care to discuss it. While I had been apprehensive about marrying Jake, I was still hurt, devastated and even a little heartbroken that he hadn't showed up to leave for our wedding. He had been pushing for the marriage almost as much as my family had been. I couldn't find him, so I went home packed a bag and got on the train. I would just stay with my grandparents for a few days and relax. Jake called that night claiming that *I* had disappeared, and he *couldn't find me.* We fought and talked until I would hang up, this repeated for a while, until I stopped answering the phone. That backfired because he started calling Bianca. Jake begged me to still marry him, Bianca called and pushed, Tina said if you don't want to, don't do it. Gavin asked if it was what I wanted, I couldn't answer honestly. I was always everyone's disappointment. Me having a bastard child, meant Bianca would have a bastard grandchild, and my grandparents would have a bastard great grandchild. So, I said yes, this is what I want.

In the three-ring circus of phone calls, Gavin fixed the situation. Carissa would pay for Jake's train ticket to get there in the morning, Gavin would pay her back double. Time would be cut close for getting to the justice of the peace's house, but it would still happen. We were a few minutes late to our own wedding. It was January 25, 1998, Superbowl Sunday. We were married in an Amityville horror look alike house. That seemed fitting. As we were read the vows, I hoped Jake would say "I don't," he didn't. When it was my turn, my voice screamed "I don't," inside my head. That isn't what came out of my mouth though. Gavin and Bianca got in a fight; he demanded her belongings be removed from his storage immediately. Jake spent the night helping Bianca move her stuff, I spent the night throwing up. I was disappointed to not have sex on my wedding night. I didn't dislike sex. I disliked having my body taken from me. I disliked that guys couldn't take the two seconds to get me in the mood or had to have it while I was sick or injured. If a guy ever told me no, which never happened, but if it did, I would simply respect that. Grandma wrote a check as a wedding gift, but it was written to Bianca. She was scared Jake would take the money for drugs, which is valid. I had to ask Bianca anytime I wanted to spend the money on anything and if she didn't approve, I couldn't have it.

We went back to my apartment in Poughkeepsie. The Dr had sent a letter to my boss that I could no longer work, so I was stuck with Jake all the time. Great thought right after getting married. I did love Jake, but I knew the marriage was a bad idea. I wanted to be with him, I wanted to work it out. But the only problem we had was his addiction, and he wasn't going to get clean. It doesn't happen if you don't want it and he didn't. He saw nothing wrong with his drug use, or with spending every penny we had on drugs. Jake didn't like being around Don, Don wasn't really a fan of Jake either. Jake said he was going to get cigarettes; Don gave him money and asked Jake to bring him back a blunt. As soon as Jake was out the door, he told me "Sorry, you know as well as I do, he went out that door he would be gone for days, come back high and there would be a bunch of bullshit. I had to give him a reason to come back. I will share my weed with him for you." Don was a dick in general, but he had his good moments. After a couple more days at my place, Jake begged me to stay at Helen's with him for just one night, so he could get away from Don. I agreed, I knew it hurt him that I had been with someone else while he was in jail. When we got there, I was all over him, I wanted and needed sex in a way I never had before. Jake was very interested but did say he was scared I would go into labor, "That's the point." We had sex, there was still no orgasm, but it was good, and I went into labor. About ten minutes after he finished. My water broke in his bed.

New Life Begins

Jake pissed me off during labor, and I tried to bite his hand off. In my defense, I had told him to stop touching my face, and he wouldn't stop. Plus, labor sucks. None of that mattered in the end; my beautiful baby girl was here. She was perfect. The day she was born, Helen and Sharon came to visit. Sharon had her second baby in December, a second boy. Both of Jake's sisters were jealous because I had a girl. Before they left, Helen gave Jake money to take the train back to her place. He never got there; he disappeared. Jake was gone for two days. His sister found him walking the streets when she was on her way to get me from the hospital. Jake was high. I have pictures of him holding our perfect daughter high. Other people can't tell, but I can. His sisters had gone to my place, packed as much of my stuff as they could, and brought it to Helen's. They left behind the antique crib and a lot of other sentimental things. No one would bring me to get the stuff. I was never asked if I wanted to go back to Helen's; they just did it. I had wanted to go back to my place – my space. I never saw Chris or Myron again. I ran into Don once. Jake and I needed to bring stuff into social services. I left him there with the baby, to run to the WIC office. Don was walking down the street and asked where the baby was, I said social services, "Damn, I knew that was going to happen," he responded. "No, Don, they didn't take her; I am on my way back there now. We just had to hand in paperwork." That was the end of the conversation and the last time I saw him.

My job wouldn't let me return to work. Jake couldn't, or wouldn't, get a job. I had an application pending for cash assistance, but it was going to take a while. I needed money to support my child. When she was three weeks old, I begged my manager to let me come back, even just for a few hours. My Dr faxed a note clearing me, and management agreed. Jake's entire family was against breastfeeding, which I was doing. There was some drama about it, but they got over it.

My first day back at work was a Friday. The baby was being watched by Carissa and Helen as they were both off for the day.

235

When I got home, my boobs were ready to explode, and I needed my baby. No one was there. A note was left on the table "Simone, mom got called in; I had the baby. I got called in, need the money, left the baby with Jake, Carissa." They were not there. I called Helen at work, but she couldn't come to the phone. I called Carissa at work; she said she hadn't seen them since she left for work. I called Sharon's, thinking he brought the baby over to see his nephews. I was about to call the police when he came around the corner pushing her in her stroller. I ran to her and scooped her up. My three-week-old baby smelled like a weed; all her stuff did too. Jake swore he hadn't done anything, not even weed, as he made himself a huge bowl of cereal. There were four remarkably diverse kinds; he had sweet, chocolate, fruity, and healthy, all in a giant mixing bowl. The next day I worked again. On the bus ride home, I dozed off and dreamed of Jake selling our baby for crack. Either letting someone buy her to keep her or letting people rape her. I ran from the bus stop into the house to again find my daughter gone. This time, I did call the cops. When they got there, I gave them a description of her stroller, diaper bag, blankets, and a picture of Jake, who I angrily described as a crackhead. As the cop was getting ready to get in the car to go look for them, Jake walked around the corner with the baby. I picked her up and brought her in, making sure she was okay and perfect in every way. I laid her in her bassinet and stormed back outside. The cop was asking Jake some questions; the answers didn't matter. I marched right up to Jake and punched him in the face. Jake told the cop he wanted to press charges of assault. "I didn't see a thing," the cop said as he got in his car and drove away. I didn't go back to work.

Jake got a job working overnights cleaning a movie theater. He got the job through his friend James who was also an addict. Jake hadn't been paid yet, but we got a letter that we had been approved for cash assistance. I heard Jake on the phone with James, "I don't care. I'll smoke that shit in the theater." He was going to take the money. We needed that money, babies have needs, plus Helen was moving. We all needed to find our own places. I threw one of my combat boots at him and told him he was a dick. He cried to his mommy that I was mean; I told her what the situation was. She tried talking to him, but she babied him all the time. I snuck away and called social services. I was honest with them, "My husband is a crack addict; I overheard him telling a friend he was going to use the money for drugs. I need that money to get things my daughter needs and for a place to live. Is there a way it can be sent to my card instead of his?" My worker was very understanding, appreciated the honesty, and made the switch right away. Back then, the man was automatically the head of the household, and benefits were issued to the HOH card. Also, the cards couldn't be used at an ATM, you had to go to a grocery store, give the card to customer service, and they got your money for you. I said I was taking the baby for a walk because I was pissed and went to the store for the money. When Jake tried to get the money off his card, it was denied; he tried mine, which was also denied. I told him it was just running late since it was our first month. He never did find out that I got it or that I got the next two deposits.

Valentine's Day, 1998, Jake disappeared. He went to the store for the usual disappearing man things, milk, bread, and cigarettes. Jake was gone for three days. I had fallen asleep with my door open and woke up with it closed. I peeked carefully out of my room and saw he was asleep on the floor, just outside of my doorway. There was a crack stem sticking out of his pocket, and streaks of dried blood trickled from his nose. I put on one combat boot and kicked him three times before he even moved. Jake jumped up, trying to explain where he had been and what he had been doing. There were no explanations that I would accept. He tried them all, including, "They aren't my drugs; I am holding them for someone else." We fought throughout the day. That night I was on the phone with Bianca since she asked to talk to him. I heard his side of the conversation. "Well, I really only did it for the money." "I did wind up liking it, though. I did have a couple of boyfriends." I hung my head in devastation. He always said it wasn't cheating because he was getting paid. It was a job. I agreed that it wasn't cheating, but not for the same reasons. I knew about it; he didn't hide it; I stayed. Is it really cheating if your partner knows about it and still stays? It didn't matter; it still hurt.

237

A week later, while in another fight about his drug use, Jake punched me in the face. I lost a tooth. The tooth had been bothering me, and I had a dentist appointment the next day. I still went; they told me it had been a baby tooth. The adult tooth was stuck in my gum sideways; this has caused my front tooth to be extraordinarily crooked. As of today, the tooth Jake knocked out is still gone, and that front tooth is still just as crooked.

In May we moved. We went further upstate, where neither of us knew anyone. Jake got a job on a horse farm. We would have a three-bedroom, two-bathroom house, no bills except phone, and Jake would be paid two-hundred and fifty dollars a week cash. It was peaceful. First, there were deer out my backdoor, wild turkeys I could watch from my kitchen window, and there was a very friendly horse that would stick his head in my window and lick me almost every morning. There were also super weird spiders. Bug phobia is real and can be paralyzing. I spent most of every day running away from spiders or spraying them with cleaner. I was isolated and had no one to talk to except my baby. My depression was spiraling into darkness. I was always on edge, wondering what was going to go wrong. It was a small town with truly little in it. I walked everywhere, though, and in some areas, I could smell crack while I was out with the baby. Jake never had the money for the things we needed; I had no idea where it went. I didn't question anything; I accepted things for the way they were and adjusted accordingly. I returned bottles and cans to get diapers, wipes, and the little bit of formula I was supplementing. We had also gotten stuck with Sharon's two adult cats and thirteen kittens when we moved, so I got the supplies they needed as well.

Before long, people from Poughkeepsie were coming to visit, bringing drugs and chaos. Jake was paying for their gas, food, tolls if they had any, hotel if they needed to stay the night, and the drugs. I was also a slut again that was cheating on him with every person in town. Jake let his cousin Mario move in; Mario was a small-time user and dealer. He was also in a motorcycle gang, as were Jake and Mario's fathers. Jake came in after work with his jaw rocking back and forth like it does when he smokes crack. Everyone has something they do with their mouth when they are on crack. I personally chew my lips. To this day, I do it when I am really missing it. Jake tried to go pick up our daughter, and I stopped him. "You aren't going near her after smoking that shit! You aren't going near her fucking high!" Mario came to his defense, "He wasn't smoking rock. I would never give him that. It was just coke." I didn't care what it was. It was my job to protect my child, even if that meant from her own father. Also, it irritates me that so many people think crack is worse than coke. Do a little research; this is a stereotype, not a fact.

My depression worsened. I will not lie; the condition of my house was disgraceful. The only thing that was consistently clean was my daughter's room and her things. It didn't help that the floor through most of the house was just the plywood subfloor. Jake was supposed to put down real flooring the first week we were there, and it just never happened. The kittens would not litter train; Jake blamed me for it. I showed them the litter box a million times, and they just would not use it. I saw someone had stolen from my daughter's piggy bank. Any change I had went in there for her. She was five months old, and it had been half full. Now the top was off, and it was lined with a few inches of pennies. I mentioned it to Jake, and he said he didn't take it; I told him to talk to Mario. Jake swore his cousin would not take from our baby. "Well, then, who did? It was either him or you." It was rhetorical and loaded with attitude. Jake backhanded me hard enough that my head hit the wall. "If you are asking me to pick between you and Mario, you do not want to know the answer. Do not ask. I will always choose my family over anyone. He is family, and you? You are just some bitch." I never would have asked. The thought had never occurred to me; it wouldn't have. It was nice to know where I stood, though, and it was nice to know we were not a family.

The first week of August, Jake came home on lunch and asked if I wanted to visit my family. He said he had already talked to his boss and the boss's wife. The week I would leave, they would give me his pay and drive me and the baby to the train station. I was so elated that I hugged him. It had been a while since I had voluntarily touched him. I will not attempt to count the involuntary times. We will just say, I stopped sleeping because I woke up too many times being tied to the bed.

The day before I was set to leave, Jake came home early. He was in a mood; it was the beginning of withdrawal. Mario had gone on a run and was gone for two days. I was cleaning the cat mess off the floor again and showing the babies the box again. Jake started screaming at me for not training them; I screamed back that I was trying. He screamed that he had had to do dishes on Father's Day. I screamed to stop being a baby and that they were his and Mario's dishes anyway. While we were fighting, one of the kittens peed on the floor right next to the box. Jake picked the kitten up as high as he could and slammed it down onto the floor. The little baby laid there twitching and hurt. I grabbed my daughter and put her in her room. I opened her blinds and put her in her swing. Looking out the window and swinging was her favorite thing to do. I closed and locked her door since I was the only one who knew how to get it open. I told Jake to take the kitten to his boss; he was a retired vet and would be able to help it. Instead, he took the kitten to the back door and threw it down the hill into the woods. I wanted to do the same for him. I told him how disgusted I was with him and asked if he would do the same to our daughter if she had a bathroom accident. Jake felt bad, found the kitten, and I again told him to go to his boss, so the kitten could be put down humanely. Jake walked out the front door, and within seconds I heard my daughter screaming. It was a new cry that I hadn't heard before. I saw the problem as soon as I opened her door. Jake, her father, was outside beating and mutilating the kitten in front of her. The smile on his face still haunts me.

I left at five o'clock the next morning. It was several train rides away and exhausting. This was before the days of car seat stroller travel systems. However, that is how I traveled with her. Theresa picked us up at the train station and brought us to my grandparents' house. We were supposed to stay for two weeks. Jake never called to make sure we got there okay; I called him that night. Jake had a house full of people. Mario, his wife, the kid, and at least a dozen other voices could be heard in the background. Jake told me I would not be able to stay at the house for the winter, that his boss went to Florida, and he would have to go too. He asked if I could stay with family for four to five months each winter, and I told him no without asking. That was too much to ask of anyone. His next suggestion was he would rent me a place near my family, sending me money for my rent and bills each month. I told him if we were going to have a marriage like that, we might as well get divorced. "Okay, did you talk to a lawyer yet? Because I did, and I am suing you for full custody?"

I loved him. I hated him. I didn't want him. I wanted a family. We made a child together, and I didn't want what I had grown up with. I was crushed. Grandma said we could stay; the baby and I could have the living room. Dierdre brought me upstate to get some of our stuff. We had to do it on two separate trips. The house was worse than when I had left. There was a cat mess everywhere, including in my daughter's crib and throughout her dresser. Dishes filled the sink and counters; flies swarmed; no laundry had been done; food and trash laid everywhere; there were knives stuck in many of the walls, swords hung at a child's level, crack and coke were laying on the coffee table. Jake had told me Mario's five-year-old was staying there. Jake came in and was an asshole at first, telling me not to take his stuff. He softened quickly and told me he didn't want me to go, and Mario's wife had pushed him to say the things he had. I knew that was true, but I also knew that a part of him had meant it. The part that didn't want to be a clean, sober adult. The part that would never be able to change the addiction we both had battled. Everyone deals with it differently. My pregnancy and child had been enough to keep me from the addictions. My love for her was more powerful, and that just wasn't the case for him. On the second day that we went, I brought a Polaroid and an extra film. A child couldn't live there. I took a lot of pictures, and we took the kittens.

On our way out, we stopped at the state troopers down the street. I dropped the stack of Polaroid pictures and the address on the desk. They talked me into giving a formal written statement. While I

241

wrote, they pulled Jake up in the system and remarked, "We have a regular criminal on our hands." They didn't know the half of it; no one does. Deirdre and I stopped at the humane society on our way back to my grandparent's house; I hope the baby's found homes. My grandmother was pissed; people had been calling all day, threatening to kill us all. When they called again, I made it clear if they had something to say to me, come say it to my face but leave my family out of it. I made sure they had the address to meet me. Like most cowards, it was all empty threats, and no one came. Jake got two months of weekends in jail. Jake's dad died of cancer while he was in jail, and once he got out, he was fired. These things were both my fault.

Two months after moving back in, I finally found a job. I made five dollars and fifty cents an hour part-time at a pet store. I gave my Grandma every penny I could to help with the costs of us being there, it wasn't always a lot, but it was what I had. Tina watched the baby while I worked, and Bianca helped when she could, but she had a full-time job. Gavin died at thirty-six years old of lung cancer. He had never been a smoker and hadn't been exposed by his family either. Bianca only lived around the corner from my grandparents, so she would sometimes babysit on weekends so I could see friends. I opened a bank account and started saving. I was doing well; I had been clean and sober since before I had gotten pregnant until Jake made a reappearance in January 1999.

My grandparents didn't want him around, and no one did, but there was still the shadow of "He is the father of your child. You cannot divorce him" hanging around. Jake wasn't allowed to stay the night or be there while I was at work. I still hated him. I still loved him. I didn't trust him at all. Over the next week, I cleaned out my bank account to pay for his hotel rooms, taxis, and food. I snuck him into my grandparents' yard to sleep and even hid him in the house a few times. I was out of options, I had to send him back to Helen, but I didn't even have enough to get him a train ticket. Thinking back, I should have just told him to go suck a dick for the cash, but I didn't. I borrowed money from Theresa, who owed me several hundred dollars, to get him back to his mom. We agreed that he would come

242

back on our anniversary. If he showed up, I would have enough money to get us to social services, and they could help us get a place together. If he didn't show up, I was done, and it was over. Jake didn't show up; he called that night with a million excuses. I didn't want to hear them and would not acknowledge them. I wanted a family desperately, but I was better off without this man, and more importantly, so was my daughter. Jake called again on Valentine's Day. I told him I was busy; I had to go to work, and not to call back unless he had a job and was sending child support. Theresa took me to court, where I filed for divorce. During the hearing, it was recommended I wait seven years and have him declared legally dead because, as it stood, they couldn't let me divorce him. He had no address for them to serve him the papers. I knew I couldn't have him declared legally dead because his family would also have to say they hadn't heard from him; they weren't going to do that.

When my daughter was nine months old, I called the ADA. I was ready; I was being haunted by increased memories, not to mention the nightmares. I was told someone would call back, it took months, and I had heard nothing. I called every month for almost a year. Finally, I got someone who said they were the ADA I was supposed to talk to, but they couldn't find my file. They would call back. By the time they called, it was too late. The statute of limitations had run out. I would never see justice, and he would always be free.

I was remarkably close with Theresa's family. Especially her dad, Sidney. All of Theresa's friends called him Dad. I was the only one who didn't have a real dad, and I adopted him as my own. He worked at a grocery store in the same shopping center as me. He drove me to and from work every Sunday because there was no bus. While I was there waiting for him, I started talking to Savannah, who had been friends with Theresa in high school. She and I hadn't been friends. They had some kind of fight, and I knew she was only talking to me to get back into Theresa's life. I didn't care. We became friends, and it didn't matter that she had ulterior motives. Savannah set me up with a guy she worked with. I wasn't interested in him, but I figured, what the hell? He would be a suitable rebound. I know, I know, I'm a bitch.

I had sex with Gerry three days into the relationship. I was his first, but at least he knew how to put a condom on. Gerry worked with Sidney and Savannah. I hung out in the employee break room with the three of them frequently. The company didn't care and allowed us to smoke there. Things started getting rough with Gerry within the first month. He took me out to dinner at Wendy's. I ate a Jr bacon cheeseburger; after we got outside, he slapped me across the face, "You ate too much; go throw it up before you get fatter." I did as I was told and started taking diet pills along with water pills. I'm sure it isn't surprising to hear that I became addicted to them.

Sidney saw I was struggling. We were both off on the same day; he said he would come to get me, and we would go to the beach. I had a bad feeling about it right away. I didn't know why; I had never had a bad experience with him, and he was one of the few men that didn't drool over me. I told him I would not have a babysitter, so no. He showed up anyway, saw that I had no babysitter, and told me to bring the baby. The three of us loaded up into his old car and were off. When we got there, he took me to a secluded spot surrounded by dunes. I watched my daughter crawl around, play with toys, and taste sand (yes, I stopped her repeatedly). Sidney stayed behind me; I didn't think about it; I was preoccupied with my child until I felt him pulling my shirt off. I just stood there as he then removed my bra. After I was topless, he came and stood in front of me, naked. "Simone, I haven't had sex in a long time. Years. How would you like to fuck an old man? Make me happy?" My body was paralyzed, but my mouth worked. "I can't. A few years ago, I would have said yes, but that isn't who I am now." I tried to cross my arms, and he gave a firm "Don't" as he stepped slowly closer. Sidney put his hands on my hips, slid them up to my back, and pulled me in for a tight hug. I felt our bare skin touching and knew what was next. He let go, looked disappointed, but got dressed. The truth? If my child hadn't been there, I would have just done it. It was all I knew. On our way back, Sidney begged me not to tell Theresa; I said I would not and had no intention of doing so.

I found it difficult to be around Theresa. I didn't like keeping this secret from her. I was snapping at her over everything, especially the money she had owed me since high school. The money didn't really bother me, except when she knew I was struggling and didn't offer to help. Plus, when I gave her the money back for Jake's train ticket. She owed me a lot more; I felt she should have told me not to worry about it. We all have different priorities and hearts, though. I decided to just avoid her instead. If she called or came by, I would have Tina tell her I was busy or not there, and I didn't call her. I grabbed the ringing phone on my way passed without checking the caller ID; it was Sidney. He was very upset that I hadn't been around. Plus, Theresa had vented to him that I would not speak to her. I told him I had just been busy and would call her later, nothing was wrong, and I wasn't mad at him. I wasn't mad at him; I was hurt. I was confused. I was broken.

True to my word, I called Theresa later that day. I tried to keep it short and simple, but she didn't have it. I caved; that wall I had built hadn't been up long enough to be solid. I made her promise not to tell the person it was about, and she agreed. "What would you say if someone you know and trust tried to fuck me?" I asked with trepidation. Theresa asked if it was her boyfriend and then went on to question every single guy she knew except her father. I said no to all of them; hell, I didn't even know who most of them were. She could think of no other names. "Theresa, it was your fucking father." I felt her heart shatter with my own. "My father? Okay, you need to tell me exactly what the fuck happened. Now." I did and then reminded her of her promise not to say anything.

I didn't eat unless I felt like I was going to be sick or pass out. I popped diet and water pills any time I felt any emotion. After a while, I would throw up if I did try to eat; sometimes, liquids wouldn't even stay down. Gerry took me to the hospital. I was severely dehydrated and diagnosed with an addiction to diet pills and anorexia. They wanted to admit me to a treatment facility, but I refused; they gave me a referral to a group for people with eating disorders. When I was being discharged, it was made clear that if I came back in for this, they would get a court order to admit me. I didn't go back, and I didn't go to the group. Teresa, Savannah, and Dierdre were at my house waiting when I got back to my grandparent's house. Theresa demanded to know what was wrong; I told her it was nothing as I popped a few pills and threw up the water used to swallow them. Gerry told them the truth with a smile on his face. Theresa took the pills, knowing I couldn't afford more, and threw them in the sewer. They didn't know that Gerry hit me almost every time I ate. I didn't tell them. There is no point in bringing up the fact that Gerry also didn't understand what the words "no" and "stop" meant. After reading this much about my life, it should just be a given.

Dierdre was moving out of state, and we had plans to hang out before she left. Gerry had come over before work, and after he left, we were going to go to the mall. Dierdre was moving in with her boyfriend, whom she had finally lost her virginity to at almost twenty years old (still proud of you, dude!). Gerry was mad at me for something; he grabbed, pinched, and squeezed my nipple. When he wouldn't let go, I slapped him across the face; he slapped me back. Dierdre and I talked about the fight while we were out. She said it was my fault that he hit me because I hit him first. I told her yes, I did because he would not let go of me, and it hurt. "That shit fucking hurts!" I yelled while we walked. "Yeah, but that isn't the same." I didn't respond because there was no response that made sense. It absolutely is the same.

Tension was high between Teresa and me. We argued over everything. It was my fault. I didn't blame her for her father's actions, but I did take it out on her. I tried not to, especially when I would catch myself doing it, but I couldn't stop. The boiling point - "Do you believe me? About your dad?" She thought, "I do, but I don't. I do, but...he is my dad. Without being able to confront him, I guess I just can't really believe it." I was surprised she had kept the promise to me as long as she did, "Confront him then." I expected him to deny it, but he didn't. He told her he wanted to see me so he could apologize. I was to meet him in the break room of his job the next day. Gerry went with me for support that he didn't give. Sidney's apology was, "I am sorry for what we did. It was wrong."

I pulled from my pocket a baggie of coke that I had been carrying around for weeks. Since the day he took me to the beach. I put it in his hand; he walked away, throwing it in the trash on his way past. Gerry slapped me across the face calling me his "Little slut."

Does Anything Ever Really Change?

Summer came, and Jake called me on my birthday. I was greeted with "Happy birthday!" When I answered the phone. "Thanks; who is this?" I asked. "It's Jake!" I thought... "Jake, who?" I really didn't realize who it was. "Jake, your husband!!" I thought for a few minutes I had honestly forgotten, even just momentarily, that I was married and that Jake had ever existed. I told him I was dating someone. He got pissed; he told me he still wore his wedding ring and didn't have sex with anyone, ever. I laughed, "I'm sure you do if they pay." It was true, I knew it would hurt him, and I had already established that I was a bitch. Jake knew how to hurt me, too; he made sure I knew that he had been in touch with Kelly from Yonkers. He had done heroin with her; he liked it, and he was going to do it again. It was all my fault because I left him.

I had a lot of friends at work. My closest friend was an assistant manager named Bill. It was a slow night and almost closing time. I felt uneasy, spooked, like I was being watched. I felt the air in the store get hotter, and it started to burn my lungs. A fat flannel-covered stomach was coming towards my register; I almost wet myself as he placed his items on the counter. I rang up the man, who didn't look at me. He paid in cash, and when I gave him his change, he made sure his hand touched mine. My skin crawled. Bill came up to lock the doors right after the customer left; I was hyperventilating. Once I calmed down, I told him that once upon a time, I had a stepfather who abused me in every way. Then I let him know I was sure that my last customer had been him. Bill let me know he would protect me in any and every situation if the guy came back to page him, and he would deal with it. The guy came in several more times, but Bill and I were frequently the only two people working. So, if he was helping a customer, he couldn't respond to my pages. The guy started coming in daily. He always paid in cash, always made sure he touched me, and I could never get the dirty feeling off my skin.

On the fifth consecutive night, I couldn't handle it. I paged Bill to the front and told the customer I had to get a change from the office. The change was in the safe right next to me, and I had no access to it. On my way into the office, I passed Bill and nodded toward the front. "That is him!" I felt a tear drop from one eye; I watched through the office's one-way window. Bill rang him up; the guy pulled out his wallet, Bill was speaking to him, the guy smirked, and the transaction ended. Bill locked the door behind him and came to the office. "It is him, Bill. I can feel it. It isn't just someone that looks like him; it IS him." Bill gave me a few minutes. "You don't have to worry about it anymore. I told him my employee, friend, and co-worker is afraid of him, and he isn't to come in this store while you are working anymore." I had tried to hide my fear. "What did he say? "I asked. "He didn't say anything. He smiled, put his cash back in his wallet, and paid with a credit card." A credit card! I ran to the register, opened it, and started digging through the credit card receipts. There it was. I wasn't crazy. The receipt proved it. Griffith. Unbelievably, I have never seen him again. I do freak out if I see someone who looks like him. I always will.

Time passed. I got a promotion and a few raises. We got a new store manager who was older but inexperienced. When I would come in for each shift, I would be given the keys to everything, and he had given me the code to the safe. All the new hires saw me as management, even though I told them I wasn't. I was friends with all my co-workers, which was very new for me. My daughter, who was almost two, was even allowed to come to work with me when I had no babysitter. Most of the staff requested off for my daughter's second birthday party. For Mother's Day, they got me a card that they all signed and flowers. They were all amazing people, and I loved them. One girl really hated the new manager and felt that he didn't follow the company rules, she reported him, and he was fired. Our new manager, Zara, was awful. She didn't like that I was treated as management by the staff or that I was treated with more respect than her. She really didn't like that I was popular with the whole staff. Zara changed the safe code and didn't give me the keys. She thought taking my power as a quasi-manager would also take away my respect, but it didn't. Zara found out that Betty and I both liked Martin. For once, he was younger than me. I wouldn't have gone out with him...because he was seventeen, and I was nineteen. Zara told him Betty liked him, but he said he didn't like her. Zara told him I liked him; he didn't say anything. He called me that night and told me he did like me, but he would not be in a relationship with me unless he could take care of my daughter. Sweet, unexpected, but unwanted. I do not think it was even that I liked him. I liked him because he was nice, made me feel safe, the friendship wasn't one-sided, and I needed to like someone to distract me from the fact that Gerry was a dick. I just needed to like someone, and he was the guy I happened to be closest to at the time.

During times of severe stress, I often had blackouts. I wouldn't remember who the people I was with were, where I was, or how I got there. This happened a few times when I was with Betty and Martin. Between that and Zara telling everyone I talked about them behind their backs, I lost all the friends I had. I loved going to work; I loved my co-workers, and I loved my job. I had reached a place where I was content in everything except my relationship and where I lived. I sank quickly into depression. I put in my two-week notice and left three days before it was over. Before I left, I turned Zara in for theft; I gave them dates and times to watch the cameras. She had been stealing hundreds of dollars in pet food and supplies. Zara was written up and made to pay for what she took. She knew it was me and put me in the system as not eligible for rehire.

Gerry decided to teach me how to drive. I had my permit, but the only driving experience I had I had been drunk and or high. With my daughter strapped into her car seat, the three of us went to a small residential neighborhood. I was doing well; everything was simply perfect, even the weather. Until I took a right turn too wide. I was in the wrong lane; I knew there was time to straighten the truck out and keep going. I panicked and hit the gas instead of the brake, then I panicked again and let go of the wheel. I hit a tree. Luckily, I have always been big on car seat safety. My baby girl only had a bruise from her car seat strap. I had various injuries. I hit the steering wheel with such force that it bent around my breasts (last I knew, Gerry still had the steering wheel); the seat belt didn't lock, so my head hit the windshield, and I had a concussion and a lot of bruising. The Dr told me my uterus was crushed so badly; I would never have more kids.

Two weeks later, I was trying to tell Gerry I was in too much pain from the accident to have sex. He was laying behind me and just shoved it in any way. We had been using the not-so-reliable pull-out method for a while, but I felt when he finished, there had been no pull-out. "Did you just cum in me?" I snapped at him. "No," he answered as he blushed and looked guilty. "Yes, you did; I felt it," I said firmly. "Why does it matter? The Dr said you can't have more kids, and I am in your ass anyway." I was absolutely dumbfounded as I asked, "My ass? That isn't my ass. Why would you think that?" I couldn't keep the "You are a fucking idiot" tone from my voice. "I'm behind you. That means I am in your ass." Yes, you can facepalm now; I did. I knew at that moment that the Dr had been wrong, and he had just gotten me pregnant.

I started my new job at the photo lab of a drug store shortly after. A few days before my twenty-first birthday, I took a pregnancy test. I did the test in the mall bathroom while Gerry waited. I came out with the test in hand, "We have a problem," I told him. "It's nothing," he replied. I put the positive test on his face, "It isn't nothing. It is a baby." he didn't believe it. We went to a pregnancy clinic for a test; he still didn't believe it. Over the next three days, I took sixteen tests that were all positive, and Gerry still didn't believe it. I became terrified that the Dr had meant I would not be able to carry, not that I couldn't get pregnant.

I told my job I needed to switch departments because of the photo lab chemicals and being pregnant. They refused to move me. Dierdre had an office job, and she got a promotion, leaving her old position open. I begged Tina to watch my daughter full-time during the day; she agreed that I would tell her why I needed the job so badly. I told her, and she made me tell my grandmother. Bianca had begun a relationship with Bart. She moved into his house with his two nearly adult kids six months into the relationship. Bianca took my daughter occasionally overnight, or even for a weekend, so I could job hunt, interview, go out, or do whatever I wanted. The weekend after I found out I was pregnant, my daughter was there. I was picking her up with Savannah, and Bianca knew right away that something was going on; she pushed me into the bathroom and would not let me out until I told her. "You need to learn how to sit with a nickel between your knees," were the words I still hear an echo of. Side note – for all the jackasses that preach, "Keep your legs closed" or other similar things, you can absolutely have sex with your legs closed. It is fabulous; you should try it.

Theresa, Dierdre, Savannah, Gerry, and I produced a plan that we would save money and rent a place together. We put some living room furniture on layaway and were supposed to take turns paying for it. I covered them often. It became clear we couldn't afford to do this, and we only knew one other person that would go in on it with us. Sidney. He and Eileen had finally separated, and he was struggling to make ends meet on his own. The group of us met him in the parking lot of his new job to discuss the situation. Sidney congratulated me on the baby that I wasn't happy about. The baby that I knew in my heart was a boy. The baby that I was secretly thinking about placing for adoption. Theresa took over, explaining the situation to her dad. Our eyes met for the first time since the day on the beach, "And us? Are you going to be okay? Comfortable around me? After what I did?" My eyes showed nothing as I had trained myself not to show emotion so long ago, "We're good." I even hugged him. But I saw a future of him trying to fuck me every time we were the only ones home. I saw a future of me saying yes, just because I had been trained to make men happy. To give them whatever they wanted.

I met a couple who wanted to adopt. We went to Chuck E Cheese, so we could talk and my daughter could play. Alex and Mark had been married for fifteen years and knew after five that she was infertile. They didn't have a lot, but they could provide a child with a stable, loving home, all needs, and some wants. I told them right away that I was undecided about what I was going to do. Gerry was disconnected from everyone and everything; that was just who he was. Alex and I became close; we spoke on the phone daily, multiple times, if there was a doctor's appointment. On the day of my sonogram, I called her as soon as I walked in the door. She sounded withdrawn and depressed as she told me she knew I wouldn't be able to go through with giving my baby up and to please not call her again. I tried to tell her I knew the gender; she said you have known since the beginning it is a boy; I never doubted you. I wrote her letters; they were returned unopened. I never saw or spoke to her again.

I had been laid off from the office job after only three weeks, and Dierdre had as well. I couldn't find another job because I was visibly pregnant by twelve weeks. I got unemployment and made it stretch as far as I could. I refused to go to Gerry's house until he told his family I was pregnant. His mother's initial response was for me to get an abortion. I was pro-choice, but for myself, I couldn't do it. She then wanted us to get married and move in together before the birth of the baby. I didn't tell her that I was already married to someone else or that I didn't even like Gerry. We were looking for apartments for just the four of us, though.

My OB was shocked and appalled at my lack of diabetes management when I was carrying my daughter. He explained the actual dangers of diabetes in pregnancy, which include stillbirth. The records from the car accident were faxed over. "Simone, you were told your uterus was crushed. It wasn't. It was bruised; your pregnancy isn't in danger at all." I was at the doctor's office frequently for lack of fetal movement; I had a very lazy baby who liked to sleep a lot. Gerry waited until I was seven months pregnant to say, "I don't want kids." Before I had gotten pregnant, he had always said he wanted kids someday.

My grandfather, who I talk about rarely and makes a little appearance on these pages, was an asshole. He saw there was a particular soda I had been drinking a lot of, so he picked some up for me. I had been waiting to thank him in person; we were not often home at the same time. I was getting ready to walk out the door for more job hunting when he came in from the store. I was waiting for him to turn; he was hard of hearing and would not have heard me with his back turned. "I saw you've been drinking those sodas a lot. You don't even have the courtesy of a thank you," he began while putting a bag on the floor. He stood and faced me, a smile on his face, stroking his beard, "You're worthless. You're useless. You'll never amount to anything." He walked away. My grandparents had three kids. Denise, who lived a few hours away, couldn't hold a job and had her hand out begging them all the time. Bianca, my mother, had owned a home, ran a business, then owned her own before going back to working for others and renting, but still, she had a life and made things happen. She did need help from time to time. Tina was in her mid-late forties and had never left home. I grabbed the latest letter from Denise and walked after Grandpa furiously, and tapped him on the back. Our eyes met with equal hatred; he started stroking his beard at once. I held up the envelope and pointed up the stairs toward Tina's existence. "If I'm worthless and useless, what the fuck do you call two of your three kids?" He smiled wider, but his cheeks darkened. "You have a point, "he admitted. I gestured to his beard that he was still touching, "And at least I don't worship pedophiles, asshole." He still didn't shave it.

I was induced at thirty-nine weeks. After ten hours, I begged for the main med, and all I could have was an epidural because the baby's heart rate kept dropping. I hadn't had any pain meds with my daughter, the thought of a needle in my spine was terrifying. I caved and had it done; I didn't even feel it over the contractions. Moments later, they told me they needed to take blood from the baby's head to find out what was causing his distress. This test must be done rapidly. They ran from my room; the results showed he wasn't getting enough oxygen. I had to have an emergency C-section. Gerry had been asleep on the floor since we got there. Savannah was in the chair to my right, holding my hand; Bianca was in the chair to my left and had just fallen asleep. As I was wheeled out, I reached back for her, "Mommy? Mommy, I'm scared," I said with a cry. It was the first time I had called her mommy since I was 14. It was also the last. "I know you are, baby, I know, I am here," she said as a nurse handed her scrubs and told her to put them on over her clothes. It was a moment of comfort from my mom, who had always been so distant, and who I always felt didn't want me. She was by my side during the surgery. I didn't react well to the epidural. I shook violently; my eyes rolled in my head, I threw up uncontrollably, and I could only say, "My baby, my baby, my baby." I saw him for a split second as they ran him from the room, and unconsciousness took over. I awoke in a room alone with no light, hooked up to machines everywhere, and every part of me hurt. I was released the day before my daughter's third birthday. I had complications from the surgery for over a year.

The night I brought my baby boy home from the hospital, Gerry slapped me across the face. It happened in my Grandma's kitchen, in front of Bianca, Tina, and Grandma, while I held my new baby. I handed the baby to Bianca and went after him; I had had enough. I had just had surgery, I was in indescribable pain, and he hit me holding our new child. I was going to beat the shit out of him, and he was never going to put his hands on me again. "Simone, let it go," Bianca commanded. "Ma, he slapped me! You saw it, you all saw it!" I yelled. "Yes, I saw it. But you were asking for it. Besides, he is the father of your child. You just take it and keep the family together. You accept it and move on." It was the shock of her words that kept me from hitting him. It was the shock of her words that made me accept it, move on, and keep coming back for more.

I received my last unemployment check while I was in the hospital. By the time he was a month old, I was broke. I called Gerry and asked him to bring diapers after he got off work. He said a small pack if I blew him, big box if I fucked him, and if I did both he would get wipes too. So, I whored myself to my child's father, in exchange for our child's needs. This was consistent until our son was six months old. When I really couldn't bear to do it, I used credit cards that I couldn't pay, and were defaulted on. I got a job when the baby was six months old and got both my kids in day care. Tina had been obsessed with my daughter. She had always wanted, but never had, kids of her own. I didn't want her watching either of my kids. The job sucked, I got to walk around the mall and beg people to do surveys. Two days before I started the new job, I had a D and C. I had still been in constant pain from the C-section, and the incision kept opening. The results gave no conclusive answers, the pain went on, the incision continued to open and close.

I had told Gerry many times before I got pregnant that I didn't want to be with him. Each time he would leave, but the next day he would be back. His slaps had become punches, the sex became more forced. During the pregnancy he had hit me less, but he had still been hitting me. I continued trying to end the relationship and he continued to come back. I told him early in the pregnancy that he needed to stop coming over that the relationship was just over. He said if I left him, he would kill himself. This went on for months. I told him I wanted to see other people, we could still see each other, but other people too. "I don't want to see anyone else," he said with a smile. "Okay well I don't want to be with you at all, so we see other people or just leave." He chose the open relationship. I made no attempt to see or meet anyone else while I was pregnant. I waited until our son was nine months old, and my daughter was almost four. I started talking to men on the internet. I wasn't interested in them, but they were a distraction. My job was awful, I was at risk of losing my day care grant because I wasn't getting enough hours, Gerry being a dick was increasing at an exponential rate.

It was winter and the sky was as gray as my forever dying heart. I had lost my job at the same time I was going to quit. I hated talking to people, especially strangers. I hated the disdain in people's eyes as I would approach them to ask if they would do a survey. I understood it was annoying, they didn't understand I was just doing my job. I had reconnected with an old friend, Spencer, online. We had been friends and there had been a spark, but we were both in other relationships. He was now single, and my relationship was open. Gerry drove the two kids and I to upstate New York and dropped us off. Spencer told me where the key was, as he would still be at work when I got there. The kids and I went in to wait, it wasn't long before I heard the door opening and boots stomping on the floor.

The four of us had an awkward dinner. Spencer looked like the guy I had known, but there were a lot of differences as well. I put the kids to bed and went back to the living room. Spencer stepped toward me slowly until I was backed against a wall. "You aren't the Spencer, I thought you were, are you?" I asked in a hushed whisper.

Our bodies touched and he shook his head. I felt his hot breath and hard dick as his lips pressed against mine. I was tied to his bed within minutes and fucked till I bled not long after. He untied me before he went to sleep. I called Gerry after Spencer was asleep, he didn't answer. I knew he turned his phone off when he went to sleep. I left five messages that I needed him to get us right away, and not on Sunday. I didn't sleep; I grabbed a knife from the kitchen and sat outside the door my kids were behind. I was prepared to die protecting them. This Spencer was a normal everyday person in the morning and throughout the day, when the sun went down and the kids went to bed, he was a monster. I didn't hear from Gerry that day. He came to get us on Sunday as he was originally supposed to do. I had never been so happy to see hi, hell I had never been happy to see him at all. I asked him why he never called back or came the day before, he just shrugged and smiled.

I returned to my grandparent's house hiding a lot. My body always told the tale of my travels, at least for a little while. Bruises were prominent around my wrists and ankles. Whip and belt marks ran across my back, stomach, tits and ass, in some of these marks there had been bleeding. I hadn't cried though. I hadn't shown fear. Those things were for the weak. It was too late for me to be weak. I was already dead inside.

I would still sometimes see a car parked outside my grandparents' house, and feel like I was being watched. When I had worked at the mall asking people to do surveys, co-workers told me they saw a man sometimes who appeared to be watching me. When I would ask what he looked like, they described Griffith every time. Bianca married Bart in July 2001. It was the first time Brady, and I were around each other since I was a teenager. We spent most of the night talking. He reminded me how I had given him not only his first cigarette, but his first joint, too. We didn't talk about any of the bad. I forgave him that night, with no words spoken. Brady was never smart. In my collection of memories, there were many, where Brady and I had shared a room, and he saw the things that Griffith did. At the time of our preteen and early teen years, I honestly don't think he knew or understood that what he was doing was wrong. He is the only one I have ever forgiven. I still hate him though. He is the epitome of everything I hate. He is the racist homophobe we were both raised to be. I am thankful every day that as I grew up, I developed my own brain and the ability to think for myself.

Memories

The nightmares returned after my weekend with Spencer. My childhood memories still come in mostly clips and flashes. I remember things I don't want to. I remember an old woman's hand, not her face, just her hand. Her skin was soft but cracked brittle and sunken around her pronounced veins. I would try and poke her veins back in. I have been told this woman was Griffith's grandmother. I remember nothing else about her, but I know I loved her.

I remember my dogs. The first one we got was mine. Someone in Griffith's family had found her. Luna had been homeless and abused. We were all staying at Griffith's dads house (Grandpa W) while waiting to move into our house. She was supposed to be a family dog, but she was mine. The first time Griffith's hands touched my body, it was because of my dog. I was sitting in a rocking chair watching TV, rocking softly. My hair was held out of my face with a light blue headband, that matched my blue and white stripped short set. "Stop rocking! You're hitting the dog!" Griffith screamed startling me. I looked down and saw Luna there. The chair was just barely touching her, I never would have hurt her and felt bad thinking I had. I sat still and watched tv for a while. I moved my leg from under me causing the chair to rock slightly, "That's IT," Griffith's voice rumbled as he charged towards me. He ripped my tiny body from the chair and threw me over his large shoulder. I was carried to his father's room and thrown on the bed. Griffth crawled up beside me covering me from the waist down in a big warm blanket. Tears fell from my eyes as I cried loudly. Griffith's body pressed against mine. "Shut up before someone hears you. Shut up or I will beat you like you deserve!" He angrily whispered in my ear. His hand maneuvered under the blanket and between my legs. I tried to stop crying like he told me to, and I couldn't. His other hand began to pinch my inner thigh, "I won't stop until you shut up! Only the weak cry, shut the fuck up you little bitch!" I didn't stop crying, but I cried a lot quieter. His hand went inside my shorts and underwear and then there was pain. Intense pain that felt like I was being murdered from inside of me.

259

Bianca was coming, we both heard her. His hand bolted to my face as he roughly dried my tears. "I can tell mommy!!" I thought fleetingly as he whispered, "Tell her I was tickling you too rough, or I will kill her." The threat was a whisper, but it was clear. Bianca appeared wrapped in a towel, "What's wrong with her? Why is she crying?" She asked with annoyance. "He was tickling me too rough", I lied probably for the first time ever. "Well stop," she commanded and disappeared. Griffith's pants opened and he rubbed himself up and down my leg as his hand returned to where it never should have been. When it was over, he told me, "Next time you will be a good girl, or it will happen again." Griffith lifted me up off the bed and tossed me firmly on to the floor. I looked up and saw Griffith and Grandpa W shake hands in greeting in the doorway. I was saved! I adored Grandpa W; he would help me.

He approached and I reached my small arms up to the big man. He had the same build as Griffith, but he was mostly bald. His remaining hair and beard were gray. Grandpa W lifted me gently off the floor. "It hurts. Daddy hurt me," I whispered in his ear. He laid me on the bed with his body over mine and smiled. "He didn't hurt you. He punished you," his hand went up my shirt to touch the flat chest that would one day get a lot of attention. He stood up straight and his hand went up the leg of my shorts. The same pain was back, tears formed and rolled steadily down my cheeks. When he was finished, he again leaned over me. He whispered in my ear, "Only the weak cry." He vanished from the bedroom. I went and curled up on the floor with Luna. She licked my tears away.

I remember sitting on my bedroom floor coloring, right after we moved into our house just after my fourth birthday. Luna's head was in my lap. I remember her sleeping beside me in bed, keeping me safe. She was my best friend; she was my everything. I remember Brady and I being alone after school, when we were too little to be alone. Brady hit Luna and threw things at her. I would scream and cry for him to stop, he would laugh at me. If I tried to physically stop him, I became his target. Brady beat us both every chance he got. If I fought back, he would show Bianca and Griffith the marks I left on him. Griffith would get the wooden paddle and beat me,

260

Bianca would watch. The marks on me didn't matter, the bruises and cuts were invisible.

When I was five, I remember praying to God. I asked him for everyone to be healthy and happy, and if it wasn't too much trouble, could Griffith maybe stop hurting me? Griffith still came to my bed. Griffith told me it was "because I was bad." He had a whole list of reasons, "Because they were things Bianca was supposed to do, but she wouldn't, so he had to do them with me instead." I would beg him to ask her and ask if she knew he had to do it with me and he would tell me "Mommy can't know. If mommy knows she will die. If mommy dies, you and Brady will die and then I will die too. Do you want us all to die?" Of course, I didn't, I just wanted it to stop. I wanted us all to be a happy healthy family, I didn't want any of us to leave, die or go away.

I remember being around five, sitting in my bed as he entered my room and closed the door. I remember the look of terror in my eyes as he got closer and closer. I remember trying to hide. I would curl up under my bed and go to sleep, or in my closet. I remember the nightmares. They were all the same and simple. They were just hands, skeleton hands made of lightning. They would reach out from under my bed or out of my closet to get me. I can remember the fear I felt in those nightmares.

There were nightmares that would send me to Bianca in the middle of the night. I would try and snuggle next to her for comfort. Griffith would pick me up and put me next to him. He would turn on scary movies (I never did get over the original *Poltergeist*). First, he would calm me, comfort me, make me feel safe. As I would fall asleep, I would feel his hand creep into my clothes, and I would have a different kind of fear and pain.

I remember being five and having a crush on a twenty something who worked with Bianca. I remember thinking he had a nice butt. I didn't question if it was normal for a five-year-old to think that way until recently. The same year, I was in kindergarten. Some fifth graders dared me and a boy, Kevin, to kiss. He was in my class, and

I had a crush on him, too. We kissed and they said no, like in the movies, as they giggled. Kevin didn't know how, but I did. I kissed him, with tongues, like in the movies Griffith would turn on. I remember being five, six and seven, playing during recess. Three boys, Kevin, Chris and William, with three girls, Elana, Stephanie and me, would play catch and kiss. The boys would chase the girls, if they caught the girl, they kissed her. I remember they only actually chased me. I was often caught by all three of them.

Bianca took me to a classmates' birthday party. The ice cream they served wasn't a kind I had ever had. I didn't like trying new things (I still don't), I cried. She took me to the bathroom and yelled at me. I was never allowed to go to another birthday party. I was hit anytime I did anything they thought was weird or not normal. Speak only when spoken to, kids should be seen and not heard.

I remember my sixth birthday. We were going to one of my favorite places, the arboretum. My favorite was the Weeping Willow Trees. I could hide under them and be safe, I could tell them my secrets and their leaves would hide my cries. Grandpa made me breakfast since I had stayed the night. I was given cereal, toast and a pear. I tried the pear and didn't like it; I didn't eat the crust from my toast. Griffith got there and I ran to him, happy, laughing and excited, my dress flowing all around my short legs. Griffith scooped me up in a big bear hug as I continued to laugh. Grandpa told him about my breakfast, that I had wasted food. Griffith beat me. The willow trees got extra tears and secrets that day.

I remember that we used to rent out the other downstairs bedroom in my house. I don't remember most of the people that lived there. I do know, one of them has some answers for me, the key to some things my brain has not unlocked. I know she does, because as Griffith came to my room, there was a woman with long straight blonde hair taking pictures of the things he did. I almost remember her voice whispering, "I am so sorry."

I remember a neighbor boy when I was seven babysitting us a couple of times. He would shower at my house, then sit on the couch in nothing but a towel. When Brady wasn't looking, he would open the towel and show me his penis, while making kissing faces at me. There were several babysitters. One took us out in the yard, which was special, we were rarely allowed to be outside. She raked up a big pile of leaves and had us jump in it. I wore blue jeans and a white sweater with pink and blue hearts and stripes across the chest. I laughed and jumped in the leaves, I rolled around and threw them up into the sky. My jeans got a grass stain on the knee, I was beaten, that babysitter never came back again. One of Bianca's friends watched us for a while at her house. She was married and had two kids, I don't remember any of their names, or really even their faces. I was a picky eater and almost never ate what she cooked for dinner. I had to sit alone in the dark for hours before I was allowed to give the food to the dog. I was very scared of the dark and they knew it. The woman's husband would pick me up by my head and swing me around. No one listened when I said it hurt, I was slapped if I cried. When I was seven, Griffith came to my room and Luna was waiting for him. She growled at him, he backed against the wall. Griffith looked at Luna with hatred. I knew in that look that he would hurt her. Before I could say anything, she charged at him, her paws planted firmly on his shoulders, I saw the aggression in her eyes, and the fear in his. He struck her with such force that it sent her flailing into the wall. "NO1" my brain screamed as I tried to run to her, he caught me around the waist. Luna stood whimpering and left my room limping. I flailed and cried as he lifted me off the ground and threw me back into the bed. "Bad dog and bad girl," he snarled as he removed his belt and whipped first at Luna sitting just outside my doorway and then across my thigh.

I remember being five or six, it was summertime. We stayed at Griffith's cousins house a lot during the day. There were a lot of kids. There were ice pops, sprinklers and frozen cream filled cupcakes. There was another little girl. I remember her hair, brown straight and thick, with bangs that framed her face that I cannot recall. Griffith would bring us both to a bedroom. He would touch her and make me watch, then touch me and make her watch. The promise afterward was always the same, if either of us ever told he would kill the other one.

I remember being seven years old and being tied naked to a tree. Griffith, Grandpa W, and several other men that I don't know, were laughing at me. They were drunk, I remember the smell of beer on their breath. They threw things at me, traced their hands up my unfortunately already developing body. They put things inside of me. Mostly beer bottles. I hung my head in shame as one of them, pulled out his penis and peed on me. I was punished for that later.

We got a second dog when I was seven. Much to Bianca's dismay, our new dog, Socks, preferred Brady over everyone else. She was a rambunctious mutt, who could and would drag me down the street if I walked her. We went out to dinner one night, leaving the dogs home. When we got home the wooden paddle was broken in half and there was a big pile of dog shit on it. Griffith blamed Luna and beat her. He knew it was her and I did too. She again tried to protect me and had been hurt for it.

I don't know when he started putting bugs in and around my bed. Before I was seven. There was a hole in the closet of my ground floor bedroom. Crickets would get in all the time, and I was scared of them. Griffith would kill them and place their dead bodies around my bed, so I was scared to get up, or even move. Sometimes they would not be quite dead, and I would see their legs twitch if I didn't hide under the blanket. Several times, bags of dead spiders and bugs were put under my blanket. I have a severe phobia of all bugs to this day. I once broke my toe, as an adult, trying to get away from a cricket. I cannot handle pictures or even drawings of bugs. This has made being a Papa Roach fan difficult.

When I was seven and had run to Bianca fleeing a nightmare, she ignored me as she always did. Griffith put me in their bed and fell asleep with HBO on. A man appeared on the screen who said "If you want something bad enough, you can will it to happen! It is that simple. Just want it with everything inside of you, with all of your heart, and it will happen." I was filled with joy and the kind of excitement that only a child can experience. I ran to my bed, jumped in and covered up with the blankets. I tried, with Luna already at my feet, I tried. I wanted it with every single part of me and that man said if you wanted it bad enough, it would happen. I wanted it with

264

every part of me, with all my heart. I willed it! I willed it! I failed, as I tried to will myself, to die.

When I was nine, I tried to run away. I didn't have anywhere to go; I had no friends there. We had spent the last two years going to a school almost two hours away near Bianca's work. She had tried for those two years to sell our house, with no success. I didn't know anyone here; I hadn't gone to the school there since second grade. I didn't know what else to do. I had tried and still did try, to ask God to please make him stop hurting me, for Bianca to do what she was supposed to with him, so it wouldn't have to be me, to please help me be good enough that I wouldn't need to be punished. I had tried to die. I tried so hard to be a good girl, I was never good enough. I didn't want anything bad to happen to anyone. I wanted us to be a family, all four of us and our two dogs. Please understand, I tried so very hard to be a good girl. No matter what though, I always seemed to need to be bad and have to be punished. I felt I would never be good enough, even praying to God for me to die didn't work. I begged God, not to hurt anyone, just me, take me away. My prayers were unheard and unanswered. I had to run away; it was the last option I had.

I wasn't allowed to leave the house or cross the street. I climbed out my bedroom window and snuck around the house. I walked along the fence that ran alongside my house. I had already broken a rule by leaving, that was bad. If I got caught, I would need to be punished. I didn't want to cross the street and break two rules. Being that bad would be a worse punishment. I could think of nothing worse, but I knew somewhere in my heart that it could be. Behind my house was a mall, and shopping center. The back lot was directly behind our fence, and no one ever used it. I walked diagonally through the parking lot towards the shopping center. I saw there was a car parked, not in a spot but near one. It was weird to see a car in that area, but I was nine, I didn't really think about it. I knew it gave me the creeps though and I didn't get too close.

I walked to the stores stopping to look at things in the windows. Where did I go now? Where would I sleep? How would I eat? I saw my reflection in a store window. One tear ran quietly down my chubby face. Maybe I had made a mistake. I decided to go back home. If I got there before anyone knew I had left, I wouldn't need to be punished. I turned and went back the way I had come, by the time I was at the end of the sidewalk, I could see that the car was gone. Halfway through the parking lot, I could see something laying on the ground, I got a little closer and saw it was a Polaroid. Closer still, I thought it was a picture of a puppy. Just steps away I bent down to look at it. That was no puppy! It was a dick! I stood straight up, every muscle in my body tensed, there was a faint noise behind me, I turned and saw the car that had been there. I felt my eyes widen. The windows were so dark, I couldn't see inside. It was moving toward me very slowly. I ran. I ran as fast as I could. I broke all the rules and crossed the street. I couldn't run home; they could follow me. I simply ran until I couldn't run anymore.

I crashed into a boy. A teenager. His name was Mikey, and he knew I was in trouble. He offered to help and at first, I told him no. Mikey seemed different, he seemed safe. I told him I thought someone was following me and I was scared to go home, in case they were watching. He started walking with me, he was smoking something, that I knew wasn't a cigarette. Mikey told me it was weed, and I was too little to try it. I asked anyway, I had after all been smoking cigarettes on and off since I was five. He finally did let me try when we were near my house. I don't remember the feeling, just that I liked the smell. Mikey gave me a boost back into my window and stayed in my yard until after I was asleep. We stayed friends for a long time. He was the same Mikey that was the nephew of Todd.

I don't remember much of being nine or ten. We got a third dog when I was ten. Stinky was one hundred percent Bianca's dog. I remembered the months preceding telling when I was eleven. Luna was old and sick. Bianca and Griffith wanted to put her to sleep. I screamed at them that they were murderers and trying to take away all I had. I have no justification for that, other than I was young, I loved her, I couldn't imagine the pain of my world without the existence of her love. It was Veteran's Day, 1990. We were going to work with Bianca and Griffith for the day. We were waiting for Bianca to finish getting ready, so Brady and Griffith took the dogs out to the yard before we left. I looked out my kitchen window to see them both throwing things at Luna and hitting her. I ran out the door just in time to see her limping run down the street. Bianca protested that we had no time to ride around looking for her it wasn't the first time she had left the yard, she would be there when we got home. She always was.

That afternoon I asked Bianca, if she really thought Luna would be there when we got home. She said she did, she always was. I felt something though. A heavy pain in my heart. It felt like my heart was crying. I knew she was gone; she was dead, I could feel it inside of me. In that moment, I stopped believing in God and I never prayed again. God couldn't be real. If God was real, children would not suffer the way I was, and my only friend would not be gone. I had prayed to God that morning, harder than I ever had in my eleven years of life. I prayed for him to give the rest of my family health and happiness, I fell to my knees in hysterical sobs, praying and begging him to kill me, please God please just kill me. Take my life so they can be happy. So, Bianca and Griffith could be like a real married couple, so Brady could be an only child and not be made fun of because I was smart, and he was stupid (Not my words), please God please, without me there everyone else could be happy, and I would not have to be hurt anymore, I couldn't handle it, PLEASE, GOD, PLEASE! After I prayed, I dried my eyes, and looked out that window. God's answer to my years of prayers, was to take my only friend. Luna wasn't there when we got back. They both said they drove around looking for her. Bianca said they found no trace of her. Griffith said he found her in a hole she had dug, and he stomped her to death.

Griffith did deliveries for the store. I liked going because people would tip me. Griffith stopped at a store, I started to get out and he leaned his fat belly against the door. "Not this time," he said as he walked away. He came out with a flat brown paper bag and started driving. I kept my position against the door, knowing what it meant when he pulled me into the middle seat. Griffith kept looking at me and I felt something coming. Something bad was going to happen. We made a left hand turn into another parking lot and my door opened. I rolled from the gaping door across the hot asphalt. Griffith scooped me up and threw me back in the truck like I was a doll. I was covered in blood, dirt and tears. He looked angry. I thought it had been an accident for years. As I got older, I realized it was a warning.

When I was thirteen, Bianca and I got in a heated debate over politics. She said we are republicans, and we vote republican no matter who the candidate is. I told her I didn't yet know what I was, she insisted I am whatever she is. "Hey ma? Are you pro-choice or pro-life?" She looked at her feet as she responded pro-choice. "Well, you should have aborted me." She looked up and our eyes locked, "Yeah, maybe I should have."

I had heatedly confronted Bianca with my memories of her eyes being open when he was touching me. She claimed she saw nothing. She claimed she sometimes slept with her eyes open. Grandma told me it was true; she had slept with her eyes open since she was a little kid. I had never seen it happen any other time though.

Wondering what happened to my other dogs? Did I ever have any other pets? Socks he kicked off the bed. It broke her back, and she was put to sleep. Stinky he let out of the outdoor cage, knowing she had been alone all day and would be hyper. "She ran out in the road before he could catch her." The way he told me about her death? He called and said, "I just got done burying the dog." The puppy he got me when I was fifteen and living with my Grandma? He threw her out the window of his moving truck going down a highway. I had rescued a baby squirrel, he put cocaine in its water. I had a gerbil; he gave it D-con. We had a bunch of rabbits, most died of natural causes. The last one I had left, he shot in the head, in front of me. Then he forced me to watch as he cleaned it, cooked it and ate it. Harry's house was a puppy mill. I think it was listed as a dog kennel, but it was a puppy mill. One harsh winter, one of the females was having a hard labor. She was brought into the basement to keep her warm. I sat with her and watched her birth her babies. I helped her take care of them by taking care of her. I went back to school after they were a few weeks old. The next time I was there Griffith told me to go downstairs and feed her. There was a smell I noticed as soon as I opened the door. There were no sounds from the mom and babies like there should have been. I got to the bottom of the stairs and saw her lifeless body, already sunken, a puddle of pee under her, a few feet away lay her pile of four dead puppies. There were boxes of D-con all over. I screamed for what seemed like forever. I woke up with my arms around the dead mama dog. Another mom had another liter. The puppies were beautiful. Some seemed sick and they slowly started dying. The ASPCA was involved and demanded the rest be taken to the vet. Griffith and I brought them. I waited in the waiting room while he was with the vet. One of those puppies was supposed to be mine once it got old enough to be weaned. Griffith came out and told me all the puppies except one tested positive for parvo. The healthy one was the one that was to be mine. The rest would have to be put to sleep. He disappeared back into the vet's office. Once he returned, he carried a large cage. Inside was a large lump covered with a towel, and one small one covered separately. I cried softly as we walked to the car, I had tried to ask where my puppy was, and he would not answer. I wasn't allowed to sit in the front seat on the trip back to Harry's house. Griffith placed the cage full of dead puppies next to me, removed the small lump and placed it in my lap. Before closing the door, he removed the towel, "Carry your puppy home" he told me as I cried with the dead puppy in my lap. I clung to her lifeless body and cried. I was made to bury them when we got back. I overheard Griffith telling everyone the next morning, while laughing, how he had told the vet to put the healthy one to sleep too, "just because."

There will be more time for memories later. For anyone reading this, it is just a story. For me, it is reality. It had been my life. It has been my slow death since I was really just a baby. For me it is pain, anger and more tears than you can imagine.

Run, Run Away

Shortly before my daughter turned four and my son turned one, I started talking to a guy online. Okay, so there were several guys. A few I was interested in. James was on Long Island, Marco lived in Texas and Derrick lived in Maryland. Gerry and I were still in an open relationship, he saw all of my actions as cheating, but an open relationship means I was innocent. I really did like James. He was different than any guy I had ever talked to. We made plans to meet a few times, but I kept backing out. I was scared that he would see me and not be interested. I had never had that problem before, I had never been rejected, I attracted men. I still have no idea why. I am hyper aware of what I look like, and I have never understood what always kept me surrounded by drooling guys. However, I always seemed to attract the wrong kind of men. James was so different from everyone else, maybe he would have been the right kind. Maybe that is what fueled my fear of rejection.

After talking online for a couple of months, I moved to talking to Derrick and Marco on the phone. Derrick told me he had a beer after work every day and he would not stop for anyone. I told him I didn't care, and that I no longer drank. Marco confessed to some drug use, primarily ecstasy, acid and mushrooms. Before you wonder if I ever did ex or 'shrooms, the answer is yes. I had kids though and I was determined to stay clean. Since before I found out I was pregnant with my daughter, I hadn't had a drop of alcohol (with the exception of Bianca's wedding). I hadn't done drugs since I was seventeen (with the exception of weed occasionally, which isn't a drug, and I don't care if you think differently). I had also quit smoking during most of both pregnancies.

My connection with Derrick got stronger. He confessed that he was living with his ex-wife and her family, but he was looking for his own place. He promised me that he was sleeping on the couch, and there was nothing going on between him and his ex. I told him that was fine because I was still kind of involved with my son's father. I explained the open relationship, that only existed because of the suicide threat, he understood. Gerry was getting increasingly

270

more volatile, irritable and abusive. He was again hitting me anytime I ate, if he wanted sex, we were having sex, if I was going out with Dierdre it meant I was screwing someone else. I didn't talk to Theresa or Savannah anymore; Dierdre was my only friend.

Everyone in my family made it clear I was to stay with him, even when they saw the bruises. I already had two kids with two men, he was the father of one, and I had to stay with him. I felt the "If you leave him you have to leave," hanging in the air. And so, I did what I do best. I ran.

I am generally a very honest person. But I lied. I told everyone I was going to Maryland to look at a school and see about finding the kids and I a place to stay, I would be back in a week or two. Gerry brought the kids and I to Maryland in May 2002. Derrick was worried I would cheat on him, or his friends would hit on me. All of his ex's had cheated on him, many of them with his friends. I told him I would wear something that would make them hit on me, and he could watch as I broke their arms.

Derrick had moved in with friends, a married couple, Allie and Steve. I had spoken with Allie on the phone many times. The way Allie and Derrick interacted made me think maybe they had had a thing at some point. I asked him he said no. I hadn't actually seen Derrick before meeting him. Cameras on computers and phones were not common then and the quality was horrible. He had sent me one picture; it was extremely dark. All I could see was that he had a large tattoo on one arm. When I met him, I wanted to run. Back home, Texas, another planet, anywhere. He would not have been bad looking if his teeth weren't rotting out, he was also dirty. I decided to stay though, I had developed feelings for him for who he was, not what he looked like.

The first night, my two kids fell asleep in Allie and Steve's room, I was told it was fine, they didn't use their room anyway. They slept on separate couches in the living room. I had previously told Derrick I wasn't having sex with him the day we met. I was waiting at least a little while. I was getting the kids blankets out of my bag when he came in his bedroom, closed and locked the door. He started kissing me and suddenly we were in bed, and he was on top of me. My fishnets were torn, and my underwear were slid to the side. I hadn't protested in anyway; I hadn't had time to. It happened so fast I didn't even have time to blink. When he finished, which was only about fifteen minutes, he fell asleep on top of me. Derrick was only around one hundred and forty pounds, but the dead weight on top of me felt like so much more. With a bit of effort, I finally got him off of me. I was headed to go check on my kids, when I discovered the lock was stuck. After trying for a while to unlock it, I heard my son crying for me. I called him over to the door and tried explaining to him that the door was stuck. He wasn't even a year and a half old though. I spent hours trying to get that door open. I could hear no one else in the house moving. Derrick would not wake up. I couldn't get out the window and even if I could, then I would not be able to get into the house. I held my babies' hand under the door until he fell asleep. I was ready to go.

First thing in the morning I told Derrick I was using the phone to see if someone could come get me. He wasn't happy about it, and I didn't care. I made it clear that locking me in a room where I couldn't get to my kids all night was fucked up, and not something I would tolerate. I called the few people I knew, no one could come except Gerry, and he couldn't come for two weeks. Derrick showed me how to get the door unlocked, I told him if it happened again, I would break the door down and I didn't care whose house it was. The kids started staying in Derrick's room with me that night on a couch. The next few days went smooth. It was weird though, that Derrick didn't go to work. He was self-employed, he fished over the winter and crabbed over the summer. I asked him about work after five days. He said he wanted us to spend time together, work could wait, rent was paid several months in advance.

Derrick stopped drinking the day after I got there, I never asked him to, he just did it. After two weeks, I decided to stay a little longer. I called home and let everyone know, I would be staying at least two more weeks. I also let Gerry know. He asked if we were still in a relationship. "To me we haven't been in a long time, but are

272

you going to kill yourself if I say no?" I asked. He said he would kill himself if we were over. "Well, I am with Derrick, but whatever you want." He was quiet for a few minutes before asking if it was a "Committed relationship" or not. "I broke up with you months ago, this hasn't been a committed relationship." I hung up. Gerry started dating Dierdre shortly after. I wasn't upset about him moving on. I was pissed however, about him being with my friend. I was pissed at them both. Derrick brought me to the courthouse and asked to fill out for a marriage license. I told him I couldn't marry him; I was already married. He insisted they didn't check, and I refused to lie on the form.

Derrick seemed sweet and caring. If I wanted or needed to go anywhere, he walked with me so I wouldn't get lost. He wanted to go everywhere and do everything with me. It had been three weeks and he hadn't gone to work though. I had brought money with me and plenty of cigarettes, but the money was almost gone, it had mostly gone to groceries that weren't eaten by me or my kids. Allie and Steve were both heavy smokers who never had their own cigarettes or money, so those were almost gone too. I sat Derrick down to talk about him not working. He confessed that he was scared to leave me because if he wasn't with me, I would cheat on him. I reassured him that I would not and if it made him feel better, I wouldn't go anywhere unless I had no choice. He went to work the next day.

Once he started working again, I found out a lot of things from other people. Allie was best friends with his second wife Penny. Penny and her kids were over all the time. Derrick's ex-girlfriend Jasmine moved in. He was given temporary custody of his daughter, Angela (who wasn't biologically his, but he was on the birth certificate), which meant I was now responsible for a pre-teen. His first wife Rae, moved in with a friend across the street to be closer to her daughter. The amount of tension in the air was thicker than the smoke. After a couple of weeks, I took the kids for a walk to the park while Derrick was at work. When I got back Derrick was there and mad because "something could have happened." We argued a little and I said, "How do you think I feel trapped here all day with every woman you have ever fucked?" He got the point and explained he had just been worried.

Derrick wasn't particularly good at his job. Most days he brought home no money, he never brought home more than sixty dollars, and often by the end of the day, he left owing people money. Steve drove us to social services so I could apply for help. Derrick was adamant that I couldn't work. I wanted to work, as long as I had someone responsible to watch my kids, I wouldn't have left a pet bug with the women that were always at the house. Derrick said I wasn't allowed to work, because I could meet another man and cheat on him.

Allie had her friend Lee from high school come visit. They had had a sexual relationship; she was hoping he would still be interested. She hoped if he wasn't interested in her, he would be interested in Jasmine. He wasn't interested in either of them, he was interested in me. I admit my wrong doings freely. I didn't cheat, at least not by definition. I did flirt and I did flash him. I did have long phone conversations with Lee and lie about who I was talking to. Sort of, I would call a friend, then three-way Lee into the call. If Derrick wanted to talk to whatever friend I was on the phone with, I would give him the phone, and Lee just would not speak. It didn't last long before Derrick found out, Allie told him. The same day she told him about me and Lee, she told me she had had an affair with Derrick before I met him. I didn't care that he had been with her, I did care that he had lied about it. I also found out that most of Derrick and I's online conversations weren't Derrick at all. He had asked his best friends' girlfriend, Roberta to talk to me the way a girl would want to be talked to. Everything that had made me like him, care for him, and want to be with him, had been a lie. I had nowhere to run back to. When I had called to tell my family, I was staying for two more weeks, they said okay, but cleared out, stored or got rid of all of my stuff.

Allie and Steve were kicking us out, rent hadn't been paid since mid-May. Another lie for Derrick. I got approved for help from social services, I gave them back rent and paid two months in advance. They used it to gamble in Delaware instead of paying bills. We had no hot water and they had a foreclosure notice on their

274

house. I went for a job interview at a convenience store on my birthday. The manager hired me on the spot, she said anyone that would come in for an interview on their birthday was a good employee who wanted to work. I was a good employee, at every job I had. I always came in early, stayed late, didn't take breaks, helped co-workers, and my job was always done. Derrick couldn't handle my son while I was at work. My poor baby would carry around my shoe and a picture of me, crying until I got back. Derrick started bringing my kids in to my job. He would park my son's stroller across from the counter so he could see me. That was all the baby needed to be calm. My daughter would run around playing. Derrick would play the old Pac-man machine. September came and my daughter started half day school, it was the only day I took a break, to watch her get on the bus. In October something happened to my legs. I could barely stand and couldn't walk; the pain was incredulous. Steve took me to the hospital where they wanted to admit me for tests, but I couldn't leave my kids that long. I signed myself out. I lost my job; Derrick got a job at McDonald's where he would have a reliable paycheck. We moved into our own place in November which was closer to Derrick's job, and he wouldn't need to pay someone for a ride to work.

We discovered while moving in that the place was infested with roaches. I tried everything to get rid of them, except an exterminator because we couldn't afford it. Nothing worked. Both the front and back doors had dead bolts that needed to be locked and unlocked with a key from the inside or outside. Derrick started locking us in the house when he would go to work, "Don't go anywhere, if you do, I will know," he would tell me. I was smart as a kid, and smarter as an adult, but because of my traumatic childhood, I confused a lot of emotions. I took his statements for cute jealousy, caring, worry and fear. Not control. I had to climb out a window with my two kids to get my daughter on and off the school bus every day. I didn't know how to get anywhere. Anytime Derrick took me anywhere, we walked a different way, sometimes it seemed we walked in circles before getting anywhere. The day came in late November where I had to leave without him. He hadn't gone to the store the day before and I had nothing to feed the kids for lunch. After my daughter got home, the three of us made an extra trip out the window to find a store. It took longer than it should have to get to the store, we took a couple of wrong turns. When we were on our way home a man I didn't know asked "Aren't you Derrick's girl?" I hesitated, "Yeah, who are you?" I asked. "Just a friend of Derrick's." He said with a smug smile. When Derrick got home from work, he got in my face demanding answers as to why I had been out of the house. I explained that I had nothing to feed the kids and he felt it should have waited until he got home, and I should have stayed in. I had just started thinking that maybe his issues were deeper than a little jealousy and insecurity. That maybe I should contact some agency to help us get out. But it was already too late. I found out in early December that I was pregnant. I was trapped.

I had to use medical transportation to get to all of my Dr's appointments. Gerry and Dierdre came to visit a few times. Bianca came and took my daughter for part of the summer. Gerry was court ordered to pay child support, he wanted no visitation and offered to sign his rights away. Bianca had been irate over my third pregnancy. "Now you will have three kids by three different men. What will people th-" Nope, I didn't want to hear it. "I don't care what people think, ma. And as far as what you think goes? It shouldn't matter to you who their fathers are, or that they have more than one. All that should matter to you is that they are mine." She never said another word about it.

My second daughter was born in August 2003. It was a repeat c-section, I had an allergic reaction to morphine. My new baby stopped breathing and had to be resuscitated, I also stopped breathing and needed resuscitation, twice. Luckily during the second half of the pregnancy Derrick had stopped locking us in the house. I had only gained ten pounds during the pregnancy, but it still would have been impossible to get out the window. Derrick had started leaving the back door unlocked, I was still only to go to the bus stop. The new school year started, and a day came where I got a call my oldest had been hurt at school. I had two small kids and no stroller. We had a grocery store shopping cart, that would have to do. It again took a while to get there. It was a mile and a half away, and I didn't

276

really know where I was going. I got in trouble again for leaving the house. Derrick said if it happened again, he would start locking the doors again.

We had been on the waiting lists for several income-based housing complexes. Finally, a letter came that we were next on the list. We moved to our new apartment in April 2004. Derrick and I fought a lot because he could no longer lock me in. He had been bringing friends home since I was pregnant. Joe, Jack, Tom and Paul were always over, before and after the move. Those were the people I was allowed to talk to. Jack was mid-thirties, as was Derrick, Tom was in his early twenties, Joe was fourteen, Paul was almost seventeen. All four of them were interested in me. Tom was the most forthcoming about it. He told Derrick "When she gets tired of your shit, give her my number." Joe and Paul followed me around like lost puppies. Jack was the quietest, and really only verbalized his desire when he was drunk. After we moved, I started talking to Melanie, one of my new neighbors. She had a daughter the same age as my oldest, they were in the same class, she had another daughter a year older, and a son that was right between my younger two. Derrick hated her. She had a reputation for being a slut and a whore that she was proud of. Derrick nicknamed her C.P. (for community pussy). Any time he came home, and she was there, we would get in a fight. I felt a spark of the defiant teenager inside of me. Yes, Derrick was ten years older than me, but I no longer needed a father, I needed a partner. Derrick helped with nothing. He came home from work at two pm, napped, went to his friend's house, ate dinner, slept. I slept on the couch with my kids, because Derrick was a bed wetter. He hadn't bothered to tell me. I found out six months into the relationship when I got peed on.

Joe had come over when we first moved in to help out. Derrick was at work, Joe got brave and started trying to touch me. I slammed him backwards into the wall holding him there by his hands and made it clear he wasn't to ever touch me again. I was tired of being touched without it being wanted and I certainly didn't want to be touched by a child. Derrick came home and saw me holding Joe against the wall and thought there was something going on with us.

277

The only children I had room for in my heart were my own. Not long after, Joe tried to convince me he was in love with me. Jack stopped coming around when he developed an addiction. The only people left I was "allowed" to talk to were Tom and Paul. Paul had moved and I heard from him rarely, no one else heard from him at all. Tom was over frequently and called me nightly. Derrick was so insecure that I was going to cheat on him, but I could only talk to guys, and the guys liked me, if I told him those guys hit on me, he would laugh about it. If any other guys outside of those four, spoke to me, it meant I was cheating. It could be a "How are you today?" From the cashier at the grocery store, and I was sleeping with him. When Tom was over, he behaved himself, but on the phone at night, the conversations were inappropriate. I hung out with Melanie as often as I could just to be defiant and have a little control of my life. Despite the arguments, he wasn't being violent. It was all fine, because it wasn't abuse.

Derrick would not allow me to buy things we needed. I had to steal diapers, wipes, clothes, and shoes for the kids. I couldn't buy household supplies, I had to steal toilet paper, he stole trash bags and bleach from work. On Halloween, Derrick wanted me to dress slutty. He always wanted me to look the part, he wanted me to dress like a slut all the time. Halloween was the only time I obliged. He couldn't keep his hands off of me. It was almost time to take the kids trick-or-treating, and he wouldn't give up. I rolled away from him in the bed, and he took what he wanted from behind. When he was done all, I thought was, "You just knocked me up." I was tired of sex that I wasn't getting anything out of. I had still only had one orgasm, eight years earlier. At least that was the only one with a partner, I had at least figured out how to do it myself. Sometimes, that was the only way I could sleep.

I was right, I did get pregnant. Derrick had gotten his license, and we had a minivan. He was never around to take me to my appointments though. Melanie took me instead, then Derrick would yell at me for being with her. Melanie was the one with me when I found out I was having a boy. Melanie was the one next to me in the operating room, Derrick didn't want to be in the room. Baby boy number two was born in July 2005, six weeks before baby three turned two. It was my third c-section. My first had been traumatic, second was easy and third was in the middle. If Derrick had helped it wouldn't have been that bad. He didn't even bring the other kids to the hospital until after the baby was born and I was in recovery. My third was very clingy, and sickly from three months to three years. I had to carry her and her new brother everywhere. Right after a c-section that's not a good thing to be doing. Derrick had barely fed the kids when I was in the hospital. The night I came home from the hospital, I had to fry ten pounds of chicken because his friends were coming over for dinner. I got my GED when the new baby was a few months old.

I went and filed for a divorced again. Jake and I had been separated for seven years. He still called every so often. The conditions of being granted a divorce without having him declared legally dead, weren't too awful. I had to write letters to three people he may be in touch with, stating who I was and why I was looking for him. I had kept in casual contact with his mom, but it had been a while and I didn't have a current address or phone number. A quick internet search got me Carissa's number though. I called and explained what I needed to do. She gave me her address, Helen's and a friends, she said she would tell them all to not reply. I had to send a letter to his last known legal address, that was simple it was where we had lived together. Lastly, a notice had to be posted at courthouse, saying who I was, who I was looking for and why. His old boss at the horse farm didn't reply either, and the notice was posted. My divorce was finally granted in the Fall of 2006, we had been separated since August 1998.

A month later I got a call from Helen. We caught up and she said she needed to tell me something. She insisted I should sit, I didn't, I need to pace when I am on the phone. I expected to hear that Jake had died. I had time to wonder while she was telling me to sit, if it had been an overdose, a deal gone bad, or if he stole from the wrong person. "Simone, look I know you're trying to find Jake to divorce him. I know you need that to move on. I didn't respond to your letter so it could move forward. But you should know, Jake is in prison. In

Florida. For murder." I guess I should have sat down. Helen told me what happened from Jake's perspective. He and a friend were planning to rob an older woman for drug money, but when Jake walked in the room, she was dead, and his friend had killed her. Helen went on to say that Jake, had been stupid enough to touch both of the murder weapons, which is why they had arrested him. His fingerprints were on both, his hand print was on the wall in her blood. I found out through an internet search that his DNA was also found in her shoe. I thanked her for the information and let her know the divorce was already over.

It took days, weeks, to process this information. Initially, I just didn't believe it at all. Jake wouldn't kill anyone. He wasn't generally violent...except when he was. I saw myself on the island, hiding under our plywood tent, covered in bruises with a bloody nose and a fat lip. I saw me showing up at the youth shelter in the Hamptons, in June wearing pants and a turtleneck. I saw his fist as it connected with my face and knocked my tooth out. I felt the beatings that to this day I have never told anyone about. I felt guilt that I should go find this woman's family and apologize for what he had done. I felt rage that he had taken a person from the world, a person from their family. At the end I believed it, and most of the time I still do. I followed the trial as much as I could. Jake and his friend were both found guilty and sentenced to life in prison.

Six weeks after having my fourth baby, I desperately wanted to be pregnant again. I hate pregnancy, it's awful, and because I have to have all C-sections, recovery can be hard. I couldn't help it though and started having sex with Derrick every chance I got. In December of 2006, I married Derrick. It was a courthouse wedding, just the kids and Melanie were there. Melanie got us a cake and made us dinner at her house. She and Derrick still hated each other, but she was there for me and supportive. I told everyone I was so happy. "The happiest day of my life" I told Bianca in a video message. I even cried when I made the video. Why did I say it? Because that is what you are supposed to say. Why did I cry? Because I knew I was lying to myself. I again, didn't have sex on my wedding night. Derrick got drunk and passed out on the couch. I hated having sex with him. I did when I had to or when my hormones were acting crazy. I never told him no, because if I even hinted that I wasn't interested he accused me of cheating. It was just the notion that you are supposed to have sex on your wedding night. Not just sex, but good sex. I was twenty-seven years old, had had one orgasm with a partner, not through sex, ten years earlier. So, on my second disappointing wedding night, where I again thought, "I don't," but said "I do," during the wedding vows, I gave up on ever having good sex, and orgasms.

I caught a virus from the kids. I had a fever, throwing up, chills, pain, I was miserable. Derrick wanted to have sex. For the first time in our almost five-year relationship and about a month after we were married, I told him no. Derrick pulled my pants off, pinned me down and raped me. There is no way I can sugar coat it. I cannot tell myself that isn't what it was, like I do and have done with so many other situations. I cannot even say he pressured me or coerced me, which is what ninety-nine percent of our sexual relationship had been, because that wasn't the case. He raped me.

I cried most of the next day and was still crying when he got home from work. Derrick kneelt on the floor in front of me begging me to tell him what was wrong. I didn't want to say it, that made it different, saying it made it real. He wouldn't let it go. "I said no, and you did it anyway. I said no, I was just sick and said no, and, and, and you raped me." It came out on one long sobbing breath. Derrick wrapped his arms around my waist and laid his head in my lap, "I'm sorry. I'm so sorry. I didn't mean to hurt you," he cried with me. I began to comfort him. I hadn't wanted to hurt him. "I know you didn't mean it. It's okay." It was okay; people make mistakes. Derrick looked up at me, in the eyes, "It will never happen again." But it did. All the time. Sometimes daily.

In the early spring of 2007, we hit a rough spot financially when he overdrew our bank account, racking up over three hundred dollars in fees. I had still been sometimes trying to get pregnant. It hadn't happened, and I figured it wasn't the best time. I stopped trying, and a month later, I was pregnant. Baby five was deemed safer out than in a month early and was born in November 2007. I had three boys and two girls. I was twenty-eight years old. My first baby was three months away from ten. Derrick again didn't come to the hospital until after I was in recovery. Melanie was there the whole time. My oldest took care of the cooking for herself, her siblings, and Derrick. I had gotten easy meals because I knew he couldn't cook. Frozen pizza, hot dogs, macaroni and cheese...he still couldn't do it. I even wrote down the directions. During all my pregnancies, I had access to doctors, medical care, and prescriptions. When I wasn't pregnant, I didn't qualify for insurance, so I had nothing, not even insulin. That changed around the time of my fifth baby's birth. The laws for medical assistance changed, and I got to keep my insurance. I finally went to the Dr and had my hip pain checked out. It started when I was fifteen. Bianca said I was making it up and wouldn't take me to a Dr and told my Grandma not to. Brady had hip surgery at around the same age and was insistent I was making it up for attention. I was diagnosed with junior arthritis in both hips and knees.

I started going to a general practitioner for medical care in the summer of 2007. The Dr told me that all of my medical problems were due to my weight (one hundred and sixty pounds) and said I was a type two diabetic, even though I had been diagnosed with type one at fifteen. I was given pills for my diabetes. I stopped eating and exercised compulsively. I lost thirty pounds in six weeks. The pills did nothing, so the dose was increased until I was maxed out, another pill was added, then maxed, and another was added, then maxed. I begged the Dr to just give me insulin. He wouldn't. I saw this Dr for four years. On my last visit with him, I brought all of my medications in a bag as he went over my vitals for the day. Again, he blamed my weight and smoking for my medical problems and the pills not working. I dumped the bag of medications at his feet. "I am a type one diabetic. If I was a type two, these would have done something. Yes, I am overweight, but I am not morbidly obese like you imply. And you really shouldn't be lecturing patients about smoking with your nicotine-stained nails. You are a fucking moron and an asshole. Please stop practicing medicine before you kill someone." I didn't go back to a Dr again unless it was an emergency for another four years.

I complained to Derrick that our sex life was boring. He did know that I never had orgasms with him; I had given up faking it long before. It wasn't worth my time or energy. His solution was to buy fuzzy pink handcuffs. We tried them out once, but they popped open in two seconds. A year later, I complained again about the sex. He bought me a vibrator that never got used, either.

Shortly after my fifth was born, I found something saved on my computer. It was a response to a Craigslist ad. The poster was a woman in an abusive relationship. The response was, "I will save you, baby." Melanie was at my house when Derrick came home from work. I simply asked him about it; I wasn't accusatory at all; we had a lot of people that came over and used our computer; it could have been anyone. He said it wasn't him; I said okay, and I went back to what I was doing. Derrick showed no indication that anything was wrong. Until the door slammed, I looked out the window to see Derrick punching our van. I walked outside; Derrick sat in the driver's seat with the door open; I knelt next to him on the floor of the van, asking what was wrong. I didn't notice the keys in the ignition. I had seen him angry before but not like this. The door leaned against the bottoms of my bare feet. Derrick wouldn't talk to me; he would just glare at me and shake his head. After several minutes I told him I was just going to go in. His hand clamped around mine on the steering wheel; the key turned in the ignition, and his foot hit the gas. "I am tired of you always accusing me of shit!" He yelled in my face while speeding down the road. One of my feet had fallen, and I was half hopping, half being dragged down the road. "Derrick, please stop! Please! You're hurting me!" He went a little further and hit the brakes. I slammed my side into the door and dashboard with force. He released my hand, and I walked back to my house as I heard him speed away. I hadn't accused him of anything, not just that day but ever. My foot was bleeding, and walking really sucked.

I didn't really care for a lot of Derrick's friends or co-workers. I had bad vibes about a couple of them. Dawson was one, he was always drunk, occasionally high, but those weren't the only reasons I didn't want my kids near him. Derrick said it was all in my head until I found his friend Dawson on the sex offender registry for child molestation. I showed it to Derrick, and he agreed Dawson would not be allowed at our house anymore. A couple of weeks later, I told him I was going to take a shower before he did an oil change on the van. When I got out, my two toddlers were sitting on Dawson's lap, reading him a book on my couch. Derrick was outside, starting the oil change. I told Dawson if he ever came near my house or kids again, I would kill him. I confronted Derrick for allowing a monster near our kids. He justified the actions that he had to associate with him because he was a co-worker. "You have to do your fucking job with him. You don't have to be friends with him. You don't have to associate with him. You don't have to be friends with him. And you sure as fuck WON'T allow him around my kids." I stormed into the house and locked him out.

The other one was Carlisle. There was just something about him that made my skin crawl, and my kids felt the same way. Derrick didn't know anything about really fixing a computer, but he faked it enough that he could charge his less intelligent friends. Carlisle brought his computer over to be fixed. After digging through the computer, we found a large collection of child pornography. Derrick asked me to wait until we confronted Carlisle. I made sure the confrontation happened immediately. Carlisle said it was a shared computer, and everyone used it; it wasn't him. Derrick said we would not report it, but if it happened again, we would. I walked away and made the call right then; I didn't care who had done it; it was still someone at that address. It was never investigated. Within six months, Carlisle needed his computer fixed again; this time, he gave assurance that he was the only one who had access to the computer. It had been kept in a room that only he had access to, plus it was now password protected. He was very adamant that there would be nothing inappropriate on the computer. He lied, of course. It wasn't even well hidden. I reported him in front of Derrick, even though he asked me not to. There was, again, no investigation. A

284

year or so later, Carlisle was arrested for inappropriate contact with a minor. He had sexually molested his girlfriend's niece. The child was twelve years old but was disabled; during court, it was disclosed that she had the mind of a seven-year-old. If they had investigated the two reports for child pornography, it would have saved that little girl. No one ever listens to me.

Derrick was always accusing me of cheating. Melanie heard a lot of the arguments; she had a plan for me to prove to him I was faithful. She wanted a tattoo but was scared, so she said she would pay for me to get his name on me if she could watch. That was fine with me; I got Derrick's name on my upper arm. Melanie chickened out and didn't get one done. Derrick was mad it wasn't on my lower back. "My name should be your tramp stamp; that way, when you are fucking someone else, they can see my name and know you're my tramp." A week later, I paid Melanie back for the tattoo.

Gerry would visit once a year, usually at Christmas time. Dierdre always came with him, even after they broke up. His last visit was when our son was eight. Anytime my daughters went to the table for more food, he followed them, he put his arm around my oldest (who was eleven) a lot, and if the girls sat on the floor, he would put them in his lap. He paid no attention to his own son. It all made me uncomfortable. I asked Derrick to watch his behavior; I wanted to make sure I wasn't paranoid due to my own history. Derrick said I was crazy and to drop it; he saw nothing wrong with Gerry's behavior. Dierdre approached me and let me know she and her boyfriend were uncomfortable with the way Gerry was acting. I asked my son how he felt about his father being there, and he told me he wanted him to leave because he wasn't paying any attention to him, just his sisters. He also said he didn't want his father to ever come back. I allowed him to voice how he felt to Gerry. His response was laughter. Gerry refused to leave because of road conditions, and Derrick told him he was welcome to stay. I had the girls spend the night in a room together; I told them to lock the door and put the dresser in front of it; I sat in the hallway on the outside of the door all night with a baseball bat. The next morning, I grabbed a few neighbors that I knew would help. Caleb and Chad were both big intimidating guys; once I told them the situation, they came over immediately. Gerry was physically removed from my house. He and his belongings were both tossed out into the snow. We haven't seen him since.

Derrick started doing the driving for Caleb, a local drug dealer. I didn't care as long as nothing was left in the vehicle, nothing was brought into the house, and gas was covered. The sixty-five dollars a week I received in child support for my oldest son went to driving all Derrick's friends around. I then had to come up with additional gas money if I needed to go anywhere. If the kids had a doctor's appointment, I had to pay Derrick gas money. If we needed groceries, I had to pay Derrick gas money. If I didn't have gas money, I had to walk, but that meant leaving the house without him, which meant I was disobeying his rules, and it meant I was cheating. Any time I was seen out of the house, he was told by someone. It was like the whole town watched me. The only way I was less noticeable was if I was with Melanie. A passenger isn't seen as well as a pedestrian. Derrick had even insisted for a while that I was cheating on him with Melanie. We were spiteful and petty; we wrote Melanie and Simone, Just Married all over her truck and left it that way until it damaged the paint.

Six months after my fifth was born, they remodeled our apartments. Melanie's son had set a fire in her apartment, so they hadn't renewed her lease. She moved about forty-five minutes away, and I thought we would never speak again. We had been friends out of loneliness, convenience, and defiance. We were complete opposites, though, in every way. Right down to taste in men, she liked cops, and I liked inmates. She called, though, and came to visit as often as she could.

A year after they remodeled, Derrick took pictures of my tits while I was wearing just a bra. He posted the pictures on a social media site that still exists, but it isn't what it used to be. A lot of people started messaging me. I ignored them all. One of them was Derrick's friend Damian. Damian asked about coming over to fuck while Derrick was at work. I told Derrick as soon as he got home.

He blamed me, smashed my computer, told Damian's wife, and made sure I knew I belonged to him.

At some point, while I was busy having babies, Bianca and I became close. We talked on the phone every night from nine until midnight. As long as the topic of Griffith didn't come up, things stayed civil. Brady had gotten married. Bianca hadn't been invited to the wedding, but Grifitth had been. That infuriates Bianca to this day; she says she would have been civil for the sake of her son. I could see her going to the wedding and staying clear of Griffith, but I knew her; she would have interacted with him. That does hurt. I know in my heart she has always wanted me to justify her actions and forgive her, even though she thinks she did nothing wrong. I have justified her actions for years. I have said many times, "Well, she was at work all the time; she wasn't really around." I thought I had let go of the anger I had for her long ago. I never admitted it to her, but I always agreed with Judge Rankin's ruling, which was, "There is no proof that you knew anything, but if you didn't, you sure as hell should have." When Bianca brings it up and how angry it makes her, I say nothing. Although I don't talk about my childhood much, if it does come up, I simply say, "I was raised by a pedophile," which brings up the inevitable, "Oh, I'm sorry, where was your mom?' To which I reply with the words I heard her say throughout my life, "She was at work. She worked over an hour away and was never around." Writing all of this has given me a different perspective.

Bianca did bring Griffith up from time to time. Most notably, she told me he had been in a car accident. I chuckled a little and told her, "That's funny." She didn't think it was funny. "What do you mean? That's a horrible thing to say. He almost died. They had to use the jaws of life to get him out." I exploded with laughter. She grilled me about my reaction angrily, and I told her the truth, my truth. "Had I been a bystander, I would have told the rescue personnel exactly what he is, and maybe they would have gone a little slower, and he would have died." She processed this statement in silence for a few minutes. I listened to her silence and felt her anger. It amazes me how many people don't realize how much their silence actually says.

"Simone, that is sick. You're sick." There was anger and fear in her voice. I laughed some more. "Maybe I am, but not everyone deserves to live, and it's adults that fuck babies that are the real sick ones." I hung up on her and didn't talk to her for a few days. She still says I am the sick one. I don't see anything wrong with my reaction, and I still laugh at the thought of the accident.

Her other profound thought was, "Simone, what happened to you is worse for me than it is for you." I heard this statement at least a dozen times and ignored it before asking how she could possibly think that. "Ma? How the fuck do you figure that? How does that even make sense in your mind?" The words that came out of her mouth were abhorrent and inconceivable, and I most likely would have hit her had we been in person and I had been younger. "I have to live for the rest of my life knowing what my husband did to my child. That is worse for me than it is for you." I snapped, "You don't even know what was done to me. I don't talk about it. To you or anyone else. Never have and never will. I am the one who has to live knowing what was actually done to me. The flashbacks, looking over my shoulder, the nightmares, the fear of sleeping, the fear of letting anyone watch my kids and not being with them. And a million other things that **you** just won't ever get." This, of course, made her push for more details of what was actually done to me. She will never get that information, and she still thinks it was worse for her than it was for me. She says it should have no impact on my adult life or who I am now.

While we mostly got along and talked daily, she always found a way to get in some digs, usually about my weight. After having five kids, I was the same weight I had been at fourteen years old. I stayed between one hundred and fifty and one hundred and sixty pounds. I wasn't happy with my weight, but I didn't think I looked bad for having five kids and four c-sections, either. She told me once, "Simone, the only thing you do right is make cute kids." It hurt, but she was right.

Setbacks

I had never stopped wanting drugs. I had never stopped wanting to die. I had had more suicide attempts as a child that I didn't write about. I spent countless hours from my teen years through my mid-twenties on the phone with crisis and suicide hotlines. My biggest salvation was my kids. When things were hard, which was always worse when the sun went down, I would go look at them. I would picture their world without me to care for them. If they wound up with my mother, she would have the finances to care for them, but there would be no love, caring, compassion or empathy. She would not understand that some of them are different, if they wound up overweight they would be bullied. If they went with their father's, they would be neglected at best. I had made a promise to myself and my kids when I was pregnant with my oldest. "My kids will never see me act in violence towards another human unnecessarily. My kids will never see me high or be exposed to drugs. My kids will have childhoods." I held on to that promise every day. When it was hard, I would watch them sleep, when they were little, I would sometimes lay with them and cuddle. The addict in me, the part of me that desperately wanted the pain to go away, be it through a temporary high or a permanent death, needed them. I needed them just as much as they needed me. They are how I have managed to leave drugs and death alone for twenty-five years.

Derrick made it clear early on, I wasn't allowed to drink or use drugs, including weed. He had a lot of rules and I obeyed them all. The not using drugs had nothing at all to do with him. I was also not allowed to be on birth control, unless I went to get it myself. After my fifth was born he told me "If you get pregnant again, you better have a fucking abortion." Yet I wasn't allowed to be on birth control. I walked to get my birth control faithfully every month, even when I got hurt and had to walk with a medical boot. I was now one hundred percent pro-choice and had been since the birth of my first child, but no one was going to make that choice for me. Derrick would not watch his kids, so they had to walk with me, and there would always be a fight because I left the house.

In the spring of 2008, Derrick brought me a small brown paper bag, "Happy early birthday," he said with a smile. Jack Daniels. My old friend. The kids were asleep, I wasn't pregnant or breastfeeding, So, I drank. He had gotten himself a six pack as well, I drank most of that, too. He later told me that he had bought me a drink so he would be allowed to drink, I pointed out that I never told him he couldn't. I didn't give him rules. My only "rule" was no drinking and driving, or under the influence of anything. That isn't even a rule, it's fucking common sense. I was passionate about that. You do not fuck up other people's lives, because you're an idiot. Before long Derrick was bringing me drinks almost daily. Then he brought me a joint. By day, I was mommy of five and everything was under control. By night, I was buzzed, stoned and eating all the kids' snacks. This progressed until I was day drinking, I woke up in the morning and had a shot and had another every few hours all day. I was never drunk or even buzzed during the day, and they never saw me drink. That isn't to justify or excuse it, it just was.

When my fourth was about two and a half, I got a panicked call from Derrick. It was after dark, and I hadn't known where he was. When he called, he told me he was drunk and there was a cop behind him. He said he wasn't far away from home, I told him to park and walk here. When he got back home, smiling and staggering, I was waiting for him outside. Derrick tried to hug me, and I rejected him. Derrick was an overgrown child; he had a tantrum. He slammed his way into the house and punched a wall. I followed him to the bedroom where he had laid in bed next to our son. He crossed his arms angrily and stared at me. I told him how wrong what he did was, he screamed at me for not hugging him. I screamed at him for risking other people's lives. "I don't need this shit" he slurred and got out of bed knocking our son off the bed and into a wall. My son and I ran to each other, I checked his head and confirmed he was okay. I walked up behind Derrick putting my hand on his shoulder, he jerked back elbowing me in the eye hard enough to knock me over. Luckily, I didn't drop my son. Derrick came to me apologizing, I believed it truly was an accident, I was still trying to show him he had knocked our son out of bed. I wanted him to see that his drunk careless actions, had hurt a child, our child, without him being in a

291

vehicle. He didn't care, the more I tried to call his attention to our son, and the more he tried to see my face. I had a black eye, it wasn't a big deal, and it wasn't the first time. He was so sorry, "It would never happen again."

I gave the standard lines when people would notice things. I was in a thrift shop in the winter, one arm was in the sleeve of my jacket and the rest was wrapped around my shoulders. Why didn't I have my other arm in? "I fell down the stairs and hurt my shoulder." Why did I have bruises on my arms? Legs? Face? "I'm clumsy. I banged it on something. I walked into a wall." Alone, at night I would think about it all. The present day, the past, and what would happen in the future. What happened to me didn't really matter. I was already dead. Brad had brought me back to life once, when I hadn't known I was dead, but that was a long time ago. I was dead again, and I knew it. Even if I hadn't been able to pinpoint when or who had killed me, it was too late for me. I had to protect my kids though. They still had so much life inside of them. I had fought to make sure they hadn't lived my life. I needed to keep my body alive, because if left with him, they wouldn't make it. I again, stopped drinking. I did smoke weed once in a while though.

Memories Part Two

It was always at the time of greatest stress that the memories would come more often. They would be more intense, more frequent, and more vivid. The images in my head that would destroy more of my present with my past. Maybe I needed them to make me angry and to make my adrenaline flow. Anger and adrenaline almost felt like life.

I am sure by now; it is blatantly obvious that I am an alcoholic. I am sure anyone reading this is wondering how or when that started. The truth is I don't remember, so here is what I do remember- I was five years old and Griffith would crack a beer, "Want a sip?" I would take it and drink the entire can without stopping. Bianca made him stop drinking, he didn't really stop he just cut down and hid it. At seven years old a double shot of Jack was the cure for a sore throat. How did I start smoking? Another valid question. Bianca had smoked when I was little, I hated it and begged her to stop. She left a not quite out cigarette in the bathroom ashtray, so I tried it, wanting to know why she liked them so much. I was five, I coughed until I was sick. I thought that meant I had done it wrong, so I kept trying until I got it right. She quit smoking when I was seven and by then I was a pro. I started stealing them from my Grandma anytime I was there. I became a semi regular smoker at eleven or twelve when I would get them from people or stayed at Harry's. By fourteen I smoked daily and late that year was when Griffith was buying me at least a pack a day.

I remember Stu who worked for my mom when I was around seven. I loved to draw pictures. I drew pictures of everything. Stu pointed out to Bianca that my pictures all looked like penises. Penis people, penis dogs, penis houses, penis clouds. After he pointed it out, it was clear to everyone.

No matter where I was Griffith's hands always seemed to be around. In the car late at night on our way home from their job, his arm would start leaning on the center seat. Once Bianca and Brady were asleep though, his hand would drop into the back seat. His fingers would creep up my leg and end where it always hurt. I would rest my head on the car window and try and force myself to sleep.

I know everyone will think I am crazy, and that's okay. I probably am and if you had lived my life, you would be too. When I was seven, I started seeing ghosts. We had one TV, and it was in Bianca's room. Brady and I were often alone after school. Cartoon Networks cartoon express would come on in the evening. During the commercials right before it started were when Brady and I would race down the two flights of stairs to get ready for bed. We aimed to be back before the shows started. There were two bedrooms downstairs, the one Brady and I shared, and one that stayed empty, the door stayed closed. I was scared of that room, it gave me a creepy feeling, especially when I was alone. Brady was bigger and faster than me, he passed me on the stairs and ran into our room. I was on the stairs when I looked at that closed door, it felt like I was being watched. *She* floated out of the room, right through the doors. In reality it was probably more of an *It* than a *she*, but she looked just like *The Good Witch* from *The Wizard of Oz*. She had the dress, the hair, even the fucking wand. I remember her lips moving, and me replying, but I don't remember the conversation. I knew she wasn't really good; I could feel the evil coming off of her, and that room. She came out and spoke to me often.

On a Sunday when Bianca was home, we had just changed our sheets, I stuck my tongue out at the closed door. The next time she appeared was the only conversation I remember with her. "I saw what you did. That wasn't very nice, was it?" She even had the witch's voice. I shook my head and sat down. "If you do that again, I will have to spank you again. Do you want me to spank you again?" My body tensed and shook, I tried to back up into the stairs as I again shook my head. I had no recollection of this woman, this thing, ever touching me, but I was terrified.

I only saw her once after that, she had left me alone when I had gone to my room to change. I averted my eyes from that door on my way passed it. Brady and I were on the second flight of stairs on our way back to the Tv when she came out. Brady and I both looked down at her frozen. Her neck stretched all the way up until her face was even with ours. As her neck rose her mouth opened revealing huge vampire fangs. Her eyes flashed from normal to black to red a few times. She vanished into a flash that was first blue, then red. She never came back. Brady claimed it never happened.

I had told Bianca and Griffith about this ghost, this witch. Griffith told me a crazy person used to live in our house, who had died there. He said the person was obsessed with the movie and had collected costumes and props from the set. Bianca thought I was possessed by the devil. She sat me on the steps by that room and read me the bible, I had to look at the door as she read. It didn't work. I never saw the witch again, but I could still feel the evil there right up until the day we moved. I had also had dreams that year that Bianca was a witch and was trying to kill all of us.

That same year, I confided in Bianca fearfully that I thought I was going to hell. She laughed and asked me why I would think such a thing. I whispered in her ear, "I think I like girls." She asked me why and I couldn't explain it. She asked if I had looked at girls and compared myself to them. I said yes, but only because I didn't really know what to say, it was kind of like that. It wasn't really IT though. She told me it was natural for girls to compare themselves to other girls, we all did it. She read me more of the bible though, just in case.

My eleventh birthday I was given my own stereo, with a tape player. I was also given two tapes, *Meatloaf's Bat Out Of Hell* and *Billy Joel's Piano Man*. Bianca and Griffith listened mostly to country, these were two of the exceptions. *Meatloaf's Heaven Can Wait* was the first song that I can say, saved my life. I remember the tears streaming down my face as I sang along that Heaven could wait as I held a knife against my wrist. I loved both albums then and did for years to come. I still do for the most part. There is only one song I cannot listen to off of either of them. The memories of his hot hands slipping up my shorts, forcing inside me, violating me, betraying me, ripping everything away that I was supposed to be, while listening to and singing a certain *Billy Joel* song has destroyed it forever. That's also a large reason I can't listen to country music. I started listening to rock and metal, initially because I knew it would piss off Bianca, but the lyrics spoke to me. I had found my music.

I remember the first time I hit Bianca. We were arguing, I was almost twelve. I was standing on the stairs, and she was at the top of them. We screamed at each other, "You're nothing but a bitch!" I screamed. "You're just a stupid slut-" I can't hear her anymore, it blacks out, but my memory reads her lips "-fucked my hus-" and she back handed me across the face, hard enough that I fell down the stairs. Blackness consumes my brain as I charge at her, I grab her around the throat, push her against the kitchen cabinet and shake. The world comes back, I see her face and what I'm doing. Now calm, I release my grasp and let go. I sat on the couch and saw her coming toward me with her hand raised. I put up my leg to block her and she hit my knee. I left for school. On the way I told Tiffany about what had happened that morning with my mother. All of us troubled kids had a crush on the school social worker, Mr. K. Tiffany used my morning trauma to see the cute social worker. I spent much of the day in the office and was told a mobile crisis team would be coming to pick me up from my house that evening. I would be going for a psychological evaluation.

I went home after school angry and waited. I had short hair that piled on top of my head in unruly unmanageable curls. I was so angry I brushed it until it was straight. Bianca and I were taken to the hospital in separate cars. I was taken for a psychological evaluation, and she was taken for a physical. I waited in that plain boring waiting room for hours. I was fed a nasty sandwich and talked to some of the other people waiting. A nurse sat closed in a little office occasionally looking out the window that protected her. A man was brought in in handcuffs, he was put in the chair next to me, we smiled at each other. I was suddenly embarrassed by the pink and white jumper I was wearing. One of Bianca's picks meant to bully me into losing weight. He stuck out a hand for me to shake, "Hey, I'm Kenny," I shook his hand and my heart fluttered. Kenny and I spent hours talking, which led to flirting. The desk nurse caught on to it and made sure he knew how old I was, he did I had already told him. Kenny was twenty-seven. After a while we were holding hands and touching each other's legs. The nurse had enough and put me in a room across from her window, alone. There was another entrance to that room though and that one couldn't be seen from her window.

He was sitting on the table with me when the nurse realized he was no longer in the waiting room. We were just leaning in to kiss when she charged in. The large room with two doors was able to be divided. She pulled the wall divider from each end, and they met in the middle. I was to stay on my side, Kenny was to stay on his side. Just for good measure she put a lock around the double handles on my side. We were still able to open it about six inches. That was enough that we could talk and hold hands. We were leaned in remarkable close together, our bodies pressed into the gap. His fingers popped open the first four buttons on my jumper. His fingers grazed my bra and our lips almost touched when the nurse yelled "Hell no! Not on my watch!" The security guard was called in and Kenny was handcuffed to a chair on his side of the wall.

Shortly after, they finally came to get me for the evaluation. The psychiatrist was an older mostly bald man. First, I did the Rorschach test (ink blot). I stared at the first one for a while, long enough for him to get annoyed and start to flip to the next one, "Wait!" I yelled excitedly, "I know what it is." His eyes widened, "It's an INK BLOT!" His disappointment amused me. On the next one, I repeated this only saying, "It's a fucking ink blot you idiot." He only tried a couple of others before giving up. He asked questions that I answered sarcastically. He tried to show no emotion in his questions or excitement in my answers. "Do you see or hear things that aren't there, Simone?"
"Yes, I see ghosts."

"Oh, and do they talk to you? Do they tell you to do things? Do they tell you to hurt people? Do they tell you to hurt yourself?" He tried to hide it. But his excitement to the possible answers to these questions echoed off the walls. "They don't tell me to do things. They don't even talk. There is one here now though." He sat straight up in his chair and leaned forward while scribbling on his yellow legal pad. "Try and find out what it wants Simone. Does it want you to hurt someone? Me? Your mom?" I looked off into the area of nothingness behind him, and then at the empty chair next to him. "It's a man. He says he was one of your patients and you didn't help him. He says it's your fault he killed himself." The bald Dr got up and gathered his things without a word, he looked pale. He didn't come back.

Another Dr came in, he wasn't as eager to hear what I had to say. "Simone, did you know that the Dr you spoke with last, did recently have a patient commit suicide?" I gave no answer, but honestly, how would I have known that? He asked a series of other questions that I gave no answer or reaction to. "Simone, did you know your mom is having a physical evaluation? Did you know you hurt her badly? She is having a spinal tap done right now. Do you know what that is?' He asked with curiosity. "No, but I am sure you're going to tell me." He did tell me; I didn't react. "Do you care that you hurt your mom? She has an exceptionally large bruise across the side of her hand. She also has whiplash. "I said nothing; my body language showed my irritation. I guess dear old Bianca, didn't tell them the bruise was from her hitting me, or that the whiplash was from the car accident she had been in the day before. "Do you want to hurt your mom again?' He asked. "No," I was tired now. "Do you want to hurt yourself?" This man wouldn't give up. "No." Just like that I was discharged. On my way out the second Dr told me the bald Dr, had quit and checked himself into a hospital as a psych patient. I believed it then, now I think he just said it to play with my head the way I had played with theirs. Touche, Doc, well played. I still won. I got to leave.

I went to a therapist after I told the first time, her name was Barbara, and she smelled bad. I don't really remember much about her. Twice she saw us as a family. The first time I shut down and refused to speak. The second time I attempted to do the same. Until someone said something, I don't remember who or what it was, but it made me mad. I stood and told each of them how I felt about them. I don't remember what I said to Bianca or Brady. To Barbara it was "You smell bad." and to Griffith It was "You're a pedophile." I

298

stormed out leaving the door open. Barbara told Bianca she believed "Griffith did something inappropriate but not criminal." I feel the same way about that statement now as I did then. What the fuck does that even mean?! We never went back to Barbara.

I got a new therapist. Michelle was wonderful. I loved her. I could talk to her about the bullies at school and she would give me genuine advice, instead of just ignore them like Bianca always said. I daydreamed of her taking me home and being my family. She brought me journals. Real ones in assorted colors and patterns, with built in bookmarks. I could write whatever I wanted in them, and I never had to show anyone, not even her. I filled those pages with laughter, nothingness, anger, fear, pain, tears, and pieces of my dead soul. We never talked about Griffith, until the day came when he had to bring me for an appointment. Michelle invited him in to join us, I didn't want him there, but I couldn't say that. That's when she brought it up. This happened twice. My accusation. I dropped my eyes and confirmed that it never happened. I couldn't say it in front of him. I didn't understand why she asked in front of him. After the second appointment that he came to, I told Bianca I didn't like Michelle anymore and didn't want to go back. She didn't make me. She hadn't liked Michelle anyway; she was jealous because I did.

Griffith used to tell us all about Bianca's money. He said she had money stashed away in several bank accounts. She just didn't want to spend it on us she wanted it for things for herself. That's why I was bullied, because I didn't have nice clothes, accessories, a horrible haircut. My stuff was all cheap and came from *Kmart* or *Caldor.* When Griffith would tell us about her money and how she was selfish I would get angry, it was her fault I was bullied so badly. She probably laughed at me just like the kids at school.

My seven-year-old curiosity about girls had laid dormant until the spring before my twelfth birthday. I had forgotten all about it. Griffith and I had stopped at a 7-11, there were two blonde girls standing in the middle of the store kissing. Not just kissing but *kissing* and hugging. It was different than the feeling I got when I saw a cute boy. I know now that was the first time, I was ever aroused. Griffith had to pull me away because I just stood there and stared. One of the girls waved at me, the other smiled. When we got outside Griffith kept telling me how disgusting that was, how unnatural and against God. I started looking at the *Heavy Metal magazines* he would leave in the bathroom. Just for the record I have never explored this part of myself. To the world I am straight and inside, I know I am actually bisexual.

My mountain bike needed new brakes; sometimes Grandma would send me to the store or for fresh bagels on the weekend. If you have never had New York bagels you don't understand, so don't try. Twice on trips like this Griffith had replaced or worked on my brakes. Twice I almost died getting across a highway and finding I had no brakes. After that I just used my boots for brakes.

I remember riding in the car as a kid. I would stare out the window and daydream about my future. I knew I was born to be something, someone great. Whether it was through a job, humanity or a family, I would have kids and they wouldn't be bullied; they would be involved in whatever they wanted after school. I would do arts and crafts with them, bake with them, and teach them things. I would have a nice house, and of course, a couple of dogs. I would have a husband who loved me. He would hug and kiss me every day. He would be good to me and our kids. He would never hit us or throw things at walls when he got mad. He would not have scary hands. I would usually fall asleep in the car. When we would get to our destination, they wouldn't wake me up, they would just leave me there. I know now that the greatness I was born for, was already gone then. The child that was born for greatness, had been murdered, and no one mourned, no one cared, no one even noticed.

I remember after I told the second time, every female in my family had a story to tell. My Grandma told me how a friend of the family would pick up her sister, and his hand would be somewhere it shouldn't have been. My Grandma told her parents, and they stopped being friends with the guy. Some guy would hide in the bushes and flash my Grandma on her way to school. My aunt Denise was raped in college. Bianca was fondled once by an uncle when she was fourteen. My aunt Tina had an affair with that same uncle (related by marriage but still disgusting) when she was around seventeen after his wife died. My only cousin, Rose, who is three years younger than me, was molested by a babysitter when she was five. I had heard the term cycle of abuse before. It's a pattern that runs in families, some are abused through generations, and some are abusive through generations. I knew then my mission was for it to end with me. I was angry at all of them. They never passed down their experiences because "You don't air your dirty laundry in public." But had anyone said anything, I could have been saved instead of killed.

I found out when I told the second time, Bianca never notified anyone that I had recanted my initial statement. All those years the case had still been open. If I had told the second time, one month earlier, they would have been able to charge him with the crimes dating back to when I was eleven. I found out Bianca never told the police, from Detective Lorenzo. I asked Bianca about it, and she confirmed it was true, I never found out why she didn't tell them. When Bianca was notified that I told the first time, he was with her. She said she turned and looked at him while listening to what they were saying, and the look on his face was that he knew what they were saying. He knew what she was being told. When I told the second time, Bianca called Griffith and told him. He knew before she did. Regardless, she told him how I was "At it again," that she had warned him to not let me sit in his lap, not hold my hand, and not be around me. He didn't tell her he made me do those things. What Griffith did tell Bianca, was that I wanted it, and I started it. He told her that I had come on to him. Bianca said she told him that if a child comes on to an adult, the adult is supposed to stop it. I never came on to him. I never loved him in anyway other than the father he was when he wasn't a monster. Even the adult men that I had consented with, I never started anything, not even with Brad who I had loved.

I remembered that Miss Olsen wasn't the first person I had told. I told Brady I had a secret that I was scared to tell. Brady put stuffed animals and the dogs on the couch and told me to tell them. He ducked behind the couch, so I could tell "them" without looking at him. After I told "them" he wasn't mad. He didn't even beat me up. He did say I must be wrong though, sometimes things could feel uncomfortable even when they weren't meant that way. Brady even hugged me to make me feel better. Sophie also told me when we were in our early twenties that I had told her, but she didn't know what to do.

At eleven years old I wasn't allowed to bathe myself. Bianca insisted I didn't get all the soap out of my hair, so it had to be done for me. I remember crying, begging, pleading, to be able to do it myself. When she would refuse, I would ask if she could just do my hair then, just not him. She never would. She didn't have time. She would sleep, or sip coffee while he did it. I would undress in the hallway, try and cover the important parts with my hands and arms, as I would slowly walk into the bathroom. My face flushed, staring at the floor as I felt his eyes dance across my body. I would slide into the tub putting my back to him, one hand across my chest and the other trying to cover everything else. My knees would pull tight against my body and hold my head, as the hot water would hide the tears rolling down my cheeks. He was so rough washing my hair, that he would lift me off the floor of the tub by my hair. When my hair was done, he would wash everything else. Years later when confronted with this, Bianca would tell me "Well, you would leave soap in your hair, and you would be irritated *down there* because you didn't rinse properly." I heard this several times before I ever gave a response. "*Down there?* Really, ma? Did you ever think there was another fucking reason I was irritated *down there?* Or are you just a fucking idiot?" She cried and walked away. She will always tell everyone how horrible I was to her, but the things that were done to me as a direct result of her negligence, never happened.

When I was twelve and in the sixth grade, we had a guest speaker. The speaker was there to discuss sexual abuse. I felt like the whole class was looking at me. Like they could see it every time the speaker would tell us that at least one person in that room was being sexually abused. I felt dirty and ashamed. I also, remember thinking that it was a normal part of growing up. That it was happening to all of my friends, too just no one talked about it. The fact that I had told a year before wasn't even real to me anymore. By telling Bianca that I must have imagined it, because that's what she wanted to hear, meant none of that had ever happened either. I believed it happened to everyone, because that's what I needed to believe.

Sheldon sat next to me in math. He was forever throwing things at me. His goal never changed, it was to get anything he could down my shirt, so he could have something that touched my tits. Me having to hand him things that hit the floor worked for him too, he would get to see down my shirt. He grabbed my tits once when we were leaving class, I bent his fingers backwards I was sent to the office. The school was divided into three sections called houses. Each house had their own office and their own principal. My house two principal was Mr. T, I told him why I did what I did. I got the typical "get over it, boys will be boys," lines, I was punished. I had to work in the house two office during lunch for a while. Mr. T was pervy too. I caught the long glances at my tits when he would drop files on the floor for me to file. In time, he started swatting me on the ass anytime I would walk past, sometimes, he even did it in the crowded hallways. I wasn't the only one he did it to. It went on for the rest of the school year. I thought about telling, there was no point. No one ever fucking listened to me. Mr. T's behavior started again the following year, I wasn't in the same house anymore, but anytime we shared a hallway, his eyes or hand were on me. When I was in eighth grade and dating Kyle, some boys I went to school with threatened to beat Kyle up. They bullied me so they tried to bully my boyfriend, too. Kyle went after them; it was in school. He had come to see me one morning before classes started. The boys that caused the drama reported it to Mr. T. I was called in and tried to explain what had really happened. Mr. T ordered me to "Stop with the editorials," because he wasn't interested in the truth. He lectured me in front of the boys, then sent them away. I didn't want to be in a closed office with that man. Mr. T told me privately that my punishment would again be working in his office, he mumbled that I should wear skirts more often. I whipped my head around and asked him "Mr. T would you also like me to preform my duties on my knees?" The look on his face was a shocked yes; I walked out and never showed up for my office duties.

Sophie and I were walking around the shopping center by my house. A car pulled up next to us and asked "Can you girls tell me how to get to..." Sophie took a step towards the car, and I yanked her back. She looked angry at me when she asked what I was doing. I told her the guy was either trying to grab us or he was jerking off, she told me I was crazy and turned back to the car. He asked again for directions, but the destination was an incoherent mumble. As she stepped closer to the car, I stepped next to her. It was her first time seeing a dick, as she leaned a little too far to see that he was indeed jerking off. Sophie jumped backwards and looked at me startled. I gave her a smug "I told you so," look as I gave the guy a one finger salute and told him to fuck off. Some other sicko in my town liked to collect Ziploc bags filled with moths. Before he would dispose of the bags, he would jerk off in them. My friends and I found several bags of dead moths in a sticky crunchy residue. I was the only one of the group that knew what it was.

I remember how I was raised to believe I was evil. Griffith called me the devils daughter. Frequently, when I would wake up in the morning he would remark that the devil himself was scared because I was awake. He told me how Heaven didn't want me, and the Devil was scared I would take over. As a young child he often drew three sixes behind my ear. Everything in my childhood had a sexual or evil innuendo. Bianca saw and heard all of these comments, and chose to close her ears along with her eyes.

Fuck you, I remember. Fuck you, I remember. Fuck you, I remember. Fuck you I remember.

Almost Time to Move On

Time passed. It was 2010. My oldest child was twelve and had her first boyfriend. A lot of people disapproved of the relationship. Some of her friends' parents disapproved so strongly that they weren't allowed to be friends anymore. People generally didn't and do not approach me. Apparently, I come off as a bitch. Derrick was, however, a lot more outgoing than I was. "Why would you let your daughter date that boy?" He was asked a lot. He would answer that she chooses who she dates, not him, and he would act like he didn't care. In the house though, he showed how he really felt. Derrick would jack me up against the wall by my throat, "Why are you letting her date that N*****?" I curse. I curse a lot. I am not offended easily and generally not by words. I don't tolerate racism, slurs, homophobia, or any other hate speech. For the first and last time, that day, I used the same word he did, only in its correct definition. "I only see on N***** here, mother fucker and it's you," I spit the words out at him as his arm pressed firmly, and then suddenly released. I fell to the floor gasping for air, he left and didn't come back until after dark. I found myself wishing he would get into a fatal car accident frequently. Bianca and Brady also disapproved of the relationship. Bianca told me over the phone how wrong it was, I told her to shut the fuck up. Brady commented on my daughters Facebook picture, that it was disgusting. I logged into her account and blocked him. He is still blocked to this day.

Theresa and I started talking again in 2008 through social media. I confessed to her that things between Derrick and I were not good. She got me to talk to her aunt who ran a domestic violence shelter in New Jersey. I told them the basics, and they said they could help. They would come get me and my kids while Derrick was at work. He wouldn't know I was gone until he got home. I was worried about leaving our stuff behind, they said we could bring it all. They had storage units and even houses. We were a bigger family and could get placed in a house. I took a few days to think and let them know I had to wait until the end of the next school year. My daughter would be starting eighth grade the next year and my son fifth. I knew

305

how hard it was on a kid to move at those times. I didn't want to cause them any more stress than necessary. They tried to convince me to do it that summer instead, I insisted, and they understood.

A lot of friends from childhood had found me on Facebook. I started to think of Brad. Before I even knew what I was doing, I typed his name into the search bar. There he was, with the same smile and almost the same hair, he was heavier, but it was definitely him. I snooped on his page; I saw that he had two kids and was married to a woman named Marissa. I didn't know if it was the same one, but I had a feeling it was. He was still cute, but I didn't find him attractive anymore. I sent him a message –

February 25, 2010, at 2:55 AM

"The last time I called you, I was 15. I called you from a hospital room to tell you I was diabetic. I was hysterical. The girlfriend you had at the time told me you guys broke up and that she didn't know where you were. In my hysterical cries of needing one of my closest friends, the only words that came out of my mouth were 'fucking bitch'. I wasn't referring to her. But to the situation itself. I see you are now married to a woman named Marissa. If it is the same one you were with back then, I want her to know I wasn't calling her anything. She hung up on me after I said it, and rightfully so. I told about Griffith and what he had been doing to me for so long. I went through many trials and heartaches. I was homeless and pregnant when I went before the grand jury. I miscarried and blamed it on the stress. When the case was to be held in criminal court, I was pregnant again and told them I was having my baby first. DA's changed, and my file got lost. The statute of limitations passed, and I could no longer do anything. He now lives freely with his wife, her daughter (who I think is grown now), and the two kids he had with her. I moved on to be another statistic. I was a teen mother and now have five kids, a husband, and a GED. I sometimes wonder why you stopped calling me. Why all of a sudden, we weren't friends. I don't know what made me check Facebook for you today, maybe cause so many old friends found me here. Maybe because I still need closure after all this time. I would really like to know, though. If you could find an answer, I would appreciate it. Please note I do not expect anything to result from this message. I do not expect us to be friends again or anything. Just to know why you never called me again. Your children are beautiful, by the way." I figured I would get no response or a lie that I had the wrong person. When a message, a very honest one, appeared, I was surprised.

February 26, 2010, at 12:20 AM
"Well, it's hard to explain but I'll take a shot. I loved a child, and you were her and it wasn't right in any fashion. I failed you as a friend. I couldn't deal with the reality you were a child in need of what I was trying to provide. A safe someone. Also, when I left, I couldn't be that hero for you. Marissa and I got back together, and we are married. I moved back to my hometown upstate. I lived near your hometown for 10-11 years. I became the captain of the EMS division. Don't think I moved on without wondering about you. I always wondered where that chapter of my life had gone. Griffith was an asshole and someday he'll get what he gave. If it's ok, I'd like to be friends again, if you don't, I would understand. And hey I'm a statistic too. I have a GED..." My heart leapt in ways I didn't know it still could.

It didn't matter that I was no longer attracted to him. What mattered was the second line. "I loved a child, and you were her" he admitted it, in writing that couldn't be burned. We sent a few more messages and he asked for my number. He called, and it was like old times. We talked for hours. It was late at night and Derrick was asleep, or I never would have been allowed to talk to Brad. He was the one who brought up the taboo subject of us. He told me he had felt guilty all these years for having sex with me, "Why?" I asked with a laugh. "What do you mean why? How old were you?" He asked. "Fourteen," I said with a smile. 'Yeah, exactly, and how old was I?" He asked sounding a little heated. "Twenty-two," I smiled and saw a flash of us. Kissing, touching, loving, hugging, dancing, laughing. "Brad, you have nothing to feel guilty for. You were my first -" He cut me off, "I know I didn't take your virginity," I paused. "Not in the sense of tearing a little piece of skin, no. I don't honestly remember how that happened, and to tell you the truth I don't want to. But you *were* my first. It was the first time I wanted it. It was the first time I remember. It was the first time it was my choice. You were my first love. Most girls look back on their first time with regret. Either who it was with or where, or something. I don't. I believe everyone's first time should be with someone they care about who cares about them. That's what I had. With you." He was silent and I heard a sniffle. "Thank you. I'm glad I got to hear you say that." After he could really talk again, he asked, "What if it was your daughter though?" The thought made me angry. "My daughters are completely different. My daughters are kids. My kids have normal lives. My daughters would never be in a situation to have a relationship – any kind of relationship, even friendship – with a grown man to begin with." After a climactic pause he said "Exactly."

Yes, I suppose on some level, the relationship Brad and I had was wrong. But fuck it was real. We talked more about our lives, our families, the world. He confessed he cheats on Marissa, that didn't surprise me. He had cheated on her when they were first dating, with me. He asked if I cheat on my husband, and I told him no. He asked if I would, and I said probably not, but maybe. I told him it would depend on the situation and the person. "Would you with me?" He asked and I could see the smile on his face, I knew the look in his eyes. "With you? Yeah, I would," I am sure he could see my face too. We talked about love, and he asked if I had been in love with him back then." You know, back then, I thought I was. I never told anyone. People knew though. They all said the same thing. You think you're in love with him but you're a kid. Wait until you grow up and then you'll know what love is. Well, I'm grown, and I know what I felt then. I remember it clearly. It was real. I may have been a kid, but we both know I wasn't *really* a kid." We talked until the sun was starting to come out and I heard Derrick's alarm going off. I got off the phone, laid on the couch and pretended to be asleep.

I had held onto my memories of Brad for so long. It had been those memories that got me through a lot of my teen years, and it was the only reason I believed I wasn't completely unlovable. I had always known; he had loved me. While I was no longer attracted to him, despite what everyone thinks, I am happy I didn't wind up with him. I liked knowing I could have him again even just in bed. For a few reasons, he was the only man I had ever been with who had always given me a choice. Even though Marissa would never know about us now (If it ever happened, he does live five hours away), and could never know about us then, I would know. I would know that I had him first, I had him during the earliest part of their relationship, and I could have him during their marriage. The part of me that never got to be a child, was still there, and admittedly petty. I'm sure you're wondering why I'm happy I never wound up with him. Well, that's easy. If I had wound up with him, I would have been the stupid wife sitting at home or at work, while he stuck his dick in everything that walked by. He had called himself a "serial cheater" and a "Man ho" while we were on the phone. I didn't want to be the stupid wife, that just wasn't me. Even though he had told me I was his "One that got away" which he probably doesn't even remember saying.

Things continued to escalate between Derrick and I for the rest of the year. He continued driving Caleb around, he was the only person that put gas in the van, so I really didn't care. Caleb though started bringing me liquor. He said it was my van too, so I should get something as a thank you. My grandparents were frequently sick, and I hated that I couldn't go see them. We had gone to New York a handful of times. The trip was expensive and extremely hard with five kids. Both Tina and Denise were now living at my grandparents, mostly to mooch off of them. My daughter and her boyfriend broke up because he moved. Derrick got my name tattooed on the side of his neck. I was very against it, but he didn't listen. Paul was hanging around a little bit again. His mother, who had been abusive to him as a child, was dying of cancer. He was living at her place to take care of her.

In March 2011, my grandfather died. I took the news pretty hard. I expected to feel nothing when he died. I certainly didn't expect a single tear. Instead, I got a flood. I didn't stop crying for days. I loved the man because he was family, and you just love family. But as a human being, I fucking hated the man. Five weeks later in April 2011, my grandmother died. A woman I had loved and not just because she was family. A woman who had said horrible things and I continued loving anyway. I shed one tear and went to bed. I expected the tears would come in the morning, but they didn't. It's been eleven years and it still hasn't happened.

Our van was stolen as a result of Derrick's involvement with dealers and drug transport. We got it back after a few days and it barely ran. The DVD player had been stolen, the transmission and control system were shot. I told him it was a good thing there wasn't going to be a service for my grandmother. If I had missed it because of him and the people he hung out with, I would have killed them all. He didn't care. I was thankful he wasn't around more often. I hated him more every day.

I was tired of not being allowed out of the house. I was tired of having to do everything for everyone by myself. I was tired of being lonely. I still had a year before I could go to New Jersey, and it would be long. I ran into Paul at the post office, where I wasn't supposed to be. I hadn't seen him in a month or so. His mom had died the same day as my grandfather. Neither of us had anything to do so he came back to my house. Derrick wasn't happy when he came home. He had never had a problem with Paul being here before and, in the past, had brought him over and dropped him off for hours. Apparently, that was only okay when he did it. Paul had gone out and got us a case of beer, that was also a problem, I was only allowed to drink what Derrick provided when he provided it. After he drove Paul home, he forced himself on me. "This is mine and don't you ever forget it," he said as he shoved inside of me.

After that, Derrick was regularly accusing me of fucking Paul. We fought about it all the time. I had done nothing wrong, and I knew I hadn't. "I want you to stop talking to him," he commanded on a day he had brought Paul over. "Why? You have never had a problem with him being around before, what is different now? And you bring him here and leave for at least eight hours, I don't understand how that is supposed to work if I am not supposed to talk to him." he laid in bed staring at me, "Are you really going to tell me Paul doesn't like you?" He got up and started moving closer. I stood my ground and showed no fear as I planted my feet as I had been trained to do. "No, Derrick, I'm not going to tell you Paul doesn't like me because he does. He always has. I used to complain about it to you and you didn't care. Actually, he doesn't like me, he's in love with me. But it never bothered you before. He was one of the approved people, remember? Why is it different now?" Derrick grabbed me by my shirt, turned me around, pushed me backwards onto the bed and unzipped his pants. "You'll see," he said as he pushed his way inside me again. The very next day, Derrick got home from work late, because he stopped and picked up Paul. He dropped him off at our house and went to his friend's house until well after dark. Fights over Paul became a daily occurrence by July.

This wasn't the first time Derrick had been like this. If I asked a male employee where something in a store was, I was sleeping with him. A male server brought out our food and I said thank you? I was flirting. We got the same male server on more than one occasion? I had called ahead to let the guy know I was coming. It never ended and it had been that way since the beginning. I had just overlooked it as being overprotective and insecure. This was the first time it had been consistently about one person though. Whenever I had told him a guy had said or done something inappropriate, he either thought it was funny or didn't believe me. When something was innocent, he saw the end of the world.

Paul and I had an unusual friendship. When Derrick had first brought him home from work, I was pregnant with my third baby. I saw the "I want to fuck her" eyes immediately and decided just as quickly that I didn't like him. He was almost seventeen then, I had just turned twenty-four. I had no patience or time for anyone who looked at me like that. Besides, he should have been able to hide his lust by that age anyway. He was an annoying kid who followed me around, he was also a target for the other guys that hung around, especially Joe. There were a lot of teens who hung out at my house back then, they would work on their bikes with Derrick in our back yard. A lot of them liked me besides the main four (Paul, Jack, Tom and Joe) that I had mentioned. Paul was the only one who couldn't hide the look though. I was pregnant and had two kids under five to care for, plus everyone that was always over. Joe started beating Paul up regularly, Derrick frequently instigated it, and then encouraged it to continue. I broke it up and pulled Joe off of Paul. Finally, I put my foot down and said that if anyone laid a hand on anyone else, they wouldn't be allowed to come over anymore. Paul was annoying, but he didn't deserve to get his ass kicked every day.

Paul came and went from our lives from the time we met (Summer of 2003) until May 2011. He would keep in touch with me via the internet more than he would anyone else. Since he was one of the only people I had been allowed to talk to, we talked. By the time he was eighteen, I had decided he wasn't so bad and started to think of him as a friend. By then, I also thought I had been wrong about him liking me; I thought he was gay. I told Derrick I though Paul was gay, and he told me he had heard rumors about Paul and Jack. Paul moved closer to us again when he was twenty-one. He was dating a woman with three kids whom he had met online, and they were renting a house not far from us. So, I was wrong about him being gay, it happens. Regardless, the whole time we had known him, he would appear for a few days, weeks or months, then disappear again. We were always in touch at least occasionally though.

Summer was coming and Derrick decided I should hang out with his friend Tino's girlfriend, Trish. Derrick started bringing the kids and I over to their house. They had a pool and a yard; it was nice to see the kids playing. We didn't live in a good neighborhood, and they couldn't often play outside. The big problem was me, I had always been socially awkward, and after being closed in the house for so long, it was worse. My birthday came, and I fell getting out of the pool. My knee was fucked up pretty badly, Trish wanted to take me to the hospital, but Derrick wouldn't allow it. Several hours later, he brought the kids and I home. When we pulled up, Paul was outside talking to my neighbor bailey. He came immediately to the truck to greet me, "happy birthday," he said as he opened my door. "Thanks" I murmured as I tried to walk. My limp was obvious, it was Paul that caught me when I started to fall, it was Derrick that laughed. Paul helped me inside but couldn't stay. I made it to the couch after he left, and only managed to move when the kids needed something for the next few days. Trish wound up taking me to the hospital on the seventh, the day before my fourth baby turned six. It was the first time Derrick had watched the kids except when I was in the hospital having one of them.

I was given an immobilizer and told to stay off of it as much as possible. I don't exactly know how anyone could think I would be able to stay off of it. The very next day I was making my baby his birthday cake, walking the three miles (round trip) to the grocery store for party supplies and food, and hosting a birthday party. Two days after that I was walking to the pharmacy for my birth control. Then we got a letter saying we had a housing inspection. My housekeeping suffered the most when I was severely depressed or physically injured. Paul showed up and I told him I couldn't hang out, I needed to get ready for the inspection. He held up a case of beer, so I invited him in. I could drink and get ready. Paul started helping, which was weird, and I kept telling him to stop. Finally, he said "Simone, you shouldn't have to do everything yourself. Derrick should be here helping but he's a dick. I'm here so I'm helping." I guess his mission with that statement was completed, because I shut up.

Laying on the couch with my leg up and the immobilizer off, I needed to figure out what Derrick's issue with Paul was. He said it was that Paul liked me. That couldn't be it though, Paul had always liked me, and Derrick had never cared. Derrick used to laugh when I would complain about Paul following me around like a puppy. All those years he didn't care about anything related to me and Paul, so why now? I closed my eyes and replayed my friendship with Paul. Being irritated with him following me around, coming in to see him getting beat up, pulling Joe off of him, internet chats, bringing over his new truck, celebrating new jobs, getting away from his crazy girlfriend, a whole lot of nothing. I fast forwarded to the more recent memories. I needed to see whatever Derrick saw. I looked at the more recent memories through Derrick's eyes. Paul popping in with beer, watching movies, researching things online, drinks, and then there it was. I saw my face, every time I saw Paul for the last few months. There was a spark in MY eyes when he was around. I opened my eyes with one clear thought," Holy shit. I do like Paul."

Battleground

July 15, 2011, seemed like a normal day. The kids were all at the summer program that used to be held here. Paul had been picked up and dropped off by Derrick that morning. We had walked to the liquor store and picked up a case of beer. I went to the kitchen to start dinner, with Paul following close behind. He said something flirtatious behind me. I don't remember what and honestly, I forgot the second the words were out of his mouth. "Paul stop," I said with a smile, "Stop what?" he said teasingly. "You know I like you," I said with my back towards him. "Yeah, I know you do," he said as he slid into the corner of my kitchen, out of view of the window, "Come here," he said quietly. I took the two steps to him not knowing what he was planning. His lips gently touched mine in the most intense peck. I stepped away, walked in a circle and went back to him. I fell into his arms as we kissed. And kissed. And kissed.

Everything else in the world ceased to exist when we embraced, and our lips found each other's over and over. We moved in circles until I was pressed against a wall. Paul began kissing down my neck, I let out a soft moan of pleasure, as I became turned on for the first time in years. I felt his smile in his kiss, as my breathing deepened, my breaths quickened, and my moaning continued. He reached his hand between my legs and whispered, "Oh my God, so wet," and placed my hand on his hardness. What I felt was very unexpected. This man was five-foot eight and about one hundred and fifteen pounds. I had always called him crack head because of his build, he had teased a couple times that I just didn't know where all his weight was. I now knew he wasn't lying, and I knew that this needed to slow down. My kids would be home soon and to be honest I was a little afraid of what I felt.

I pulled back from him and told him the kids would be home soon. We calmed ourselves, and I went back to prepping dinner. He found it hard not to touch me, so he kept poking me, anywhere, abdomen, arm; he even got my nose once, and every time he said "Poke," so I grabbed his hand and showed him exactly where I wanted him to poke me. Again, I was against a wall in an instant;

his body was pressed against mine in all the right places. My leg wrapped around him, and as we began to grind against each other, my back arched in a pleasure I hadn't experienced before. I pushed away just seconds before the kids walked in. We started talking as I cooked; I needed to know, "Why me? Why now?" I asked. "Why you? What do you mean why you? "He seemed surprised by my question. "Paul, we're friends; I know your type. You have a ton of people staying in your house, including Erica, who has the perfect body and walks around naked. You like skinny girls, girls a little younger than you. Girls who wear dresses and make-up. I am not your type." He looked at me very seriously, "It's all here," he said and tapped my head. "Erica is nice to look at, but I wouldn't touch her with a ten-foot pole. I've dated girls younger and older, hell my first was thirty-two, and I was sixteen. I don't care about clothes or make-up, never have." So many girls would love to have a guy who wants them for their minds or for who they are. I know that. Those are generally the girls that are seen by themselves or society as stupid or bimbos. But I'm an ugly girl. I'm a fat girl. I wanted and want for a guy to want me for physical attraction, too, not that they don't, but I want to be wanted for my body. "Yeah, but you wanted to fuck me the first time you saw me," I said matter-of-factly. "Yeah, I did. I have always wanted you."

We had dinner and I set aside a plate for Derrick. Paul and I were sitting outside when Derrick got home. Paul kept touching my ass, I pushed him away telling him to stop before Derrick saw. "I hope he does see," he said. I hadn't had time to think about all of this, let alone over think it. I certainly didn't want Derrick to know, this was just going to be a short-lived affair. It would serve Derrick right. After all, he had told me he cheated on his second wife (Penny) with Allie, because she kept accusing him of it. Derrick had been accusing me of cheating with Paul for months. Before Paul it was everyone else, I was supposedly cheating with. Fuck him and his double standards. "Simone, I can't promise you the sun, the moon, and the stars. Hell, I can't promise you much of anything, but I can promise you, I will treat you a whole lot better than that piece of shit does." … Wait...what?

316

There was no time, Derrick was done talking to Caleb and walking towards us. "Paul promise me you won't say anything? Promise me you won't tell him? I need to figure this out first. Please, please, please don't say anything?" Something in my voice must have hit him because he promised and moved his hand away from my ass. Derrick took Paul home, which was a very long ten minutes for me. Paul text me and let me know he was home and hadn't said anything. The next few days we were all over each other. Melanie had moved back to town; she was staying with her ex a few blocks away from me. I knew I could trust her, so I told her the situation. She had always hated Derrick, so she was insanely happy that I was cheating on him. On the third night of us being all over each other, Melanie wanted us to meet her. She wanted to come spend the night but didn't want to walk over by herself. After the three of us were back at my house, Paul and I continued to explore everything we could about each other. Melanie made comments as often as she could, the usual telling us to get a room, asking if we needed a condom, telling us to just fuck already. I stood and pulled Paul with me to my downstairs bathroom. Once we were there, his pants dropped, mine came off and I sat on the sink. I was so in need of what he had to offer that his size wasn't intimidating in that moment. I pulled him closer, our lips met, I tilted my hips towards him, his dick barely touching me, "Really?" He asked in an excited whisper. "Well, yeah. We have been all over each other for three days what did you think it was leading to?" I said laughingly. "I just never thought you would let me." I didn't bother to respond with words, I let my kiss and my body say anything and everything that was needed. I had never been so turned on in my life.

Paul was barely inside of me when he moaned, "Holy shit five kids and still so tight." I didn't have the time to educate him on how a vagina actually works so I just said "C-sections." We fucked with me sitting on the sink, bent over the sink, laying on the floor missionary, from behind, anyway we could, until we heard a noise. We both jumped up and put our pants on, I pushed him behind the door and peeked out. I crept slowly, like a kid in the middle of the night trying to steal candy, all I saw was Melanie. I questioned her about the noise, she had heard it to, but didn't know what it was. I went upstairs and saw Derrick still asleep in bed.

317

Yes, ladies and gentlemen, I fucked someone in my bathroom downstairs while my husband was upstairs in bed sleeping. Am I ashamed of it? No. Am I proud of it? That depends on the day, but often yes. Do I find it amusing? All the time.

I had Paul leave. The second the door was closed, I felt guilty. I hid the lighter he had forgotten, and I smoked his cigarettes. The next morning, he text me wanting to come over. I told him I needed time to figure it all out, that I was married, and this was wrong. Paul justified it by pointing out that Derrick treated me like shit (he didn't know half of it, no one did). He told me he had heard me tell Derrick for years that it was over and to leave, that I didn't want to be with him, and it was over. That was all true. I had told him those things over and over, he would never leave, though, and I never pushed for him to go. Paul agreed not to come over and to continue to keep his silence. Melanie saw how distraught I was. I went through every emotion several times. I told Melanie how much I loved Derrick, which wasn't true; I didn't; I never really had. The guilt made me feel like I did, though. I was doing so badly that Melanie stayed with me for a week. She never once judged any of my words or actions. She would support my decision no matter what it was. Stay with Derrick and stop the affair. Leave Derrick and be with Paul. Stay with Derrick and continue the affair. Leave them both and be with an alien. She wouldn't judge a thing I did. It wasn't until that week that I really saw her as a friend. During that week, Paul and I talked via phone and text daily.

I had just started to handle it better when Derrick brought Paul home the day Melanie left. I told Paul I still wasn't ready and still needed time to figure things out. While Melanie had still been with me, I decided that I needed to follow through with my original plan. I had less than a year left before we were going to be picked up and taken away to New Jersey. I could start over there; I knew it was for the best. No one knew about the escape plan, not even Paul or Melanie. I wanted to come clean with Paul, but the way he looked at me...it would break his heart. I had to, though; I was about to tell him everything. He kissed me. The whole world disappeared. We had sex again, this time outside in a clearing by my house and on a walking track. Again, the deed was left unfinished by us both. I had given up on that ever happening to me, but it was hands down the best sex I had ever had.

We carried on sneaking around the next few weeks. It was a small town, and people suspected before anything was actually happening, just like Derrick had. Caleb was the only one who had the balls to say anything to me about it. "Miss Simone, I just want you to know people are talking about you and that boy. People know. Or they *think* they know." I laughed about it. A couple of days later, Caleb came to my back door to bum a cigarette. Paul was sitting in my living room; Derrick was upstairs asleep, we hadn't been doing anything but talking. We knew when it was and wasn't safe to fuck around. Caleb started laughing as soon as he saw Paul, but not Derrick. Derrick had hit me that morning, and I was still pissed off about it. I walked over to Paul and stood very close, "hey Caleb, you know what we talked about? What everyone *thinks* they know? Well, tell them this." I grabbed Paul and started kissing him. Caleb was happy for me. Turned out he didn't really like Derrick. Within twenty-four hours, almost everyone on my street knew. I now had a team of people willing to cover for me. Turned out none of them liked Derrick. I had thought they were all his friends. They would text me if Derrick came home unexpectedly while I was out with Paul. They would call if they saw him out somewhere and knew he was on his way back. They would watch my house while I snuck into the shadows of the woods. I came clean to a couple of them that Derrick had been abusive for years. They made it clear that if and when I wanted him gone, all I had to do was say so.

Paul started pushing that he wanted us to be together. He wanted a full-blown relationship. We had told each other we loved each other. I did love him, but I didn't want to go from one relationship right to another. I still didn't know how to leave Derrick. On top of that, letting go of an almost ten-year relationship is hard, especially when there are kids involved. Paul started thinking I was trying to have them both. I wasn't. I didn't want or love Derrick. I explained to him all the things I felt and why it was so hard, he understood, but he was also frustrated. The conflict within me was destructive. I didn't want to hurt either of them. I didn't want to be with Derrick; that was why I had made the plan to run. I hated New Jersey, but it was the best option. I liked Paul, even loved him, which I can't say the same about Derrick; I was being pulled in too many ways. There was no way that I could see to do any of this without hurting someone.

I thought about my entire relationship with Derrick. Climbing out the window to get my daughter on the bus. Not being allowed to speak to anyone. Having to pay him gas money to take our kids to the Dr or to get food. Not being allowed to take birth control. Not being allowed to leave the house. Having to steal toilet paper, diapers, kids' clothes, pads, and tampons, or having to make my own. I thought of him stealing toilet paper from the state parks when I refused to. I saw him knocking our child out of bed in a careless drunken stupor and not caring that he had done so. I thought of all the times he had put his friends first. I didn't consider the times he had hit me or forced himself on me. Those things didn't matter, but the rest did.

By the end of the first week of August, I knew I needed to end things with Derrick, regardless of what happened after. I tried to wait for the timing to be right. I was going to wait until after his birthday. I knew that wouldn't work; it wasn't until the second half of September. I was then going to wait until the kids went back to school in late August. It wasn't going to happen. After our daughter's eighth birthday, that was a little earlier. I thought I could wait that long. I didn't make it.

On August 11, 2011, Derrick came home, and I already had his stuff packed in trash bags. "We need to talk," I gave the famous last words that everyone knows signal the end. "About what?" He asked as he gave an impish look and sat on the couch. "I want a divorce." He stared, his cold blue eyes looking through me as we both lit cigarettes. "Why?" He asked. "What do you mean why? There's a huge list of reasons why. Do you want the fuckin' list?" We both inhaled, and neither of us looked away. "Yeah, gimme it. Give me the list." This mother fucker was serious. "You keep me basically locked up. It's not as bad as it used to be, but I'm still not supposed to leave the house. You won't let me buy the things we need. I have to steal toilet paper, for Christ's sake. I'm not allowed to have friends; I'm not allowed to have a job." I paused as I felt tears stinging the backs of my eyes. "Go ahead. There's more. Tell me." I lit another cigarette. "You're not there for the kids or me. I have to pay you gas money to take me grocery shopping for food for your own kids. I have to pay you gas money to take the kids to the Dr." Inhale. "Come on. There's more." Inhale. "I have to do everything by myself. The kids are just kids, and I know you work, but you could help once in a while or give me a break." Inhale. "Come on." Inhale. I trembled as a tear got a little closer to the surface. "You hit me." Inhale. "Come on. Let's go. I don't have all day." Inhale. "You raped me." There it was the biggest reason. It came out through clenched teeth as I fought the years of tears. "And I never meant to hurt you – in that way-I" What the fuck just fell out of his stupid face? "You didn't mean to hurt me *in that way?* Maybe, MAYBE the first time. But you kept doing it over and over again. That's not a fucking accident; it's not a fucking mistake." I was fueled by anger now, and the tears were gone. Derrick walked out the door, "You're not saying the biggest reason. You know what it is. Who it is. I know too. This isn't over. Watch. And I'm going to get custody of those kids." He got in his truck and left.

I had several texts from Paul and Bailey. Bailey was a big guy, who beat his wife Hannah regularly, but he was on my side, wife, Derrick. I texted them both, letting them know that I did what needed to be done, and I asked Paul not to come over. I needed time. I made dinner and saved Derrick a plate. Bailey came over insisting that the kids and I stay the night at his place; he knew when Derrick got home, things were not going to be pretty. I agreed and got the kids ready to go. Paul showed up not long after. I tried telling him I just needed time, but he wouldn't listen; he just wanted to be there for me. I had forgotten some things at my house and went to gather them; I passed the knife block on the counter; there was a candle next to it. I flashed to the pleasure of pain those things brought. I heated the blade of a steak knife and held it against my arm. The glorious feeling of relief burst through my heart. I didn't think about what I was doing. I brought the knife and lighter to the living room floor, sat down, and began to feel. I was burning the word "Nothing" into my arm. I was going to have to go over it several times. I was so lost in the pleasure of pain that I didn't hear anyone come in. Paul spoke, snapping me out of it. I blew out the candle and tucked the knife away. It was too late; he had already seen. I started putting things away, Paul hugged me from behind, and I calmed instantly. He held up my burnt arm and turned it to the smooth unharmed surface. He pulled out his pocket knife and held it near my arm, "If you're going to do it, at least do it right." Paul was familiar with cutting but no other self-harm. I declined the offer of his clean unheated knife. A week later, he caught me trying to burn "Worthless" and "Useless" into my upper thighs. He got mad and started throwing things around my kitchen.

I left Derrick a letter. I told him I was staying at a friend's house, not Paul's, and I would be back in the morning. I asked him not to try and find me, that I just needed time. He had called and texted throughout the evening. He made sure I knew he was looking for a girl and that he wasn't moving out. Derrick said we would just split the bills and live as roommates. I told him that was fine and that we could come up with an agreement. Neither of us could bring whomever we were seeing back to the house; we would work opposite shifts and split all the bills equally. Derrick said he would work his normal shift, six am until two pm, and then the rest of the day was his. That he would not watch the kids because it was time for him to go do stuff with his friends. That was even better for me because I didn't really trust him to watch the kids; I told him we would split the daycare bill. He said no to that also because not all of the kids were his. The kids that were not his were thirteen and ten; they didn't need daycare or a babysitter. The kids that were his were seven, six, and three. The kids we shared did need daycare. I tried to explain that to him, and he said I was the one who had the kids, and it was my problem.

Even though I had asked Paul not to come and didn't want him to stay at Bailey's, the two men insisted. We were all over each other; we couldn't help it. Whenever we had a moment, there were no kids in eye shots. We needed to be touching each other. Bailey offered us some pills already crushed; he said we needed to take the edge off. We both declined. Bailey let us know that the split of me and Derrick had already made county-wide news in the gossip mill. I noticed Paul looking at me in a different way, "What?" I asked him from across the room. "You're beautiful," he said with a smile and glowing eyes. I took a couple of steps toward him, "You're delusional. What are you thinking? I can tell you're thinking something." He pulled me in closer for a kiss. "I was thinking about something, but today isn't the day," he said and kissed me again. "Uh uh, you can't do that. You have to tell me, or I'll stop kissing you," I pulled back just a little bit." Well, it's a question," he said as he pulled me closer, and we kissed more. "Hmmmm," I said as I started to pull back again. "It's two words, and they both start with M." I pulled all the way back. I hadn't been prepared for that. I went back to his arms and started kissing him more to remove the conversation from his lips. "Is that a yes?" I kissed more, "You're right. Today isn't the day. Don't ask me that today." Marriage? I didn't know if I ever wanted to get married again. I sure as fuck didn't want to discuss it the day I told my husband I wanted a divorce.

The next morning Derrick wanted to talk, but all we did was fight. He insisted I had spent the night at Paul's house. I wouldn't tell him where I was because I wanted to make sure I had a place to escape to if needed. Derrick and Bailey had been friends for a long time; I also didn't want him to know his friends were on my side. Derrick took off, telling me what a useless bitch I was and that he was seeing someone also. It turned out he was seeing someone he worked with. He had known her longer than he had known me, and he knew she and I had a history. I was a witness to her beating her young toddler daughter. I had been brought in to give a statement to CPS, and her daughter was removed from her custody. I made it clear she wasn't ever to be around my kids, especially alone. After a week of nonstop fighting, I texted Derrick and told him we needed to make the final plans for our daughter's birthday party. He called, and I told him the date and time that would work best; he said no because it was the same day as his girlfriend's daughter's birthday. I called him out for putting someone else's kid above his own, and he laughed at me.

Derrick was treating this new girl like gold. I had been treated like a piece of shit, even in the beginning when I hadn't seen it, I did after. I cried all the time. I hated Derrick more than I loved him, or even liked him, so why was it so hard to let go of? Why did he treat her so well after only a few days, but for nearly ten years I was the doormat? What was wrong with me? Derrick came home from his friend's house one night and fund me in a ball crying on the kitchen floor. Derrick said nothing, he picked me up, put me on the counter, wiped my hair out of my face, and with soft caring, teary eyes asked me what was wrong. "It just HURTS! You treat that girl, who abused her own child like she is made of gold, but you treated me, the mother of your kids, like dog shit. Not just dog shit, but dog shit stuck to your shoe that you can't get off. I don't understand. I don't understand why I am so unlovable. Why no one has ever loved me. What the fuck is wrong with me? Why wasn't I worth it?" His tears fell. "You were. You are. I fucked up. I'm trying to take where I fucked up with you and do it different with her." That really didn't make it better. She was worth it, and I hadn't been. She was a human and I had been property.

Derrick and I talked, we decided to take a week, spend time with the other people we were seeing, and then talk again. We were talking about trying to fix us. I did talk to Paul, and he wasn't surprised. He understood how hard it was letting go of ten years, even if it had been a bad ten years. Any time Paul and I spent together was in his bed. To this day, he doesn't know I faked it every time. It didn't matter, it was still the best sex I had ever had. Derrick and I also spent time together. We talked a lot and he didn't put his hands on me in any way. At the end of the week, Derrick made the decision that we would break up with the others we were seeing. He broke this off with the girl and watched the kids so I could go see Paul. I didn't think a week was enough time. I was still confused and really just wanted time alone to think.

I walked the mile and a half to Paul's house. I didn't want to end it, but things couldn't continue how they were. I still didn't want to hurt either of them, and neither of them could see how badly I was hurting. Paul and I went to his room, he tried to kiss me, I told him I was there to talk. I told him what I had come to say, I had been honest since the beginning of the situation, I wasn't going to start lying. Paul kissed me, kissed down my neck, and took off all of our clothes. As I lay in his bed naked with him above me, I told him "I'm being honest here. I am not supposed to be in bed with you."

324

He smiled and kissed me again. My legs opened and I pulled him closer until once again we were one. Our bodies moved together in harmony, wanting and needing each other. I was dizzy with pleasure and - something was happening- my brain was fuzzy except for one clear thought "I think I'm going to cum. It's actually going to happen. It *is* real." I felt my nails dig into his back as the start of something I thought was impossible was happening. "Marry me?" He asked as my first every orgasm with a man was beginning, "Yes" I said in the heat of the moment, to the physical pleasure. The realization of what he said hit me like a ton of bricks and the orgasm never quite happened.

I left his house more confused than when I had gotten there. I was thirty-two and felt guilty being involved with a twenty-five-year-old. I had feelings for him. I really didn't have feelings for Derrick, I just didn't know how to let go of all the time and effort I had put into the relationship. I had gone there to break up with him, because it was what Derrick said I was supposed to do. I did it and still wound up in his bed. He hugged me and I relaxed. He kissed me and the world disappeared. I started to feel alive again in his arms. I hadn't felt these things since Brad. I didn't know what to say or do about the proposal. I couldn't tell him that I had been saying yes to the sex and not his question. That seemed cruel. It wasn't that I would never want to marry him, I was a long way away from even having those thoughts though. That night, Derrick raped me. Again.

School was starting and Derrick was selling our van for scrap. I told him I would need some of the money to get the kids new shoes and supplies for school. He refused and told me it was his money. Paul picked up a job with an acquaintance power washing houses and gave me the money to get the kids the things they needed. He started randomly stopping by with a candy bar, or just to say hi. None of my neighbors ever told Derrick Paul had been here, I never hid it though. I didn't know which one of them I was with, and I wanted to be alone, with no one except my own thoughts. I told them both that, but neither of them listened. I never lied to either of them. Derrick didn't have the same respect for me. He didn't show up to our daughter's birthday party, I knew where he was though. Bailey dropped me off near Derrick's girlfriends house, and I walked over to confront him. He was sitting in his truck outside of her house talking to her. She said nothing when I told him off and made it clear picking *anyone* over his own child was unacceptable. I met back up with Bailey where he had dropped me off and went home. Derrick came home that night and raped me.

I was sitting outside talking to bailey the next evening, and I asked him what he says or does if his wife doesn't want sex. I knew he beat her, but I didn't know if that was all. He said if it was all the time, he would think she was cheating. That was absurd because they cheated on each other like it was a competitive Olympic sport. I clarified my question, his answer was simple, "I go jerk off." He knew by my facial expression, or maybe lack of eye contact, that that wasn't what my life consisted of. Bailey beat his women, but he was protective of his friends. I brought the kids inside to get ready for bed, Bailey made it clear he would be outside waiting. "We need to talk."

I took an extra-long time getting the kids bathed, ready for bed and asleep. Every time I peeked out the window Bailey was still there. I knew if I didn't go outside, he would knock, so I swallowed my pride and walked out the door. "Simone, what you said...your face...you're saying?" I looked away. "Bailey, I didn't fucking say a thing. Whatever you think you saw, that's on you." I turned so he wouldn't see the tears coming. "Simone, I called the cops. They'll be here any minute." The anger chased the tears away. "You what? Bailey, I don't fucking like cops. Why did you? I didn't even say anything. What the fuck, dude?!" His face softened and I saw his whole body relax as he sighed. "You didn't have to say it. Just talk to the cop and they will tell you what to do." When the cop car pulled up, I kept trying to walk away. It was a female cop that everyone knew. Celeste was nice, approachable and admittedly not like most cops.

I walked behind my house, she followed, she just wanted to talk." I don't know what Bailey told you. He should have just minded his own business." I chewed my fingers, smoked and dug my nails into any bit of flesh I could find. "Just tell me what happened and if there's something to report, I will walk you through

326

is." A lava hot tear leapt from my eye onto my cheek. "He hits me sometimes, and if I don't want to have sex, I don't know, he doesn't care. He just kind of does it anyway." She pushed a little harder, got a tad bit more detail, and asked me why I never said anything. I turned to face her for the first time. "Well, who would believe me? This is his town. He knows everyone. Everyone is his friend. Anytime I breathe wrong someone tells him. No one here even knows my name. Besides, he is my husband. Most people believe you can't...*you know*...your wife." I didn't realize until hours later that I had been openly crying the whole time. Celeste didn't give me a choice. She put me in the back of her patrol car and took me to the commissioner. I gave a written statement detailing some of the sexual and physical accounts. The commissioner read it with a somber look, "I am so very sorry you have had to live like this" he said as he signed the paperwork granting me a twenty-four-hour order of protection. I had to go before a judge the next day to get it extended to thirty days. Another cop had stayed behind at my house so when Derrick got there he could be escorted out. I had bags by my back door to be donated to the local thrift shop, Derrick took the wrong bags. He wound up with old kids' clothes and sheets.

The next day in court I was granted a thirty-day protective order. Derrick was granted a few hours of visitation twice a week. I was granted three hundred dollars a month in financial support, and my official request for his girlfriend to not be allowed alone with my kids was granted. He would be permitted to come get his personal belongings with the supervision of police only. Before the thirty days was up, we would need to go back to get a one-year order. Two officers came with him about a week later. He wanted the living room TV. Derrick had bought the old projection TV from his boss, I had hated it, but it was the only one we had. I told him to take it. On top of the TV was a wooden ship that said DAD on the cloth sail. My son had bought it for Derrick the previous Father's Day, using the entire gift card he won in a spelling bee. Derrick knocked it off the TV smashing it to pieces. My son's face when he saw it was heartbreaking. With no real income my rent dropped to nothing, and they gave me a check for eighty-nine dollars a month to help pay my electric bill. The electric bill was over two thousand dollars because I hadn't been allowed to pay it. With Derrick gone, I still didn't have

Paul spend nights at my house. I saw him several times a week and we talked daily. Derrick had mine and my daughter's phones turned off. He then tried to have the electric turned off, to be turned on at his girlfriend's house. That would have made my life easier. It didn't work though; she had a different electric company. He also tried to have my cable and internet disconnected. It was one thing I didn't have to worry about paying for. I was one of the only people on my street that had internet. Most of my neighbors used it and used my computer. They all chipped in to keep it on.

It was peaceful with Derrick gone. It was quiet and took time to adjust. Late at night I would get the feeling I was being watched. I would check the windows and the doors. I often saw his truck, or his girlfriend's car, driving slowly by my house. Or I would see someone duck into the shadows by the trees. Everyone thought I was paranoid. Even Paul didn't believe Derrick was really there. I could feel it though. The same way I had been able to feel Griffith watching me. Derrick later admitted that he had been stalking me in those weeks. Stalking was the word he used. I hated when he had the kids. I didn't trust him, and I wasn't used to being away from them. Seven hours a week wasn't much, but when you're a worrier and an over-thinker it's really thousands. There was drama at Paul's house. Most of the people staying there were involved in some kind of drugs. Because of my own history, and the fact that I am just not social, I avoided being there. My insecurity about Erica walking around naked didn't make me want to be there either. Paul told me when she would get in fights with her boyfriend Zack, she would go get in bed with Paul...naked. He swore nothing happened and he would never touch her. I believed him but only because in our town everyone slept with everyone. This led to a large group of people having herpes, chlamydia and gonorrhea. She was one of them, he had been tested several times and was negative. Regardless, I didn't like her walking around naked, and I liked her in his bed less.

As the drama at his house escalated, I let Paul stay at my house sometimes. He didn't want to throw everyone out without anywhere to go, but he didn't want all the drama either. The house stayed trashed. There was never any food, but there was always beer. The few people that were working weren't interested in contributing, and

328

the electricity was going to be disconnected. Paul was over one night, and we were talking about the drama while I showered. Once I was done, I laid on my bed, on my abdomen, wrapped in a towel. I told him I really didn't like Erica being in his bed, and he climbed on top of me. He tried kissing my neck and touching me. I told him to wait. We were in the middle of a conversation. He said he didn't see the big deal, that I knew he wouldn't touch her, and he started trying to touch me again. I shoved him off of me angrily and told him, "No, stop." He gave me a sad face and asked why not? "Because I'm upset. You wouldn't like it if some guy was getting in bed with me naked." Paul backed off a little and rubbed my back while we talked. His hand moved to my thigh, which I didn't even really notice at first. I was in mid-word when his finger slipped inside of me, then he was inside of me. After he was done, I looked at him and very clearly told him," I said no." His expression changed to sadness and hurt. "I thought I changed your mind. You were wet." This is one of the many reasons why boys and girls should both be taught about both anatomies, by their parents and the school. If you touch parts of the anatomy, it responds, plain and simple. It isn't an indication of wanting or willingness. Besides, some females are just wet more often than not, and it means absolutely nothing. Most men understand truly little about female anatomy.

I didn't discuss it with him, and I said nothing else about Erica being in his bed. There is no point in saying words that would not be heard, and people only hear what they want to hear. They also only see what they want to see. As I got dressed, got into bed, and cried myself to sleep, he chose not to hear or see. It was even more fucked up because it wouldn't have taken much to get me in the mood. All I needed was my feelings to be acknowledged. A simple "Okay I will keep my door locked," and we could have had sex. I wouldn't have said no, and he wouldn't have disrespected me. I never bothered to say no again, I already knew there was no point.

Some of the people that had been staying at Paul's moved on, including Erica. New people came. Brittany was new, she wanted any man that would give her attention. A county troublemaker, George was staying there. He was more than happy to oblige Brittany's needs as long as his girlfriend didn't find out. Paul threw a huge bonfire, at least once a month. Bailey wanted to go, but he didn't want to bring Hannah. He told her to watch my kids so he could take me. My oldest was more than capable of watching them, but Bailey had covered for me and been there for me through the ordeal with Derrick, so I acted like I needed her. Brittany and I were the only two girls there. All the guys and I talked; I had alcohol to ease my social awkwardness. Brittany wasn't getting attention no matter how much she flirted with every guy there. She took her shirt off; She had a boyish face and figure. All the guys were still more interested in talking to me. I had to show off what I had that she didn't so I also took my shirt off. Derrick was there and was in the rounds of guys I talked to. He angrily told me to put my shirt back on many times. He even pulled me away from conversations with other people to tell me I "had" to put it back on. I refused, making it clear that he couldn't tell me what to do anymore, because I wasn't his property. "Well, I'm sure he feels the same way I do," Derrick said with a nod toward Paul. Paul stood on his back deck looking out at the pile of people and the fire glowing in the night sky. Our eyes met as I walked toward him, "Are you okay with me walking around like this?" His eyes were soft and showed no concern. "Yeah, babe. You're fine to walk around however you want." I wasn't sure if I should be concerned that he didn't care, so I asked him why he was okay with it. His answer was simple. "They can look all they want. I know who you're going home with." I went back to talking with all the guys, giving Derrick a smug look on my way past.

It was the first time I had really drank in years. It was the first time I was drunk since I was a teenager. Brittany was still upset that she wasn't getting the attention she needed. She pouted for a while, flirted more, and made it clear she would be on the side of the house alone, if anyone wanted to fuck. No one went. She reemerged claimed she was very sick and needed help getting in the house. No one went. When she came back out, she was fine, laughing, talking and flirting like she had been most of the night. There wasn't attention still for Brittany. So, she took off her pants. With enough drinks I had the confidence to take off my shirt, the pants wouldn't happen. I glanced down her slender body and started to laugh. The guys saw what I did and laughed with me." What? What is it?" I approached her calmly and slowly. "Brittany? When your pussy can

330

eat your underwear, there might be a problem. Especially if you can't feel it." The underwear she was wearing were supposed to be full coverage in the front but had disappeared into her abyss. Obviously embarrassed she scrambled to put her clothes back on, "Jealous," she said as she started past me. "Jealous of what? That you have the body of a little boy and I actually have tits? Jealous that any guy here would rather have a conversation with me, than fuck you? I may not be hot, sexy, or thin, but I could have any guy here I wanted." Everyone who heard the conversation nodded in agreement. In a later conversation she admitted that she wanted me too.

Derrick was drunk and tried to take his truck out for a drive. I had Paul and Bailey get his keys. No one would be driving that night. Not if I was there, I wouldn't allow it and they all knew it. Derrick yelled that he had lost the only thing that mattered to him, and he wanted to take the truck and crash it into a tree. He had to be forcefully removed from the truck. As we were calming him down, Bailey yelled that Hannah was on her way and she was bringing my kids. I threw my shirt on just as they were pulling into the driveway. This was a side of me that my kids would not see. I don't remember getting in the car or going home. I do remember throwing up all over the parking lot when we got there though. I woke up on my couch with someone's feet in my face. They were definitely men's feet, it had to be Paul. I sat up and tried to remember...anything. My vision cleared and I saw it was Derrick on the couch next to me. At least my clothes were still on. I wandered around my house and found Paul asleep, alone in my bed. I woke him up and asked him what happened, and how I got on the couch with Derrick. He told me they had left Derrick in a chair, and me on the couch. We woke Derrick up together not knowing if he was still going to be volatile, and he remembered less than I did.

In October, everyone left Paul's house. The electric was off, and no one had any interest in paying the bill. Paul started staying with me. I really didn't want him to move in, but I saw it as short term, I couldn't see him staying somewhere with no electricity. Derrick and his girlfriend broke up after she faked a pregnancy and miscarriage. As a human being, a woman, I believe faking a pregnancy, then the

331

death of a child, is the worst thing a female can do. Derrick had nowhere to go. he asked Paul if he could stay at his place. He didn't care about electricity; it would just be somewhere to sleep for a few hours a night. George also needed a place to go. We said they could both stay there. Derrick would send me pictures of him heating water up for coffee using a cinder block and oven rack, with a small fire. I knew he wanted me to feel bad and tell him to come home, I felt nothing.

The protective order had never really mattered. When Derrick was still with his girlfriend, he had got a message to me that they had no food. I was sending plates of food out to his truck for him, plus anyone else that was staying there. I was feeding between three and seven extra people a day. The breakup only fueled him to try harder for us to get back together. I didn't want to hurt him. I ignored his comments, or said things like "I don't know," "Maybe one day," "We'll see." I started getting lease violations for him driving his loud truck down the street at night. It was illegal for them to hold me responsible. He wasn't on their property, plus the domestic violence act of 2005 states if they know he is on the property, they are supposed to report it to the police. They never reported it. The police knew he was at my house all the time anyway, they rode by and saw him there regularly. That didn't matter though. No one had ever cared about protecting me.

Paul went away for a week in October to help his grandmother. During that week I desperately needed groceries. Derrick offered to take me, he had been decent then, and the store I needed to go to wasn't walking distance. Paul and I discussed it, and Derrick was my only option for getting to the store. Derrick took the long way there, through desolate back roads. I was increasingly uncomfortable the more we drove through the middle of nowhere. On a dirt road surrounded by fields without a house in sight, Derrick pulled over and turned off the truck. Derrick got out and walked around to my door. When he opened my door, I could see his pants were already down. I laid down and let him do what he wanted. There was no point in objecting, my protests would fall on deaf ears. There was no point in fighting, I would lose. There was no point in trying to run, there was nowhere to go. When Paul came back, I told him about it; he had no reaction.

Derrick called me nightly. As we would talk about general life, his job, the kids, or anything else, he would masturbate and make it known he was doing so. Derrick would say things that got inside my head. He would tell me how much he missed me, that I was his "One that got away," that he loved me, that he "Didn't know what he had until it was gone," that if I took him back, we could start all over and be a family. I still just wanted time, space, peace. Paul knew a married couple, Jane and Alan, who had a teen son, Sam, who needed a place to go. They would be able to get the electricity turned on and keep the bill paid, so Paul agreed. After that he went back and forth between staying at his place and at mine. Derrick's truck needed work, so he was riding a bike. Derrick would ride his bike to my house, using the back door so he wasn't on camera. He often would "accidentally" fall asleep on my couch so he wouldn't have to leave. I knew he wanted Paul to think I was having sex with him so Paul would leave me. I called Paul one afternoon while I knew Derrick was there and had him put me on speaker phone. I made it clear that as of that moment, I wasn't with either of them, and I wasn't sleeping with either of them either.

In July, when Paul had first kissed me, I had weighed one hundred and seventy-seven pounds. My highest weight ever outside of pregnancy. By October I was one hundred and thirty-two pounds. My lowest weight without the use of drugs, since childhood. I was too stressed to eat, throw in long term high blood sugar, and you have a dramatic weight loss. Derrick started to complain that whenever he was over, I was cleaning. "It's already fucking clean. I think you keep that broom in your hand to avoid doing anything else, like spending time with me. Just stop. Don't clean for one day. I dare you." I dropped the broom in the middle of the floor. We argued and he left. The next day when he came back, the first words out of his mouth? "Why the fuck is it such a mess in here?" The broom was laying exactly where I had dropped it the evening before. "Well asshole, you complained about me cleaning. This is what happens when I don't clean for a day." I knew I had made my point and picked up the broom. Whatever I did was never right, I was used to it, it had been that way my whole life.

During the thirty-day protective order, we had gone back to court, and it had been extended for one year. Derrick convinced me to go have the protective order dropped. I filed to have it modified and we went to court again. I asked the judge to cancel the protective order stating that we were working toward a possible reconciliation. The judge denied it, sighting that he saw stories like mine too often, that ended in the woman ending up murdered. The judge did agree we could have phone contact, to discuss the kids, only. That the second he said something about getting back together, I was to hang up, if something threatening was said I was to hang up and notify the police. Outside of the courthouse Derrick yelled at me," You didn't want them to drop the fucking thing. If you, did you would have told him, we were getting back together. He would have dropped it if you said we were getting back together!" Everyone in the vicinity was staring, including all the cops and court officers, who were very well aware of the situation. "Derrick, do you know what reconciliation is?" I asked him like he was a toddler. His blank stare and slight shake of the head showed me he didn't. "It means getting back together. The judge denied it, because when women like me, take men like you back, women like me end up dead." I walked away.

Derrick asked me not to let Paul come trick or treating with us. I hadn't planned on asking him to go. He had no kids and wasn't the father of mine. Paul did stop by while I was getting the kids ready to go. Derrick got there just as Paul was about to leave. Derrick had an epic toddler temper tantrum. One of my neighbors put him in his place, that Halloween was about the kids, his attitude problem would not interfere with the kids enjoying the night. Throughout the night, Derrick pouted, didn't interact with the kids at all, and made frequent comments about moving away and not coming back. Right before we began our walk back home Derrick told me "I am moving to North Carolina. You won't hear from me anymore." I had learned that statements like this were made to get a reaction. He wanted to hear me say stay. What he actually heard was "That's cool. Let me know your address when you get there for court."

334

My fifth baby was turning four. I had tried to find work with no success. I applied for cash assistance and began their job classes to receive it. Melanie took me to another town to get my son some things for his birthday. Derrick called Melanie's phone constantly while we were gone. He had been demanding when he called, even after she told him she was on the phone with her mother, and I would call him back when she was done. Finally, she got pissed off and told him to just not call her phone anymore. I found a bike for my son at a really great price. Melanie took a picture of it while we were coming out of the store, she sent the picture to Paul. Derrick called screaming that nothing about his kids was to be sent to Paul, and that once we were back together, I would never be allowed to talk to Paul again. I told him calmly that it was Melanie's phone, not to call again, I would call when I got home.

I didn't call when I got home, I didn't call at all. I ignored all of his incoming calls that night and into the next evening. I was on the phone with Paul and Derrick was calling every couple of minutes. Suddenly my back door burst open, slamming into a wall and Derrick rushed in. "I gotta go Derrick is here," I told Paul and hung up. "You didn't answer the phone! You didn't call last night! I thought something was wrong! I thought something happened to you!" He yelled at me as the door stood open, the cool fall air blowing in around him. "You didn't worry when I was walking to the store in almost knee-deep snow, to get groceries because you wouldn't take me. You weren't worried when I was carrying seven hundred dollars in groceries home in a granny cart. You weren't worried when you knocked our sons head into a wall. You weren't worried when the medication we tried him on made him act like he was on coke. You weren't worried when I begged you to spend time with me. You weren't worried when I fucked up my knee. Why worry now? Were you worried something happened to me? Or were you worried I was out fucking someone else?" In two quick movements I was against a wall by my throat. "You can't talk to me like that. You need to let me come home and stop all this bullshit. I'm tired of you telling people this dumb shit. I read the police statement and it's fucking stupid. Everyone knows you can't rape your wife. You need to do what you're told. Stop talking to Paul about my kids, let me come home, then stop talking to him altogether." This time when he released me, I landed on my feet. As I gasped for air, I told him to get the fuck out of my house before I had people physically remove him. I wasn't talking about the police, he knew it and left.

We were having a warm streak that fall. It was more like summer. Derrick stopped by to talk while most of the kids were at school. My littlest baby played in the early afternoon sun as Derrick, and I talked. Derrick asked if he could take our son with him to Paul's for a little while. I agreed and got his shoes, I reminded Derrick to make sure his shoes were on before he played in the yard. All the guys worked on cars there, there were car parts scattered across most of the yard. I figured there were at least four other adults there, everything would be fine, and I could get some uninterrupted cleaning time in. Within an hour I got a call from Paul, "Hey you hear from Derrick yet?" He asked." No. Why?" I replied with confusion. "He didn't call you? They're on their way to the hospital. I got them a ride with my friend Jason who's staying here. Derrick left the baby in the truck with the door open. He told him to come in when he was done playing. He had no shoes on. The rest of us didn't know he was even here until he came in with blood dripping from his foot. It's bad, Simone. He might lose his toe." I was dialing Derrick's number when Jason's truck pulled up. I got in and went to the hospital. Paul wasn't exaggerating. It really did look like he might lose his toe. When we got to the emergency room, Derrick didn't even come in. Jason, who I barely knew came in. I watched as they stitched it up and listened when they said just a little bit further and they would be removing it. It was Jason who caught me when I almost passed out. It was Jason who wheeled me out of the hospital holding my son, because I was too dizzy to walk. I made sure that the hospital documented what happened, where and who had been responsible for my son at the time of the incident. Afterward I made sure Derrick knew not to even ask to take him alone again, it wouldn't happen.

Derrick asked that Paul not be invited to our sons fourth birthday party. I was fine with this and again, hadn't intended to invite him. Derrick didn't show up until the very end of the party and again, didn't interact with any of the kids. I was so tired of fighting with

336

him. I was tired of fighting at all. I was tired of everything. His constant pushing for us to be together and be a family got to me. So, just days after our son's birthday I agreed to take him back, but made it clear he couldn't move back in. I also made it clear I would not end my friendship with Paul. He was the only one I had been allowed to be friends with all those years, I wasn't just cutting him off. I called Paul and invited him over. We stood in my kitchen, in the same corner we had shared our first kiss, just four months earlier. I told him it was over; I was taking Derrick back. Paul dropped to his knees, wrapped his arms around my legs, and cried. He told me how much he loved me, wanted to be with me, marry me, spend forever with me. Above him I also cried. I didn't know if I was in love with Paul, but I did know I loved him in a way I had never loved Derrick.

For the next three days, Derrick was at my house except when he went to work or was at Paul's house to sleep. While we were together, all we did was fight. He complained and belittled me constantly. Paul and I communicated through email since I didn't have a cell phone, and I couldn't talk on the house phone with Derrick there. I cried every time a new email popped up. I asked if he still would have kissed me if he knew how things would turn out. "Yes, because I cherish every moment I got to spend with you in my arms,I told him. I believed we would be together someday. "I believe you, but I will be looking for miss right now." For three days, I cried, which was just something else for Derrick to complain about. On the first day, I was in my boys' room cleaning up; I sat on the floor sobbing. Derrick came in and kicked me; my head slammed into a wall. "Can't you do anything besides cry?" He screamed. It had been a long day where I had done nothing right. "Well, if I'm so fucking horrible, why are you here? If everything about me is so awful and you hate me so much, why are you fighting so badly to get me back? Why the fuck do you want me? Can you think of *ONE* good thing about me?" Derrick left. After he was gone, I called Paul, and I asked him if he could think of one good thing about me. There was no hesitation, and there wasn't just one thing; there was a list. I posted on Facebook asking those that knew me well if they could think of one good thing about me. Some of the people who commented knew me well, some didn't, but in either case, they all gave lists.

On day four, Derrick called me yelling. He was furious that I had still been talking to Paul. I hadn't hidden it; I had told him I was still going to be friends with him. Derrick screamed, cursed, and called me every name in the book. He said he was done; he was going back to his first wife Rae. Before he hung up, he let me know that Paul felt the same way about me that he did, that neither of them wanted anything to do with me. I had just gotten more time on my phone, so I called Paul. There was no answer, I text and got no response. I was waiting for my little ones to fall asleep, when I saw Caleb outside. I went out and we talked. "Miss Simone, Derrick is stupid. You're smart. You being with him makes you look dumb. Paul is head over heels in love with you. Go get your boy. Lock your doors, I'll keep a look out." I had already talked to my daughter who was now a teenager and she had already agreed to listen for the kids after they were asleep. I grabbed some stuff Paul had left at my house, locked up and left.

I stopped at the store to grab a phone card for Paul, I had told him I would get his minutes for the month before we broke up. For me a promise is a promise. Paul's house was at the end of a dirt driveway on a dirt road. There were large potholes and no light. I couldn't see. I called Paul, no answer. I called Derrick, no answer. I had come that far, I wasn't about to turn around, so I navigated around the potholes from memory. With a lot of luck, I managed to not fall. Jason answered the door when I knocked, he confirmed with Paul it was okay to let me in. Paul didn't move from the table where he had just finished eating with Jane and Alan. I handed him the large envelope with his things in it and let him know there was also a phone card in it. I stood over him, wishing we were alone. I had so much to say that I didn't want to say in front of everyone. "So, I guess Derrick wasn't lying for once and you really don't want anything to do with me. It's really fucked up, because I never lied to either of you. I'm sorry if I hurt you though. Could you walk me to the end of the driveway? Or let me borrow a flashlight and I'll stick it in the tree at the end? I can't see a damn thing out there." Paul grabbed my hand as I started to walk away. "I never told Derrick shit. He had you on speaker when he was on the phone yelling at you earlier. He swore when he hung up you were going to call back threatening to kill yourself if he left you. You didn't call him back. He left to go pick up Rae since he made himself look like an idiot. I was going to call you, but my phone was dead. It's still on charge." We stared at each other, me standing above him at the table, his one hand holding mine and the other on my hip. "Promise me it won't happen again?" Paul asked softly. "I promise," I whispered as our lips connected once more and everything around us disappeared.

We were still in the same spot, sharing the same kiss, when Derrick came in with Rae. He said something under his breath as he took her to his room. Paul stood, his arms surrounded me, and we kissed all the way into his room. I paused to call my daughter and check on the kids, they hadn't woken up and everything was fine. I went back to kissing and our clothes vanished. We had sex and for the first time, with a man, and no assistance of fingers or tongues, I had an orgasm. I guess it wasn't a myth after all. A couple of days later, we were at my house when Paul told me that he had been talking to his ex, Kate, while we were broken up. He said they weren't talking about being together, just as friends. "Do I have anything to worry about?" I had been honest with him through everything with Derrick and we had known each other for years, I expected honesty. I believed there was no way this man, would look me in the eye and lie. "No," he said. His eyes gave me no reason to question him. It wasn't until this minute that I realize how odd that was. I knew he still talked to several of his ex's and was friends with them, including Kate. I had never had a problem with it, so I should have known, him confessing to talking to an ex as a friend was a lie. On December 4, 2011, Paul's phone fell out of his pocket at my house. I saw it after he left while I was straightening up. It was unlocked so I committed the ultimate relationship betrayal, outside of cheating, and I snooped. I found out that he had been talking to Kate about being with her. He had sent her a text "You should know, I've missed you," at the same time he had sent me the email that he "Cherished every moment with me in his arms." He had also told her that I had been insecure about her, that I had been scared he would leave me to go back to her. That was a lie. I was insecure because she had been a scrawny twig and I was a fat whale. But he had wanted me for so long, since well before he ever knew her. I never thought he would have left me, for anyone. Then I looked through his other texts. Erica. He had been asking Erica for nude pictures. He had been texting both of them at the same times he had either been emailing me or on the phone with me. My daughter was up, I asked her if she could listen for the kids while I went out. She said yes, I locked the door and took what I believed would be my last mile and a half walk to Paul's house.

The house was dark when I got there; I knocked lightly. No answer. I went around back and knocked on his window. No answer. I went for the old movie trick and softly threw rocks at his window To my surprise, it worked, and Paul came out on the back deck. I handed him his phone and walked away. "You came all this way to bring me my phone?" I whipped around to face him, "I looked through it. Go fuck yourself." He asked me to wait, and stupidly, I did. As we talked, I was getting louder by the syllable, so we went inside his room. He didn't understand what my problem was, so I pointed it all out on his phone in black and white text with Kate's name at the top. "But I told you I had been talking to her. I didn't lie about it." Some people are denser than others. "You said you weren't talking about being with her. You telling her you're single again, that you've missed her, and asking if she would give the two of you another chance, is, in fact, talking about being with her, not to mention the fact that you were asking Erica for nudes. The same Erica that you said I didn't need to worry about being naked in your bed. We broke up for two seconds, and you're trying to get back with your ex and see someone else naked. I'm sure you'd fuck Erica if she was around." Paul denied the accusation and tried to justify his actions. "We were broken up," he insisted. Which is true, we were, but we were back together when he looked into my eyes and lied. The problem was the blatant dishonesty. Now, I have never been a *Friends* fan, but I always sided with Ross. He hadn't done anything wrong; they were on a break. In my situation, Paul could have had sex with two hundred girls during those three days, it would have hurt, but I wouldn't have held it against him. We weren't together. If he had been honest about it, there wouldn't have been a problem. "Not only were you saying all this shit to her, but you were also doing it at the same time as you were telling me you love me, wanted to be with me, and cherished every moment with me. If you had been honest, it wouldn't have been a big deal, but you lied." Paul still didn't understand, and to "fix" it, he changed his relationship status on Facebook to engaged. Kate saw it right away and texted him, "You were single and now engaged; WHAT THE FUCK?!" He deleted the message and claims he hasn't spoken to her since.

I again cried for days, whether he was around or not, I cried. Paul who had liked me, and even fallen in love with me over our eight-year friendship, had showed me that I didn't mean much to him at all. If someone means something to you, you're not interested in someone else after just a few days. If someone means something to you, you don't lie to them. Paul knew I had issues with crying in front of people, but he had seen me cry over the years. Mostly, he had seen me cry over Derrick. He had always told me it was fine and I, "Didn't have to face the pain alone." It was different now though, he left me alone in his room and went to punch his kitchen cabinets, he put a hole in the wall of his den, he went to the yard and threw car parts around. I saw his fists curl and uncurled at his sides, like they were breathing. I kept trying to get myself together, at least cry silently so he wouldn't know, the flood wouldn't stop though. The kids and I spent a weekend at his house and after I thought he was asleep, I sobbed as his arms were draped around me. "Would you stop fucking crying already!" He snapped and his fist shook above me. I tightened my muscles and covered the side of my face to prepare for the blow. He didn't hit me, but he was close. Paul could handle my tears, as long as he wasn't the one who caused them.

Amy was a girl that both Paul and his friend Jason had dated. I guess she hadn't actually dated either of them, just fooled around with them, and many other guys. She just liked to string guys along. Paul and Jason were still friends with her, and Jason was still trying to get with her, or at least get a little action. Jason invited her to come stay with him at Paul's house for a few days. Paul was different around her. He was always all over me, no matter where we went. He was always kissing me, touching me, damn near fucking me with our clothes on. Not with her around though. All of a sudden, his back hurt too much for me to sit in his lap, the kisses were short, there were nonstop excuses to not touch me. Paul took a muscle relaxer for his back pain and went to sleep. I sat on Paul's bed and listened to Jason tell Amy how he thought we were just sex, and after it fizzled out Paul would be done. I had had that thought as well. When I asked Paul why he had been different around Amy, he said he didn't realize he had been.

Later that month after I had come to terms with it, accepted it and tried to move on, we were in bed talking. I was sitting up next to him as we smoked after sex cigarettes. A conversation about the world around us, movies that were out and just general small talk, turned into a verbal attack of me. Paul ran his fingers through my hair and complained it was too wild and thin (it had been falling out since I was fourteen). His eyes fell lower, and he remarked on my bushy eyebrows, "You have really pretty eyes though," and he continued downward. My boobs were too big and uneven, my stomach was "too chubby" I had been cursed with a white girl flat ass, my thighs were too big..." Can you stop already? I already know every single thing that is wrong with me. I criticize myself harder than you ever could. I don't need you to point out every flaw I have." I chased away a tear that had been trying to sting its way through. "I didn't mean it like that," he said sadly." Well, how else could you possibly mean it. I could point out every flaw you have, but to me those things aren't flaws. They are a part of you, which makes them cute." On another occasion while talking about my weight he told me, "You look fine. Could you look better? Yes. But I don't want you to do it for me." That one happened months before he picked my body apart. He hadn't noticed when I stopped eating. Until he took me to lunch, and I threw it up all over the side of the road, because once again my body wasn't used to food.

I allowed Derrick to take the kids on two overnight visits. He had moved out of Paul's and was staying in a camper at Trish and Tino's. The first time, he brought them back at two o'clock the following afternoon. They were filthy from head to toe and crying that they were hungry. I asked what they had eaten at their dad's house, and all three of them said nothing. They hadn't eaten since lunch the previous day. I ran outside to confront Derrick, he told me they had no food, and that the kids had refused to bathe at his house. I fed them and talked to them about their refusal to bathe there. They said Derrick had told Rae to give them a bath and they were uncomfortable taking their clothes off in front of her. That was understandable and a conversation I would have with him at a later time. The second time, I had him pick them up later in the day. We met at McDonald's right after I fed them dinner. I had packed food for him to bring with him. Hot dogs, peanut butter, jelly, cereal, milk, bread, ramen, and snacks. That would be plenty for breakfast and lunch the next day, and another meal if they got hungry again that night. Again, the next afternoon Derrick brought them back filthy and hungry, again they said they hadn't eaten. I stormed outside to confront Derrick. He again said they had no food, "I sent food!" I yelled logically. Derrick claimed he didn't know what happened to most of it, but that he and Rae had eaten the hot dogs. After talking to the kids more, I found out Derrick and Rae had eaten it all. While getting them washed, I was told that Derrick had made all three of them sleep in bed with him and Rae, both times. I also found that my four-year-old hadn't wiped his butt well. He had been potty trained since he was eighteen months old, but occasionally still needed help with wiping. He had poop dried and caked all over his butt that had been there long enough that his underwear were stuck to him and he had a rash. That was the last visit he got with them that was over four hours.

The kids wanted to spend Christmas at Paul's house. We loaded up the presents and spent the night. The family that was staying there wasn't happy about us being there, they made us all feel uncomfortable and unwelcome. Even Paul felt unwelcome in his own house. I supposed technically it wasn't his house. His mother had left no will. His brother had taken anything of value and sold it right after she died. Paul and his brother didn't have the financial means to care for the house, the people staying were supposed to be contributing to bills and the mortgage, but no one did. Derrick called and said he was going to stop by with things he had for the kids, I told him we were at Paul's. He was pissed we had spent Christmas at his house, he told me Paul had no right to see his kids on a holiday. Derrick brought each of the five kids a Christmas card, the three that were biologically his also got a candy cane.

343

Social services asked that I go to a Dr as part of being able to receive cash assistance. They needed to make sure all applicants were able to work. My Dr filled out the forms, citing that I was disabled. He checked the box for unable to work and for state reasons he simply wrote complications of diabetes. In January 2012 I applied for disability. Paul came to my house for a week in January. He was initially coming to help me get ready for a week long inspection, and to keep me calm the day before. I have pretty severe anxiety and being forced to allow people into my home, has always been a problem. It feels like I am having my space violated every time. It's like being mentally raped. I was ready for Paul to leave after a couple of days. I wanted my space, and I wanted it to be mine. I told him several times it was okay for him to leave, I was fine. He didn't leave just sat on his computer.

Most of the time I was fine with him being around. We could be doing two different things in the same room, and it still felt like we were spending time together. If I had to get groceries, he walked with me. We held hands walking through the streets and discussed the architecture of every building. We stayed up most of every night having sex, and every evening too. There was a lot of sex. On average, we had sex five times a day, five days a week, two hours every time. It was great sex. He still doesn't know I faked it almost every time. Other than that, one time when we got back together, it only happened with my assistance.

I started therapy over the summer. My therapist Patricia was amazing. She's one of the only women I have ever really been able to talk to. She had helped me work through the guilt I felt for leaving Derrick. I discovered in her office that a lot of why I struggled to leave him was because I felt responsible for him. Derrick had never learned how to take care of himself. He went from his mothers to a wife, a girlfriend, back to the first wife, to a second wife, back to the first wife, then to me. I had taken care of him for ten years. He didn't know how to cook, clean, pay bills, or support himself in any way. It had been the longest relationship he had had, and I felt I needed to continue doing everything for him. Patricia and I minimally discussed my childhood. She knew that I was raised by a pedophile, and that was as detailed as it got. She diagnosed me with depression, PTSD, and anxiety. All things I had heard before, all things that are

344

accurate. Bianca and I had stopped talking as frequently when I started seeing Paul. After she saw a picture of him, she told me, "He looks like Brad that's why you like him." I didn't see it then or now. They both are white guys with dark hair; that's where the similarities end. I told Bianca during one of our now rare phone calls about what the therapist had diagnosed me with. "What do you have to be depressed about?" I was silent, and she asked a few more times. "Ma, some people just have depression. It just happens. There doesn't necessarily have to be a why involved. It's also not the first time it's been said. Every therapist and shrink I have ever been to has diagnosed me with depression." Bianca dove further into the world we didn't discuss, "How do you have PTSD?" She questioned genuinely. "From trauma, Ma." I snapped, getting irritated. "Trauma from what?" She seemed confused. "Oh, I don't know, ma. My fucking childhood?!" This is why I don't talk to her about important things. "What about your childhood was traumatic? I don't think your childhood was all that bad." I hung up and turned my phone off. I texted her in the middle of the night that my phone had died. She never asked again.

Porn had never bothered me in previous relationships. I used to tell my ex's to "Go watch porn, jerk off and leave me alone." I didn't feel that way with Paul. Maybe because with him, physically, I felt not good enough from the very beginning. I caught him looking at pictures of women on 4chan one night and asked him to leave. "I didn't do anything wrong," he snapped. "You're right. You didn't. But if you would rather look at someone else's pussy, instead of having the real thing, when I'm sitting five feet away from you, then there's no reason for you to be here." We argued and I again saw his fists curl and uncurl in his lap. He got louder and closer to my face, I saw the rise of his shoulder and flinched. The fist that was going to connect with my face was settled by him taking his cigarette and putting it out on his hand. Once we were both calmer, I told him "I didn't care with other guys, but with you it hurts. It's one thing if I'm not around, or unable to fuck for some reason. But not when I'm sitting right there. It hurts, and I already feel not good enough for you." Paul reached out, his hand gently caressed my cheek, "But you are baby." He kissed me and we wound up in bed. In his mind sex fixed everything, sex made it all better. But I cried myself to sleep quietly, wondering how many times he had to think of someone else to fuck me.

February came, and Derrick and I had our divorce hearing. He didn't even show up. Melanie came as a witness. I wasn't sure what she was going to say; as far as I knew, she had only seen the incident with our van when he dragged me down the road. I had really never been in a courtroom without being high or having a drink first. Before each hearing for my protective orders against Derrick, I drank a beer first. Melanie stopped and got me a forty-ounce before the divorce hearing; I drank half before going in and the other half after coming out. I gave a statement about the abuse, stating that most of it had been sexual and behind closed doors. The judge looked at me with kind, caring eyes. She didn't tell me that a husband can't rape a wife. Melanie gave a statement that she had come over and seen Derrick holding me against a wall by my throat, the van incident, bruises she had seen on me, she told the courtroom about names he would call me, and that he tried to hold me, prisoner, in my home. As I had always known, you never know who is secretly paying attention. The judge calculated that based on his pay (which he had lied about)) his child support for the three kids we shared would be four hundred and sixteen dollars a month. I told her we had agreed to three hundred dollars a month and asked that it remain that way. The judge agreed and ordered it, along with giving me full custody and control of visitation, which is in the divorce decree as "Visitation as mother deems appropriate." Derrick barely showed up for visitation to begin with. He had been stopping by at random times, talking to Paul and me, and leaving. He claimed those were visits with his kids. Our divorce was finalized a few weeks later; he didn't file any exceptions to the order. The battle was over.

A Brief Intermission

For Valentine's Day that year, Paul desperately wanted to get me a Nook. I told him I didn't want it; I was fine reading books from the library. He persisted, though. He borrowed the money from me to buy it. I won't lie; I loved it. I still have it tucked away somewhere, although it no longer works. Not long after, Paul and I were browsing a local thrift store. There was a wedding dress there; it was gorgeous and in my size. It was also only ten dollars. Paul insisted that I had to have it. I tried it on as soon as I got home. While holding steady at one hundred and thirty-two pounds, I still looked and felt like a fat blob. Everyone remarked on the weight loss, and a lot of people said I looked too thin. I didn't see any difference in my appearance. I thought the scale was wrong, so I got on every scale I saw. They all said the same thing. The only thing that made me believe it a little bit was that I had to get smaller pants. I could fit in my teen daughter's clothes, and she was skinny. Even when I look back at pictures, I don't see the weight loss; I just see fat. My third child came home from school asking what a "crack ho" was. A kid in her class had told her her mom was a "crack ho." Apparently, this kids' dad was friends with Derrick. Derrick had told everyone I was on drugs which is what caused my weight loss. The classmate had overheard a conversation and repeated it to my child. That wasn't a fun conversation to have with an eight-year-old. More people believed me than I thought would. Derrick still had a following, though. I would walk to the store; people would throw trash and beer cans out of their windows at me, yelling that I was a "slut" or a "whore." There was a church on the corner of my street. The pastor, who isn't a true person of God, did three separate sermons on me. He preached about adultery for one week. How a man can do what they want and feel necessary to their wives to make sure they stay in their place for a second week? Sins of women for the third week. Yes, I was mentioned by name. It had been seven months, and I was still the talk of the town. Everyone turned a blind eye when that same pastor crashed his car looking at a twelve-year-old girl.

When things were good with Paul, they were amazing. He made me feel things that I hadn't felt since Brad. When he hugged me, all the stress I carried fell away. When we kissed, the world disappeared. I was flooded with thoughts and feelings that I thought were impossible. With Brad, I hadn't been able to imagine a future outside of friendship. I had wanted that so badly but had never let myself imagine it; I had known it wasn't possible, so thoughts of it were just too painful to allow. With Paul, though, we were grown, and there was no reason we couldn't be together. Even though his age did freak me out, and sometimes, even now, it still does. We spent almost every minute together. We watched TV, read books, cooked, cleaned, did things with the kids, there was still a lot of sex, and most importantly, we had conversations. I spoke, and he reciprocated; that was an amazing thing all by itself. I felt love, and I felt loved, I mattered, and sometimes I even believed him when he told me I was beautiful, which was more often than his nasty comments. I started to believe that maybe forever really did exist. When we worked on something together, we knew each other so well; we didn't need to speak; we just moved together in harmony.

It was getting hard supporting five kids and two adults on the exceedingly small amount of money I had coming in. Paul had no interest in getting a job. If I got a job, I would lose any chance I had of getting a disability, and I didn't actually know if I would be able to hold a job long-term. The pain from diabetic neuropathy and arthritis kept me from standing for some days. Plus, every penny I made would go to daycare. When Derrick and I split, the electric bill had been over two thousand dollars. I was barely paying enough for it every month to keep. I had tried to get a new account, but Derrick would have to call them, which he wouldn't do. Paul would take an odd job when one was available, but most of what he made went to cigarettes or whatever he would eat while he was out. Paul and I talked about the wedding. I made it clear I was in no rush. In a way, I was excited, there was definitely love there, but I was also hesitant. I didn't need a marriage to be committed. I didn't need another marriage this soon. I wasn't one hundred percent sure I was *in* love with him. Somewhere on a subconscious level, I saw the warning signs. I didn't consciously see them until writing this. Paul was looking at rings, ones that were thousands of dollars. "You should know me better than that." I took his laptop and looked up wedding rings on *eBay* and *Walmart*. He bought my wedding ring set on *eBay* for thirty-seven dollars. I bought his from some other site for forty dollars. It turned out to be the wrong size, and tungsten can't be resized. Eventually, I got him one that fits.

Derrick showed up in early May and told me his days off had changed. He said he was now off on Wednesdays and Thursdays. He would pick the kids up both days from four to seven. He didn't show up for the next eight Wednesdays or eight Thursdays. Sixteen consecutive missed visits. The last visit he had shown up for, only our daughter went. Both of our boys refused to go. That was in late April. In May, I got a call from the child support office. Derrick was in causing drama because his paycheck was garnished. Neither of us knew that he was supposed to pay the child support office, so he had been paying me directly. He had been shorting me from September through January. Once the divorce hearing happened, he started paying what he was supposed to. Derrick had been removed from the child support office after he made threats. "Somebody is going to give my fucking money back. I don't care if it's this office or that cunt, but if I don't get my fucking money back, I'm going to blow this whole fucking place up!" The child support worker thought he might be on his way to my house and was scared for me. She gave me her direct extension and told me to have it in my phone ready to hit dial; that way, if she got a call with just background noise, she would know it was me and be able to alert the police. "He just pulled up; I have to go," I hung up and entered her number just as Derrick started hammering on my door. Derrick yelled and screamed that they had him in their system as four hundred dollars passed due because he had been giving it directly to me. I pointed out all the times he shorted me and that he really was more behind than that. That calmed him down because he knew I could report it and he would have to pay more, I wouldn't, but he didn't need to know that. After a bit more huffing and puffing, he realized he was wrong and left.

On a random Sunday in June, he stopped by again. He talked to Paul, and I then interacted with the kids, which was unusual. Derrick was at my house for about an hour before he left as abruptly as he had shown up. I got a text right after he left, "You know it's fucked up. It's fucking Father's Day, and no one said Happy Father's Day to me. No one got me anything. You didn't make me a cherry cheesecake like you always do. You didn't take them shopping to get me stuff." I responded, "I didn't even know it was Father's Day. You haven't seen them in almost two months. Act like a father, and you will be acknowledged and appreciated as one." Derrick called, screaming at me. I was again a slut and a whore, and if I hadn't left him for Paul, he would have been there just like he had always been. He refused to accept that he hadn't been here before I asked him to leave. He had spent zero time with the kids or me for years before I ended it. Even at the kid's birthday parties, if we went somewhere, he drove and then slept in the van until we were ready to go. He went to work, got home at two, napped, left, and didn't come home until the kids were in bed; Derrick refused to accept that his actions were what ended our relationship; in reality, it was over long over when Paul had kissed me. I confessed to Derrick that I had planned on leaving him anyway, and I told him about my plan to go to New Jersey. In his mind, though, I left him for another man, and that delusion will never change.

On July 3, 2012, Paul and I walked to the courthouse because he wanted information on how we get married. After hearing all the information, he needed, he asked to fill out the application for the marriage license. After he filled out his portion, he passed it to me. Just because we were filling out the forms, it didn't mean it had to happen right away. The license was good for six months, and I knew firsthand that anything could happen during that time. Paul got the money from my bag to pay for the application and turned it in. I told him several times that we didn't need to pick a date right then; we could wait. He didn't seem to hear me. Paul knew me well and knew I didn't like odd numbers (I know I'm weird). July sixth was available, so he booked it. I felt my heart beat faster, and my lungs turned to fire. I didn't come out and say, "I want to wait, "because I didn't want to hurt his feelings. I didn't want to make him feel unwanted, and I had been trained to just do what men wanted.

Take Three

So, we were married. Overall, I was happy; the "I don't" voice in my head wasn't as insistent as the last two times. "I do" was definitely present this time, whereas it had been silent before. We didn't have a lot of money, so I didn't wear the dress. We would have a party at a later date, and I would wear it then. For the courthouse wedding ceremony, I got Paul a white button-down shirt from *Roses,* a discount store that no longer exists. I wore a white shirt with a white lace overlay that I found at *Dollar General* After the quick wedding. We walked back to my house, where I made chicken parmigiana for dinner, a family favorite, and baked a cake. We played music, danced, and drank a few beers after the kids were in bed. I spent the night of my third marriage taking care of Paul as he threw up from drinking too much. Paul can't have sex if he's been drinking. I knew it was a problem if he drank a lot; I didn't know it was even if he had one beer. I spent my third wedding night restless, unable to sleep, and just plain angry. Guys, if you know you suffer from "Whiskey dick," don't drink on your wedding night. Just don't do it.

I loved that Paul stepped up with housework, cooking, shopping, and even the kids. But we needed money. I couldn't support the seven of us on less than nine hundred dollars a month forever. Our small town was finally getting a *Walmart*, the building was up, and they were taking applications. I told him, and he said *okay*, but made no attempt to apply. I went online and applied for him. He was hired in August, on the same day I got a letter saying I was approved for disability. All five of the kids would be in school full-time starting that August; we were going to have a steady income, and things were finally looking up. Paul's schedule was five days a week, from four in the afternoon until one in the morning. Some nights I would walk there and bring him dinner. If I didn't, he would call and spend his hour break on the phone with me because he missed me.

That fall was nice. I waited up for him when he got home; we would watch TV. I introduced him to *Supernatural,* and we would watch it through the night. There was still a lot of sex, and our five times-a-day average held strong. Most nights, I didn't sleep. I hadn't been able to sleep at night since I was a kid. My therapist (Yes, Patricia) said it was because I was trained as a kid that it wasn't safe to sleep at night. That may be the case, or it may be genetic. My grandmother was the same way, and so are most of my kids. In the mornings, I would get the kids ready and off to school, do the cleaning, and make Paul breakfast. After I would wake him, we had breakfast and, of course, sex, then nap until mid-afternoon. Once in a while, I did fall asleep at night. On those occasions, Paul would get the kids to school and make me breakfast. We rarely argued. When we did, though, it was bad.

Paul and I had our wedding party in September. Bianca came and stayed a whole two hours; it was the first time I had seen her since 2008. Paul's cousin brought a beautiful wedding cake. We seemed happy, like the perfect couple, but we frequently made other couples jealous. We were happy eighty percent of the time. My thoughts had been plagued with increased doubts. Every time I saw his fist clench, a new doubt was born. Every time he spent money without making sure we had it, I panicked. This is how our relationship stayed for quite a while. I found him looking at porn again and the hefty stash he had on his computer, plus more in his phone. I do not believe that porn in and of itself is cheating. However, if one person isn't okay with it, it's crossing a line. If the other agrees not to watch it, then hides it or deletes it, it is a betrayal and, in some way, cheating. I was devastated. I had lost all of that weight, forty-five pounds, and I still wasn't good enough. His insistence that he had done nothing wrong only hurt more. If he honestly believed, he wouldn't have been hiding it or sneaking to look at it. I cried that I felt not good enough, ugly, and fat and that he had to look at other women to have sex with me. He assured me that wasn't the case. He even told me that with an old girlfriend, he had pictured me in order to have sex with her, but he had never done it with me. It honestly did make me feel better to hear, though. I made it clear, though, "One more time, and I'm done. I will divorce you faster than I married you."

Paul's work shift changed, and with it, so did he. He became noticeably short-tempered at anything and everything. Even asking him what he wanted for dinner could, and would, start a fight. He was no longer interested in spending time with any of us. He almost completely stopped helping in any way. If I asked him to do something, it was done eventually and with an attitude. After a year in the new position and just after two years with *Walmart,* Paul was fired. He stocked bread for a merchandiser off the clock and got paid cash for it. He didn't know it was against the rules. Paul spent the next four months unemployed. Sure, he got an unemployment check, but he needed to go do something. I couldn't spend twenty-four hours, seven days a week, with him. He sat at his computer all night, slept all day, and did nothing in any way to contribute. His attitude wasn't helping anything either. I started applying for jobs for him since it was clear he was content, once again, to sit on his ass and do nothing. I got him a job at *Royal Farms,* a shit job, but a job is a job. It was much closer to our house; I could bring him anything he needed at any time. I became friends with almost everyone whom he worked with, and most were also guys. This is something that all of my exes would have had a problem with. It would have been a beatable offense. Looking back, Paul seemed to like that all the guys liked having me around. In school, most of my friends were girls because that was what was socially acceptable. After school hours, and once I was no longer in school, I had always been just one of the guys. I don't understand women, I never have, and I never will. I usually say it's because I don't know how to "girl." In mid-2013, I started gaining weight. It had just stayed off for those few years, and as my pants size expanded, I was terrified. Paul claimed he didn't notice. But any time there was a sex scene in a movie, he would make comments about the women. Or he would say things like, "We have great sex; imagine how it would be if you looked like that." Once again, I stopped eating and started working out excessively. It didn't matter; I just gained.

In April 2014, I got sick. I had severe abdominal pain that was like more intense contractions. If I was stressed, it would get worse, and my stomach would swell, causing me to look six months pregnant in a matter of hours. The pain was around the clock, and nothing helped. I went to the Dr after two weeks when I couldn't handle it anymore. I had an infection called H.Pylori. I was put on several medications, including two antibiotics at pretty high dosages. Paul and I still had a pretty active sex life, and after a couple of weeks with no sex, we took the one day I was feeling better to make up for it. Neither of us, in the heat of the moment, took the time to think about what happens to birth control effectiveness when combined with antibiotics.

On May 20, 2014, Paul bought me a guinea pig that I had been in love with at the pet store. I carried him home in my hands, loving him more every minute. The next day, I told him I couldn't wait and needed a pregnancy test. Once we got back with two tests, he followed me to the bathroom, and we watched as it immediately showed positive. I simultaneously laughed and cried. Paul pouted; he had never wanted kids of his own. My kids were seventeen, fourteen, twelve, ten, and seven. The next morning, I took the other test, which was also positive. I woke Paul to tell him, but he made a sad face and went back to sleep. I made sure to let him know where I stood. "I know you didn't want kids. If you want to walk away from this, it's fine. I will not hold it against you. I will not hold you responsible. No child support, no involvement, nothing. But if you're going to go, you need to do it before the baby is born. You have until birth to decide what you want." I could see the fear in his eyes as he said, "I'm staying."

Paul came with me to the first doctor's appointment, which included a sonogram. When our little blob came into view with a tiny, fast, flickering heartbeat, Paul cried. The fear and anger that had been there were replaced by pure joy. I was sent to an endocrinologist who finally did proper testing; the tests proved I was a type one diabetic. My maternal fetal medicine Dr fought the insurance company to get me an insulin pump. I was thirty-six years old, so I qualified for genetic testing. We found out we were having a baby boy and that I was a carrier for a rare genetic disease called Tay Sachs. I knew enough about the disease to be terrified. Tay Sachs babies have a horrible quality of life and die by age five. For the next few days, Paul and I fought, cried, and comforted each other. Our initial decision was if Paul was also a carrier, we would have the baby tested; if the baby was positive, we would terminate. Paul was at work four days after I got my initial results; I texted him, "I am having this baby." He texts me back, "I love you." I called him at work, "I don't think you understand what I'm saying. I am having **THIS** baby. No matter what the results are." I really needed to make sure he understood what I was telling him. "Yes, I understand, and I love you." That's when I noticed the sound of relief in his voice and that, for the first time in days, I wasn't crying. My testing had been done at twelve weeks. Small-town life has more disadvantages than people realize. It took weeks to find a lab that could do Paul's test. We didn't find out until I was eighteen weeks that Paul wasn't a carrier, and there was no chance of our child having it.

Paul was great throughout the entire pregnancy. There was no arguing. He would banish me to bed any time he didn't have to work. I was told to go "baby bake." Paul cooked, he cleaned, helped with homework, and he did it all. It was a completely different universe compared to the way my ex's had been. The pregnancy was hard. The awful bus trips to regular OB appointments, and the medical transportation rides to maternal fetal medicine didn't help. My diabetic neuropathy worsened with each pound gained, and the pounds increased rapidly. I lost feeling in my left hand and most of my right. By the end I could barely walk. It was my biggest pregnancy gain ever. I had weighed one hundred and seventy-one pounds when I got pregnant and two hundred and twenty-five when I went into labor. I was diagnosed with polyhydramnios, which is extra fluid, in the last few weeks of the pregnancy. My medical team was pushing for a thirty-nine-week delivery, I knew there was no way I was going to make it that long. They were talking about doing fluid reduction at thirty-seven weeks, and I knew I wouldn't make it that long either. Just days after Christmas, at thirty-six weeks, my water broke in my bed. There are complications that can come with polyhydramnios, including the baby dying, which I was already at risk for due to being diabetic. Paul and I went to the hospital via ambulance. He held my hand during the surgery. When we finally heard the cry of our son, we cried with him.

The day after the birth, I saw Paul staring at me with a goofy look. He had our baby laying on him and his eyes were tearing. I asked him what was wrong, and he shocked me. "You grew this. You made this. He's amazing. You're amazing." It was the nicest thing anyone had ever said to me. Baby six and I were in the hospital for five days. I had been carrying enough fluid for triplets, I was swollen like a balloon for weeks after he was delivered. Just hours after I came home with the baby, Paul had to go to work. The following months were hard. My depression had been bad before getting pregnant, it worsened with all of the pregnancy complications, and worsened again with the birth. I never admitted that I had postpartum depression, anxiety or psychosis but I absolutely did. I made plans to kill myself shortly after the babies first birthday. I wanted to be there, experience all of his firsts, be in pictures with him so he could grow up seeing us together, and then be done. I was going to use my insulin pump to do it, just max it out a couple of times. My sugar would go so low so fast that no one would be able to stop it. By his first birthday though, Paul and I decided we wanted another baby and had been trying for a month. The suicidal thoughts and urges didn't go away, even though I was trying to get pregnant.

Right after the babies first birthday, Paul lost his job. He broke a cash register; he was banned from the property, and we had to pay over thirteen hundred dollars to replace it. Paul was going away on a week-long field trip with one of my boys, just days after losing his job. I called Patricia for an emergency phone appointment, in a panic I said, "I don't know how we're going to afford food let alone diapers and toilet paper!" As I said Patricia was amazing. She started collecting items for us, days later she brought by a few bags of food, toilet paper and diapers. While Paul and my son were away, Melanie came and stayed for the week. I had quit smoking three years earlier, with a smoker around for a week, I started smoking again. When Paul got back, he was again distant. He sat on his computer constantly, but never to do anything productive. All of the help he had given during the pregnancy was gone. Getting him to even hold the baby so I could do things was impossible. He snapped at everyone over everything. If I asked him to get something off a high shelf, I saw his fists clench and unclench as he got it, I saw his jaw flex in anger every time I spoke. Every time I tried to have a conversation that wasn't directly related to sex, he shut me out After three months. His fists still hadn't connected with any part of me. The walls, doors, and cabinets got the beatings instead. When he really was struggling with controlling a fist, he would cut his own hand. I still don't know that any of that was better than just hitting me. I got him a job at *Domino's*, where during his first week at work, he lost his wedding ring in someone's pizza.

My oldest moved out in November 2016, three months before her nineteenth birthday. She lived just down the street, and I saw her almost every day. We were very close and talked many times a day. We found out baby seven was on their way in June 2017. We again had genetic testing done to see if there were any signs of downs syndrome, or other genetic complications. Baby seven was as healthy as could be. The pregnancy was much easier, less weight gain, less complications, but Paul wasn't the same. He stopped caring about everything, he wanted to spend even less time with us as a family, and no time with me at all. Our sex life with the previous pregnancy had dropped from several times a day, to a couple of times a week, with the new pregnancy it dropped again to a couple of times a month. There was no sex unless I initiated it. There were no days to baby bake, and everything was left for me to take care of. In July 2017, my oldest moved again. Only this time she went over three hours away to live with her boyfriend. We stayed close despite the distance, and they came to visit every two to three months. I didn't want to like her boyfriend, but I did. He was impossible to not like and became part of our family very early on. I love him like he is one of my own kids.

Baby seven stayed in until the scheduled C-section date, a first for me. She was born just two days after my eldest's twentieth birthday. Melanie had come to help out while I was in the hospital. Unfortunately, that turned disastrous. My teenagers were calling me in the hospital constantly about one problem or another. Baby and I were only in the hospital for two days. No one came to visit us, except a bus driver that I had become close with during the eight months of frequent rides. Paul was given as much time off as he wanted, without pay, of course. He returned after a week, because we couldn't afford for him to take off longer. My oldest came to visit two weeks after the baby was born. Having everyone home where they belonged was good for my heart. The depression after baby seven wasn't nearly as bad.

Paul was at *Domino's* for almost a year when he got an offer at *McDonald's*. He had worked there before; the manager knew him and offered him a job when he was there to pick dinner up. The pay would be better, and he would get more hours, so he took it. I jumped through hoops to find out how he could get his license back and made it happen. Right before COVID hit in 2020, we got a used Chevy Suburban from someone he knew. It should have made things easier but it didn't. Paul spent all of his time doing things to the truck and on his phone. The kids and I were always in last place for his time. He continued to be angry all the time, he took his anger out on my three teenagers, which I wouldn't tolerate. There isn't a lot about my kids in these pages. I don't want them to ever be able to be identified, and this story isn't about them. They are my world. I grew with them and because of them. My body survived for them. Everything that was designed to kill me, failed, so I could be here for them. They would not (and didn't) have the life I had. I devoted every moment of my existence to ensuring they would have normal lives. I confronted Paul every time he had an attitude with my kids. I made it clear he wasn't to take whatever his issues were out on them. He swore he didn't, so I showed him where he had. At any and all of the jobs he had he introduced himself to new employees as "The company asshole." His co-workers would complain to me that he was mean. I always laughed and let them know, "He's proud to be an asshole. I don't know what you're telling me for. Out of him and I, he's the nice one." I never minded him being an asshole at work, it was different now that he was the asshole at home, too. His behavior started to resemble Derrick's. Any family plans, he drove there and just sat on his phone the entire time, refusing to interact with any of us. I started putting him in charge of taking pictures, to get him involved, and hoping he would see what he was missing out on. He never noticed.

The arguments came more frequently, "Whatever happened to I don't have to do everything by myself? You don't know a single thing about your own kids! They're still just babies, and you don't spend any time with them at all! What happened to us? Why don't you ever want to spend time with me? We used to do everything together, watch TV, go for walks, read, cook, everything, and now I don't even exist!" Paul would never answer other than to clench his jaw or ball up a fist. It's still the same argument we have to this day. When our youngest was about three we had a huge fight. He laid in bed through most of it. He had agreed he would try harder months earlier, and then gave no effort. I made plans to do things as a family, and just the two of us, he stayed disconnected. This was a night he had promised, again to do something with me, and again, forgotten. I stood at the foot of the bed yelling at him. "You can't even have a conversation with me? I want someone to talk to! I can't make friends; I don't go out of the house. You're supposed to be my partner, my best friend, we are supposed to be a team, but I don't even fucking exist! All you care about is your phone." Paul didn't respond which made me angrier, and I yelled more. Finally, he yelled back while moving toward the end of the bed, "Maybe I would want to be around you more if you didn't act like my fucking mother!" His mother had been an evil woman who abused him physically throughout childhood, he said it to try and hurt me. I looked at his area of the bedroom as he stood and approached me. "Maybe I wouldn't need to act like your fucking mother, if you didn't act like a fucking child!" I pointed to his window, covered in empty soda bottles and trash, the floor next to his side of the bed, with laundry, more trash and even used tissues. As he got closer screaming and yelling, he bent into my face getting louder. I stood my ground crossed my arms and bent back into his space. We matched cruel word for cruel word. His fists curled and uncurled faster and faster, his shoulder drew back, his arm raised, just a bit. I saw the rapid breaths catching in his throat as his eyes filled with hatred and rage, his arm froze there. "Go ahead. Do it." I matched the hate in his eyes with my own. "I have never hit you. I have never thought about hitting you." He smacked his arm into the foot board as he walked away and got back in bed. For someone who never thought about hitting me, he certainly knew what I was talking about. He went to sleep without another word.

I just wanted someone to talk to. I wanted a connection with a human. The only people I had to talk to were my kids. While I was close with them, and we talked about many things, there are some conversations you don't have with your kids. There are different kinds of human connections. I was looking for one I couldn't get from them. I was looking for the connection Paul and I had, before it vanished. In my adult life I have made three friends besides Paul. Melanie, who now lived in another state, and had developed an addiction to pills. Marie who was my neighbor, and a recovering addict. The two of them and I were all at various different points of addiction and recovery. I love them both to death. I will be there for them always. But sometimes, being around other addicts, or even talking to them, is just a reminder of who I used to be. Sometimes, it makes me want and need things that I put away long ago. And Nadine, who is one of the best people I have ever known, but there are somethings I just don't feel comfortable talking to her about. Besides, no one knew that Paul and I had any problems at all. To the outside world, we were still the perfect couple, who connected on every level, and never fought about anything. I missed Paul, I missed who he had been. I missed the man who had made me believe that forever was real, and that it was possible for someone to love me. I missed mattering and having a connection. I missed that when I was sick or injured, he would step up and make dinner. Now he would just feed them cereal and tell them to go to bed.

Paul had been at *McDonald's* for about two and a half years, he had been promoted to management. I got a phone call from my daughter, who lived two states and three and a half hours away, telling me that someone had contacted her via Facebook. The person told my daughter, that Paul worked with her niece Maggie, and Paul had been sexually harassing her. This girl Maggie was seventeen. I knew Paul had given the girl rides home from work before, and I had warned him about giving females, especially underage ones a ride. I walked into my bedroom to confront him, instead I became the monster I was destined to be. Paul was coming out of the

360

bedroom as I was walking in. I saw him, my arm pulled back and I slapped him with the power of ferocious adrenaline, so hard that he went backwards a couple of feet. My adult son (then twenty) said he heard the hit downstairs in the kitchen. Paul grabbed his face and asked me "What was that for?" The look in his eyes wasn't confusion, anger, or fear, it was lust. Pure unadulterated XXX lust. I repeated what I was told and read him the texts my daughter was steadily sending. Maggie's aunt wanted to speak with me, I told my daughter to give her my number. We talked for a while. She told me Maggie was trouble, lied a lot, liked drama, and had made similar accusations against many other men. Paul was in the room through most of the conversation. He said the only thing remotely sexual that was ever said was "Maggie was talking about two other co-worker's asses. I said, "Well, yours is no better." Paul wasn't thinking about her being a minor when he said it. Usually, he worked days and minors worked nights, with COVID though, anyone was working whenever they could. He didn't think about her being a kid when he said it. The aunt admitted that she thought the real problem, was Maggie had a crush on Paul, and he insulted her.

By the next morning, Maggie's guardians had contacted corporate and the police. It was brought to my attention that Maggie had expanded on her statement, "I gave him the finger and he asked if that was an offer." Maggie had said. I told her aunt that I had known Paul for seventeen years and that isn't something he would say. From the days of our earliest friendship, if a female gave him the finger, and he was interested, he said "When? Where? And how?" I was also told that another co-worker, Sally, gave a written statement in favor of Maggie's side of the story. I confronted Paul as soon as he walked in the door. There had been a meeting between him and upper management, plus he had spoken to the police. So far there were no co-workers saying that he did anything. The security footage which included audio was being reviewed by the police and management. I repeated the version of events, I had been told. He said every single employee was going to be asked to give a written statement, even the ones who worked mostly nights and weekends. That would include one of my kids who worked there. Paul even told the regional manager and co-owner that I had hit him. The regional manager had known me just as long as Paul had, she said, "Well, I know your wife. I can see that, and I don't know if I would have reacted any differently." The truth was, I hadn't hit him because I believed it. I hit him because of my past and I had warned him about her previously. It's another situation of my life that I can say I am not ashamed of my actions. I think many people, that had lived my life, would have reacted the same way. I also believe most of them wouldn't admit it.

Paul came to me and told me he thought Maggie might have hit on him; I asked for an elaboration. "It was hot in there one day. I pushed the sweat and my hair out of my face with my shoulder, saying that it was hot and I needed a haircut. Maggie replied I like guys with long hair." Some guys don't realize when a girl is flirting with them or don't realize it until after the fact. That was absolutely flirting. I told him to let management know the next day and possibly the police too. When he went in the next day, the police were there with the regional manager and co-owner. The statements had been reviewed, and the tapes had been watched. Not one employee sided with Maggie. The security tapes showed Maggie giving Paul the finger and him not responding at all, and nothing else. The conversation about asses was all there, but all of the things she had reported were not. Her comment about his hair was there as well. The investigation was closed, and he wasn't reprimanded at all. She quit and got a job at *Walmart,* where in her first month, she accused half of the male employees of sexual harassment or assault. Neither Maggie nor her family bothered to apologize to Paul, but they did take down their social media posts. I never apologized for hitting him, either. "I would tell you I'm sorry for hitting you, but I'm not." He thought about it and looked at me lustfully, "I deserved it, and it was justified," he said with a smile. Paul had been looking for a new job for months at that point. Two months after the sexual harassment accusation, in November 2020, he got a new job that had much better pay, a lot of overtime, and rewards.

Now

So here we are today. It is June 15, 2022. I have been telling Paul I want him to leave for around five years. I have tried everything I could think of to fix our marriage. I realized long ago that it can't be fixed, because he doesn't want to do anything to fix it. In recent conversations I have been brutally honest with him. I have told him," I am not in love with you. We're in this for convenience and habit. You're here because you have nowhere to go, and I take care of you. I'm here because I need a way to get the kids to their appointments." He doesn't deny it. I have told him living this way is fine, until one of us meets someone else and the remnants of love we do have for each other turns to hate. I didn't tell him I was never in love with him at all. I also haven't told him that almost every orgasm has been faked. It has happened, maybe a dozen times in the almost eleven years we have been together. I have been in the same awful income-based apartment for eighteen years. It's full of mold and falling apart, they won't fix anything. Five of my seven kids are still living at home, at least two of them most likely always will. As of today, my kids are twenty-four, twenty-one, eighteen, sixteen, fourteen, six and four. I also have two granddaughters, and a grandson due in the fall. My six- and four-year-old have been sleeping on the couch with me since May, it's been easier for me to cope that way.

Why did I sit down and write my story? Ever since I was a teenager, around sixteen, I would occasionally fall into a dark hole, mentally, of course. It usually lasts two days, never more than four. During this time, I could interact with others as needed and do the basics to care for everyone, but my mind wouldn't be in the present. During these times, I would remember something unpleasant from my childhood, deal with it, and move on. This time has been different. I fell into a dark hole in early May. It feels like my entire being is bleeding and crying like my soul is leaving my body, going somewhere, looking for something. I have remembered nothing, although some things have become clearer. I strongly believe that Griffith used to drug me, but no memories are actually new. I feel like my soul is literally bleeding out of my body. I thought writing about it would help. It hasn't.

I have discovered a lot though. I always believed all people were equal. All people should be treated equally and have equal rights. Now I know that is wrong. We are divided but not in the way most people think we are. It's not race, ethnicity, social or economic status. It's something no one can see, and most people can't feel. It's something on your soul or your spirit when you're born. There are three classes of people. The medium sized class of people are the exceptional ones. These are usually celebrities, professional athletes and musicians. They are people who are seen, heard and acknowledged. They are the people who have always had a voice that others hear. The largest class of people are the normal or typical people. This is most of the human population. They have normal everyday lives. The smallest class of people are the garbage humans. These are the invisible people. Most people don't notice them. They were born simply to be used, abused and thrown away. They are the dumping grounds emotionally and physically for the rest of the population. That is what I am. A garbage human. I was born with a mark on me that's invisible. Only those that need to relieve their anger or sexual deviances can see it. I have had my soul brought back to life once fully with Brad and partially once with Paul. Sometimes, I hope it happens again, that feeling of being alive, human, that I matter, is something I have felt so rarely. It's amazing, but when it's gone and I'm killed again, the pain gets worse each time. Most of the time, I just hope for the end. For peace, for darkness.

I have learned that in every relationship I have been in, they are all the same man. You can change the name, face, and build, but when you peel back the layers, they are all the same monster. The monster that I was trained to be with from the beginning. They are all him in different severities. I learned I have a lot of anger that I thought I let go of a long time ago, mostly toward Bianca. I have survived countless beatings, even more, sexual assaults, roaches, lice, and bedbugs; my body kept going because inside, I was dead all along. I have left pieces of myself, my soul, throughout my journey. There is some of me left behind in every house I lived in as a child, even some in the remnants of the tent in the woods. At Harry's house, where Griffith committed, I believe the worst atrocities to my body; if you look hard enough, you may see my ghost. I refer to that house as where I was murdered. One day, when it's over, I think I will get to collect those pieces. I joke about my life. I say for the life I have had, I must have been Hitler in a past life. Maybe the garbage humans are the reincarnations of the evil people of the past. Maybe this is what happens when an evil person gets multiple life sentences. Maybe that is how the garbage humans get their mark. I have learned a lot writing these pages. I have shed countless tears, but I have held in even more. I still hear the echo of his voice yelling at me, that only the weak cry.

I don't have as many physical scars as I probably should. I have some though, and although I really don't lie, I won't give an honest answer about where most came from. Years of drug use, diabetes, pregnancy, domestic violence, and a few other factors has destroyed my teeth. They are discolored and several are missing. One thanks to Jake and another thanks to Derrick. I weigh one hundred and eight-nine pounds. The weight gain is largely caused by my insulin. I have recently been diagnosed with a diabetic eating disorder, called diabulimia. It's the withholding of insulin to cause weight loss. I stop taking insulin for months at a time to make the weight come off. I also still have anorexic tendencies. I often say I collect eating disorders like other women collect shoes. Before you suggest good old diet and exercise, I have a list of gastrointestinal issues and what I can eat is already severely limited. My arthritis and neuropathy pain are so bad that some days, I cannot even walk.

What's next for me? I am trying to find a way out of my marriage. We have been approved for a mortgage. But if my marriage ends after we buy a house, my kids and I are on the streets. It is also not a whole lot of mortgage for house prices in 2022. Paul swears that he wants to stay together, that he loves me and is in love with me. Yet at times while I have been writing this, I have sat at the table crying uncontrollably, while he sits next to me staring at his phone laughing. That's not love. I have asked that he not touch me much over the last few weeks, which he has also not respected. I've made it clear that he will know when it is and isn't okay to touch me, he only does during the times when it's not okay. I still see his fist clench and unclench any time I try and discuss our relationship. He is emotionally abusive; he will not accept any of the responsibility for the problems in our marriage. Paul doesn't lock me up like Derrick did, but he does ensure that I can't go anywhere. If I go anywhere, I have to take the kids. If I don't they call me the whole time, or I come back to a completely trashed house. Oh, and the last time I left him with the kids, he forgot to feed them. I have been begging him for a break for the last four years. I have not ever had a break in my twenty-four years of motherhood. He still hasn't actually hit me, but I can feel it coming. I would like to say that when he does, it would be the final straw. That I would involve the police and end the marriage. I would like to say that I would hit him back, but he has admitted that he likes it, it's a turn on. The truth is, I would stay on the floor and apologize to him for whatever I did. I am sure, whenever it happens, and it will, I will have deserved it. I deserved it all. It is what I exist for. I am sure that anyone who has ever really known me, knows that when I die, it will be by my own hand. I thought maybe that's where this writing was going. I thought maybe it was an epic suicide letter. Sometimes I still think that. Maybe not though. So, what is this? What happens to it? I'm not sure yet. I do know I have been silenced for too long. I have been beaten into submission and obedience, and I'm tired of following other people's arbitrary rules. I am tired of being silent because the truth would hurt other people. Although I dress in a way to not be seen, I want to be emotionally seen and heard. I want to scream from a stage to the entire world that these things happened. That there are others like me. I want to be validated, I want to be, and I want my pain to be acknowledged. So, I am thinking of sharing this with an exceptional person maybe more than one, maybe they can help figure out what's next for the invisible girl. Maybe they can help me have a voice, maybe I could borrow theirs, just like once upon a time almost thirty years ago, I borrowed life from Brad. Just like when I was a kid the universe would pull me to a safe person to tell my secrets to, I feel that pull again, towards a few exceptional people.

What have I had to do to get through writing this? I occasionally smoke cigarettes, I vape constantly. I smoke weed whenever I can, it's the only thing that helps the physical pain, or helps me sleep. Until I sat down to write this I rarely drank. I had gotten to the point that I could have a drink here and there, and not finish the bottle. I had my first real alcohol relapse in twenty-seven years writing this. I drank almost twenty-four hours a day during the initial writing, through two revisions, and through three quarters of rewriting it. I will not confess how much Jack Daniels I have consumed during the writing of these pages. I think during the initial twenty-three days it took me to write the first draft, my blood became whiskey, and my flesh became music. I needed the alcohol to cope with the demons, I needed music to sing out the pain. I have not engaged in self harm, not really. I have dealt with that over the years by taking showers so hot that they burn. I have thought about it though and I am sure that by the end, I will have a knife and a lighter stashed somewhere.

In the hardest moments of writing this, I have had to tell myself that it isn't real. I have had to tell myself it's just a made-up story. I have had to tell myself it happened to someone else not me. If I share this with you, if you're reading this, I will probably try and tell you afterward the same thing. I may have to say that to deal with the way people look at me, or that they see me as less than human when they know. And that's when people simply know, "I was raised by a pedophile." I still have my separate lives, just like I did as a kid. My old life, I try not to let mingle with my present. I try not to let them touch. It's unavoidable sometimes, though.

During the writing of these words, these pages, I needed support. I have none. I have never told another human the things that are in these pages. I have never spoken them aloud. I can't. So, I resorted to childhood when I had imaginary friends. I made up my own support system in my mind. It's not like *Sam* and *Dean Winchester (Jared Padalecki, Jensen Ackles – Supernatural)* could come in and kill my monsters. I can't make a deal with *Crowley (Mark Sheppard, Supernatural)* to get revenge on those who murdered me. Even the angel, *Castiel (Misha Collins, Supernatural)* cannot come and zap my memories away. Detectives *Olivia Benson* and *Elliot Stabler*

367

(*Mariska Hargitay, Christopher Meloni, Law and order SVU*) cannot come catch the pedophiles and rapists that have plagued my life and get me justice. I know there is no chance that *Rio (Manny Montana, Good Girls)* could magically appear in my kitchen, giving me the guaranteed income of laundering money, so I can get out of this dump. *Chester Bennington (Linkin' Park)* and *Marvin Lee Aday (Meatloaf)* can't come back to life and sing the lyrics of the pain in my heart. *Jacoby Shaddix (Papa Roach), Matt Walst (Three Days Grace)* and *Brent Smith (Shinedown)* still do a kick ass job. My favorite author, *Stephen King* couldn't write a salvation for me. There is no monster he could create greater than those I have known. These people though, I have imagined them here with me. Not their characters, but them. They were there for me during the hard parts, they never judged me, not even when I cried, and they were the friends I never actually had. Why them? I have seen enough of their public persona, to believe they are decent exceptional people. The same way I used to pick a safe teacher at school. Those teachers were normal, typical people. But they were capable of seeing the garbage humans, they really saw me. I believe that these exceptional people would too, see the real me. The invisible, overlooked, broken, used, abused woman, who carries more scars in her heart than human flesh could possibly have room for. None of you know me, but I would not have been able to write it all, live through it all, without the imaginary presence you have had in my head and heart. For that, I thank you.

Where Are They Now?

If you're anything like me, you're probably wondering what happened to several of the people in these pages. I'll give the information I know to the best of my ability.

Brady lives a few hours away from me with his three kids. We don't speak, and I often forget I have a brother. I have not seen him since 2007 or 2008. As far as I know he still has contact with Griffith. We have vastly different world and life views. I strongly dislike the human being that he is.

Derrick remarried a girl young enough to be his daughter. She is the same age as the girl he raised as his own. They are expecting their third child together. He tells me all the time how he doesn't want more kids, but he keeps having them. He works a five-minute drive away, but he never sees our kids. He started to show an interest in seeing our daughter when she was in her mid-teens but has not reached out to either of his sons.

Jake is still in prison for murder. I still waver on whether or not I believe he's guilty. I talk to his mom from time to time. When our daughter was pregnant, most of his family came for her baby shower. Jake calls every so often or sends a letter. He believes in what he needs to believe in to get by. I have been hearing for the last ten years that he's getting out in two years. In his mind, we are still together. In October he called, he had seen pictures of my family (thanks Helen). He believes my oldest son is his. The last time I saw Jake was in January 1999. My son was born in January 2001. I'm sure you can figure out the math on that yourself.

Charles, my good old dead-beat dad, is still in New York. He had been helping raise his grandkids; last I heard, because his stepdaughter was a "bad mom," his words, not mine. We had reconnected when my third was a baby when I needed a family medical history from him. We talked for two hours, emailed for a year, and then he just stopped responding to my emails. I no longer wonder what was so wrong with me that my own father didn't want

369

me from birth. I know that being a garbage human has destined me to just be unlovable.

I found Myron on Facebook. We caught up, I told him I was surprised he remembered me. He said you always remember your real friends. That meant a lot to me. I asked him whatever happened to Don. He said he hadn't seen or heard from him in years, but the last he heard, Don was seen running through the streets of Poughkeepsie with a group of women chasing him. He had tried to have several girlfriends at one time, and they found out about each other. Sounds just like Don.

I reconnected with a lot of childhood friends through Facebook. Tiffany abandoned her four kids and lives in Georgia with her husband. Sophie, who had actually been my best friend from the time I was ten until I was fourteen (at school anyways), is still in New York. She's married and has a son. Nora has moved to North Carolina and has three kids. Dierdre and I grew apart after her husband told her he didn't want kids. She always had, and I think talking to me when I have an army is painful. We also, no longer have anything in common. Theresa, I keep in touch with more than the rest. She wasn't a good friend then, but she is the only one who bothers to check in on me now. I have severe anxiety and I am not capable of being the one to reach out, which she understands. Raynelle and I lost touch when I was bouncing around group homes. I found her on Myspace, and she had no interest in reconnecting. I strongly believe she had lied about her brother trying to touch her. Her Myspace page was dedicated to what a great person her brother is, he joined the military of some sorts, and she seems to worship him. All of my other friends from my grandparent's town, I simply lost touch with while running away. I have found some on Facebook and we're "friends" there but don't talk.

Kyle, did I ever actually break up with Kyle? I tried to. We got in touch on the phone in 1998, when I was pregnant with my daughter. He wanted to stay together and said we could get married and raise the baby as ours. I told him no; he sent me a hundred dollars and told me to take care. We have reconnected through

Facebook as well. He lives in California and has two sons. His wife is a lot bigger than I ever was.

A lot of people I have written about, are most likely dead. Mary, Kurt, Drew, Lettie, Ziggy, Richie, Todd, Mickey, Johnny, and Keith, I believe they all have died. Most of them I never knew their last names, so it's impossible for me to know. The truth is some of them may have been using fake first names as well. I changed almost every name (I dare you to figure out which names are real) mainly to protect my kids if this ever became public, and myself too. I don't need people all around me to know the details of things that were done to me. I thought I saw Mary once when I was fourteen. I was just coming home from school, and I thought I saw her standing at the library looking at me. I really had to pee, when I came back out, whoever it was, was gone.

Brad lives in New York with his wife and their three kids. He cheats on his wife "because she doesn't like sex", which I think is just an excuse to justify his infidelity. I look back on my time with him fondly. I was deeply in love with him no matter what anyone says, kids can in fact fall in love. Especially those of us that were never really kids. Brad and I talk occasionally, usually just a quick hi on Facebook. We tend to keep our distance, we know that there is still love there, and how easy it would be to spark what we had again. I miss our friendship; he was one of the only real friends I ever had. And because he experienced similar things as I did, I can talk to him in a way I can't talk to most people. Would I ever have sex with him again? That depends. From 1993 when I was sleeping with him, until Paul and I started seeing each other in 2011, yes, I would have. It wouldn't have mattered who I was with, I would have fallen into his bed at the drop of a hat. From the day Paul kissed me until 2018, I would not have. Paul had come so close to giving me the same safe feeling that Brad had, and then ripped it away. From 2018 to 2020, I may have, I'm honestly not sure. From 2020 to now, in a heartbeat. 2020 is when I officially gave up on my marriage. Right now, this minute, I would, mostly for all the wrong reasons. It would be for the nostalgia, because there is a petty part of me that would just to know I could. There are good reasons, too. He is the only man who has ever to this day, always given me a choice, cared if I wanted it, and made me feel one hundred percent safe.

Griffith lives peacefully about four hours away from me. He lives dangerously close to my daughter and granddaughters. It fills me with terror and anger to know how close he is to them. He married the woman he started dating after I told, and he had two kids with her, a boy and a girl. I have wondered if he ever did anything to his next stepdaughter, or his own daughter. I have made myself sick with guilt that if he did, it was my fault for telling. But the woman he married knew what he was accused of, she stood by him, even though she never showed up to any of the hearings. If he did hurt those kids, the guilt is in his hands, and she is just as guilty as he is. I still freak out if I see someone who looks like him, I still look over my shoulder. I still have nightmares. Sometimes, not very often the last ten years, I wake up in weird places, like under furniture or in the bathtub. I laugh it off and think, "At least it's not a dumpster." I almost never remember the dreams, just the feeling of fear and my body hurts like I have been beaten. I have also dreamed of killing him. To hold a gun to his head and pull the trigger, may finally set me free.

If given the opportunity, would I, do it? Could I, do it? Hold a gun to his head? Absolutely. Pull the trigger? Probably not. But I would carry the memory of the look of fear in his eyes with me forever. I fear that one day, the pictures he took of me as a child, will surface. The thought of my toddler/child face plastered across the news, and social media as they try and identify the "victim" is a fear that plagues me. Those pictures are my only hope of ever getting justice though. If he was found with them, he would be charged with many counts of child pornography. I guess those pictures are a double-edged sword. I take solace in knowing when Griffith is on his death bed, he will see the demons of hell coming to get him. He will feel the pain of his eternal afterlife, and he will see my laughing face. He will know exactly why he will suffer forever. Griffith will forever be the only person I truly fear. I have no memory of if the man ever actually raped me. I mean, I'm sure he did, but I don't remember it. I feel that memory coming, and I don't want it. That's

372

what the alcohol was for.

A Few Last Thoughts

I am almost forty-three years old. I have had consensual sex with seven men. I have only been naked in front of four men. I married three of them, and Drew is the other one. Well, five if you count Todd; I don't. I am seen as a slut by several old friends and exes. But all my exes have called me "The one that got away" or said, "I didn't know what I had until it was gone." They all want to know the secret to making me have an orgasm. They all think it must be feeling loved. I'm sure whoever is reading this thinks that too. I won't tell my exes what the secret is, but I will share it here. It's feeling safe. I have had that safe feeling with two people. Paul, who has made it happen, just not as often as he thinks. And Brad, so I guess it would take feeling safe and more than two seconds.

I have mentioned that I don't listen to music; I feel it. I have wondered through writing this if when the music is on and pouring through my body if I am bleeding, crying, or breathing. Maybe all three. Want to get to know me better? This is a list of songs, in no particular order, that have touched my soul. Either by giving me the anger and adrenaline I needed to go on, keeping me alive, or ripping the words from inside of me and letting me know I am not alone. Thank you from all of us garbage humans. You really don't have any idea what your music means to people like me. I'm sure I'm forgetting many songs and artists, but time and space are limited.

Meatloaf- Heaven Can Wait, Two Out of Three Ain't Bad, Paradise by the Dashboard Light, Life is a Lemon, and I Want My Money Back, Objects in the Rearview Mirror May Appear Closer Than They are, Everything Louder Than Everything Else, Lost boys and Golden Girls.

Motley Crue- Dr. Feel good, Without You.

Guns N Roses – 14 years, Civil War.

Korn Freak on a Leash, Coming Undone, Falling Away from me.

Queensryche - Silent Lucidity

White Lion – When the Children Cry, Wait.

Sublime – Date Rape, Wrong Way

Alanis Morrisette - Perfect, Mary Jane.

Placebo – Post Blue, Pure Morning, Meds.

Red Juppsuit Apparatus – Facedown

Soul Asylum - Runaway Train.

Bon Jovi – Always, I'll Be There For You, Never Say Goodbye.

Aerosmith - Janie's got a Gun, Cryin', Crazy, Amazing, Love in an Elevator, Angel, Dream On.

Metallica – Nothing Else Matters, Sandman, Unforgiven.

Incubus - Pardon Me

Linkin' Park - Hybrid Theory full album (except My December and High Voltage), Don't Stay, Somewhere I Belong, Lying From You, Easier to Run, Breaking the Habit, From the Inside, Nobody's Listening, Numb, Given Up, Leave Out All The Rest, Shadow of the Day, In Between, In Pieces, The Little Things Give You Away, Nobody Can Save Me, Talking to Myself, Invisible, Heavy, Sorry for Now, Halfway Right, Sharp Edges, Castle of Glass.

Three Days Grace – Tell Me Why, Landmine, So What, The Real you, Love me or Leave me, Chasing the First Time, Chalk Outline, Happiness, I Hate Everything About You, Home, Pain, Animal I have Become, Never Too Late, Riot, Lost in You, The Good Life, Human Race, Painkiller, I am Machine, Right Left Wrong, The Mountain, So Called Life, I am The Weapon, Neurotic, Lifetime, A

Scar is Born, Redemption, Chain of Abuse, Someone to Talk To, The Abyss, Explosions, Champion.

Papa Roach - Last Resort, Infest, Broken Home, Between Angels and Insect's, Blood Brothers, Revenge, Never Enough, Thrown Away, She Loves Me Not, Black Clouds, Getting Away with Murder, Scars, Do or Die, Blanket of Fear, Hollywood Whore, I almost Told You That I loved You, Still Swingin', Where did the Angels Go?, Before I Die, Silence is the Enemy, Wish You Never Met me, Leader of the Broken Hearts, Walking Dead, Not That Beautiful, Give me Back my Life, Broken as Me, Crooked Teeth, My Medication, Born for Greatness, Periscope, Help, Traumatic, None of the Above, Elevate, Kill the Noise, Stand Up, Liar, Dying to Believe, Leave a Light On, Always Wandering, No Apologies.

Shinedown - Save Me, If You Only Knew, Unity, I'm Not Alright, My Name (Wearing Me Out), Diamond Eyes, Evolve, Brilliant, Sure is Fun, Clueless and Dramatic, The Saints of Violence and Innuendo. Stranger Inside, .45, Sound of Madness, Breaking Inside, Cyanide Sweet Tooth Suicide, Bully, Enemies, Through the Ghost, I'll Follow You, Cut the Cord, State of my Head, How Did You Love, Devil, Black Soul, Attention Attention, Kill your Conscience, Monsters, Get Up, Special, The Human Radio, Planet Zero, Dysfunctional You, Dead Don't Die, A Symptom of Being Human, Hope, Daylight.

Want to connect with me? Send an email to my completely anonymous email address. I understand the need for anonymity and swear not to disclose any personal email addresses; I wouldn't want it done to me, so I wouldn't do it to anyone else. I mean hell, you read this far, and you don't even know my real name. Or just make an anonymous one like I did. It's free and easy. "Simone Petardo" May 23, 2022- June 15, 2022

Today is July 19, 2022. I have written this, edited it, printed it, edited it, and typed it again. If you've done the math, you know that I have just turned...

Forty-Three

I have contacted some of the people I have written about and have further updates. I confronted Kyle about the multiple rapes and beatings from our past. He told me that as an adult, he was diagnosed autistic. He says that because of that, he has no concept of right and wrong and cannot be held accountable if he does anything wrong. I deal with autism daily, and this is bullshit. He is just a dick that doesn't want to take responsibility for his own actions. I confronted Drew, whom I believed was dead. He said that I went to his bed willingly enough, often enough, that he owned me. That he could do whatever he wanted to me, whenever he wanted. I found my old landlord from Poughkeepsie, who I also suspected was dead. He is seventy years old; he has been clean and sober for five years. He is the leader of his AA group. I am incredibly proud of him. I found out that Myron died of cardiac arrest several years ago. I never got to thank him for being there for me during that time. I let his daughter know how amazing he was and that he had helped me through a very hard time. I told her he was my family.

I contacted my old middle school social worker, Mr. K. I hadn't slept in a couple of days, and I was in a very bad place emotionally when I spoke to him. I blurted out things from my past like it was nothing. He tried to find me a trauma counselor and told me that I was still suffering from the same trauma over and over again. He, like every other professional I have spoken to, recommended hypnosis. There aren't qualified professionals in my area. He tried, which is more than most people have done for me. For that, I am forever grateful. There aren't strong enough words in the English language to express my gratitude. I have also found and contacted my old fifth-grade teacher, Miss Olsen. She remembered me and what had happened to me then, even though I had never given her any details. We emailed each other several times, and she is truly an amazing human being. Just the fact that she remembered me, and believed me, brought tears to my eyes. I am thankful that someone remembered, someone believed. I am still trying to reconnect with Mr. B from high school. I want him to know he was the only one to ever be proud of me. I want to tell him he saved my life and that he made a difference.

I rarely talk to Bianca. It bothers me that she comments on my friend's Facebook pages about how great they look or how well they're doing. I will never and have never been good enough, though. I feel she failed me. In the last two and a half months, she has reached out to check on me twice. She knows that I have not been in a good place. She only contacted me because she was jealous that my kids were spending time with my friend Nadine. She believes you're supposed to put your spouse before your kids. Lately, I have been wondering just how deep that belief, that loyalty went. I find myself wondering how much she really knew about what her husband was doing to her daughter. I have no love left in my heart for her. I have anger, questions, and indifference.

Paul and I have discovered that if we stay here, any house we get is going to be condemnable or close to it. We started looking at other rural areas. We are hoping to move to upstate New York in the next year. We have talked, and he says he wants to fix our marriage. He says he has barely touched me for the last five years (almost) because he is scared of getting me pregnant. I have given him the information to get a vasectomy several times over the years. Yeah, fear of pregnancy may explain the lack of sex, but not the rest. He disconnected emotionally from everyone and everything. I told him if he puts in the effort, I would accept it, and I would try, also. I made it clear I would not put in the effort that he didn't. I tried for years while he sat there. I also made sure he knew I will not trust would him to not do the same thing again. On June 24, 2022, I sat down and sang to him, *Someone to Talk to* and *Home,* through waves of tears. I then read him the pages starting with our first kiss to the playlist. His only response, which I had to ask for, was, "I know I have been a shitty husband. Hell, I'm barely a husband." That was it. I still have not seen any effort. He has, however, agreed to an open marriage in the future.

Brad reached out on my birthday. He always knows when something is wrong; he always has. I always know when he's thinking about me. We talked about the past. The feelings we had. We talked about the present. I told him some details of the things that were done to me. I've had a hard time holding it in the last couple of months. Things in our conversations were different than normal. For the first time ever, we were getting nasty, mean, and bitchy with each other. We got into a fight when I confessed to him that I planned on killing myself in about a year. I wrote him an email confessing about the miscarriage. I had never told anyone in twenty-nine years. Initially, it wasn't even written here. I planned to take that to my grave. I told him about Kyle raping me repeatedly back then and that I stayed with Kyle to protect him. He got me to stop drinking. I have been sober for twelve days...again.

I confessed to walking the streets of the town Griffith lived in, drinking, getting high, and riding around with strange men. I also confessed that I knew why we had been fighting and not acting like us. It's because we both still love each other. We wanted to be together and never got to have that. We had a love, connection, and bond so strong it never broke. So, to clear the air, I said the forbidden taboo words through email. I thought that he would never talk to me again and was surprised to see that wasn't the case. We talked all night several times. One night the conversation was almost completely about sex. He made it clear that "what was then isn't now," and I made it clear I was interested and would even be his mistress. I had referred to myself as "every one's little cum dumpster," talking about back in the '90s. Brad made it clear that I was never a cum dumpster to him, and I never would be. As sad as it is, that's one of the nicest things anyone has ever said to me. Brad is currently not talking to me; I don't know why. I suspect it's because in one email I sent him, I told him that I'm happy he and I never wound up together and that I always have been. I could probably look past some of our differences. But the truth is, even if we were both single, I couldn't be in a relationship with him due to his cheating problem. He thinks that he has handled the trauma of his childhood so much better than I have. That's not true, though. He thinks he cheats on his wife because she doesn't like sex. That's not true, either. His need for sex, often and with multiple partners, is a direct result of his trauma. He needs sex to feel wanted, needed, and validated. In the right situation, I am a nymphomaniac and can't get enough. Even if he was getting it at home multiple times a day, he would still be unfaithful. It hurts that I love him the way I do, and I know that we could never be more than friends and sex. It's all I would accept with him, though. I thought maybe he wasn't talking to me because he thought I wanted more than what we could be, but I made it clear that wasn't the case. So, it was either the email I sent him, or he knows how easily it would be for him to get too close to me to want more with me. My soul aches to be with him. Once this life is over for both of us, our souls will be together the way we never could be.

I still don't know what happens to all of this now. Sometimes, I still think it's an epic suicide letter. Sometimes, I think it's meant to help people. I think I'm going to put it out into the hands of exceptional people. If I have shared this with you, even if nothing happens with it, remember me. Keep my words, my experiences, in your heart. Notice the garbage humans. Help those like me to be different, to be alive. Loan someone who is in danger just a little bit of your life, so they can feel free, alive, and human. Be a friend. Be kind. Take my words and make a movie, a show, a song, make a fucking difference. It matters more than you could ever know.

Always
The Dead Girl. Flasher, Jailbait, Lot Lizard, No one who has ever really mattered.
July 19, 2022 (and I am now one hundred and seventy-seven pounds)

Milton Keynes UK
Ingram Content Group UK Ltd.
UKHW051006231123
432971UK00011B/123